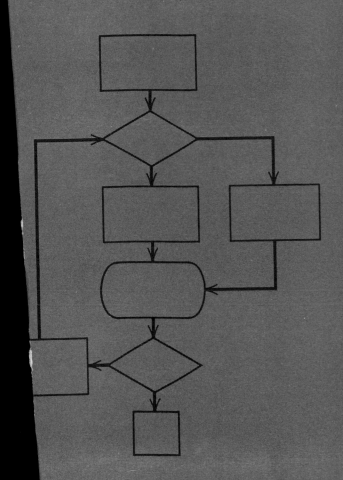

NUMERICAL METH

AND FORTRAN

PROGRAMMING

with applications in engineering

NUMERICAL METHODS AND FORTRAN PROGRAMMING

with applications in engineering and science

DANIEL D. McCRACKEN

McCRACKEN ASSOCIATES, INC.

WILLIAM S. DORN

INTERNATIONAL BUSINESS MACHINES CORPORATION

John Wiley and Sons, Inc., New York · London · Sydney

Preface

This book is designed to give the undergraduate in engineering or science a basic understanding of the numerical solution of problems on a modern electronic digital computer.

The emphasis is on carefully selected and highly practical methods for handling a variety of numerical problems encountered in modern computing. The methods presented here are not only of value in themselves; they also provide the student with insight into more sophisticated methods and prepare him to understand them in their full depth. Just as the physicist must have an intuitive grasp of the meaning of inertia before he can fully understand mechanics, so must the study of numerical *methods* precede the study of numerical *analysis*. Our goal has thus been twofold: to provide the tools for useful computation and to lay the groundwork for possible further study.

Our combination of numerical methods and FORTRAN programming is much more than the binding of two standard books in one set of covers. The introduction of FORTRAN material is timed to coincide with the needs of the numerical methods sections. The major examples of programming in most cases also illustrate numerical techniques. Perhaps most important, the outlook throughout is modern. For instance, the critical subject of roundoff error is treated in terms of *floating point* roundoff; the semigraphical representation introduced here facilitates full understanding. Numerical methods chosen for inclusion have been selected after careful consideration of their suitability for use with a digital computer.

Since we have not needed interpolation as a pedagogical device and since interpolation is less important with a computer than it is for hand calculation, the subject is mentioned only briefly. Another traditional topic not included is work with matrices.   For our intended readers, some of whom will be sophomores, there is little real advantage in the use of matrices.   Linear transformations in most cases have not yet been encountered, and it is doubtful whether such students are really helped by the introduction of matrices strictly as a notational device.

A student who completes this book will not, of course, be a finished numerical analyst, partly because of these omissions.   Our conviction is that there is great advantage to an *early* study of the material presented here, followed later by a more complete course that can build on the foundation laid by this book.

The presentation in the numerical-methods chapters in most cases begins with an appeal to geometrical intuition to motivate the student's understanding.   We then prove the central results analytically and finally make the ideas concrete by applying them to numerical examples and a case study.   This approach, we believe, is the route to most rapid and thorough learning.

The thirteen case studies have been included for three reasons. One, of course, is to illustrate the application of the ideas in numerical methods and programming.   A second is to show the combination and interaction of the two subjects.   (In this connection several case studies show the consequences of careless error analysis.)   The third reason is to exhibit some of the variety of areas of engineering and science in which computers find application.   The presentation is such, however, that understanding the material does not depend on familiarity with the application areas.   In many cases actual computer output is reproduced.

There are more than 300 exercises, with answers to many of them in the back of the book.   Some apply the techniques developed in the text to numerical examples; others apply and extend programming ideas; a third group asks the student to prove results related to text ideas or to extend them.   Many of the exercises permit the inquiring student to discover for himself topics that are developed in full detail in later chapters.

An earlier version of the book has been taught to classes ranging from sophomores in engineering to juniors and seniors in mathematics to graduate engineers.   Naturally, the instructor will select topics and modify examples to meet the needs and interests of different classes.   A judicious choice of exercise assignments can do much to match the book to the requirements of a particular class, in view of the large number and variety of exercises provided.

This book can be used for a four semester-hour course if the students have access to a computer and are expected to do a fairly large number of problems on the machine. On the other hand, it can also be used for less extensive courses, either by assigning fewer exercises or omitting chapters. The class that is not ready for ordinary or partial differential equations could stop after Chapter 9. Furthermore, the numerical methods chapters are not strongly interdependent. The instructor who wishes to slight Chapter 3 on function evaluation in order to concentrate on linear equations, for instance, will find no difficulty in doing so. Many other ways of organizing a course around this book are possible.

It is a pleasure to acknowledge the contributions of those who assisted us in the preparation of this book: Miss Agnes Kuhlke and James Griesmer of IBM, William Nyback of the Milwaukee School of Engineering, Fred Gruenberger of the RAND Corporation, Jack Hollingsworth and Paul McGloin of Rensselaer Polytechnic Institute, Eugene Golub and Harold R. Van Zoeren of Stanford University, and Charles Davidson of the University of Wisconsin. The help of these competent people was of great value to us; in their various capacities they shaped the book in important ways. Finally, we wish to express our appreciation to the International Business Machines Corporation, and particularly to Dr. Herman H. Goldstine, for the support and encouragement without which the book could not have been written.

DANIEL D. MCCRACKEN
WILLIAM S. DORN

Ossining, New York
Yorktown Heights, New York
April 1964

McCracken (D. D.)-

A Guide to FORTRAN Programming

A Guide to IBM 1401 Programming

A Guide to ALGOL Programming

A Guide to COBOL Programming

Digital Computer Programming

McCracken (D. D.), Weiss (H.) and Lee (T. H.)-

Programming Business Computers

McCracken (D. D.) and Dorn (W. S.)-

Numerical Methods and Fortran Programming

Contents

—1

Fundamentals of
FORTRAN Computation

1.1 The application of computers

Electronic computers are widely used in the solution of the problems
of science, engineering, and business. This use is based on their
ability to operate at great speed, to produce accurate results, to store
large quantities of information, and to carry out long and complex
sequences of operations without human intervention.

In this book we shall concentrate on the scientific and engineering
applications of computers, typified by work of the following sort.
The design of a new airplane consumes thousands of hours of computer time in the investigation of the interrelated requirements of
structures, aerodynamics, powerplants, and control systems, as they
would operate under numerous flight conditions. The design of a
chemical plant depends on calculations of capacities, operating conditions, and yields under a variety of circumstances. The design of
an electric transmission line calls for a study of the loads that would
be imposed on different sections of the line as the consumption changed
and as unusual conditions developed.

It may be noted in this sampling that the computer does not "solve
the problem." Instead, it helps to explore the alternatives. We do
not ask the computer, "How shall I build this new device?" but rather,
"How would the device work under this set of conditions if I built it
this way?" There are many ways in which the equipment could be
built; there are various operating conditions to consider, and there are
several different and even conflicting goals to be balanced. The computer *cannot* enumerate the design considerations, specify the operating conditions to be investigated, determine what the goals are, or

determine the trade offs among conflicting goals.   It *can* usually offer us great assistance in predicting the consequences of *our* choices in these matters.

1.2   The steps in "solving a problem" with a computer

There is much more to "solving a problem" with a computer than the work the computer does.   It will be instructive to outline the complete process of setting up a typical engineering problem for a computer solution to see just what the human does and what the computer does.

Problem Identification and Goal Definition
This is the question of choosing a general approach, deciding what combinations of goals the system must satisfy, and specifying the conditions under which it will be required to operate.   In some applications this is simple; in others it may take months.   In any case, it clearly demands a full knowledge of the problem; there is little the computer can do to help.

Mathematical Description
There are, as a rule, several ways to describe a process mathematically: one must be chosen or a new one must be developed if no standard method applies.   This step requires full knowledge of the problem and of the relevant fields of mathematics.

Numerical Analysis
The mathematical formulation of the problem may not be directly translatable to the language of the computer, since the computer can only do arithmetic and make simple quantitative decisions.   Trigonometric functions, differential equations, integrals, square roots, and logarithms, to name a few common examples, must be expressed in terms of arithmetic operations.   Furthermore, it must be established that any errors inherent in the data or introduced by the computations do not invalidate the results.

This is an entire branch of modern mathematics.   One of the goals of this book is to introduce the student to the elements of numerical analysis.

Computer Programming
The numerical procedure must now be stated as a precisely defined set of computer operations.   There are usually two steps to this part. In the first the sequence of operations is written in graphical form in a *block diagram*.   The procedure must then be stated in a "language"

that can be "understood" by the computer or which can be understood after a preliminary translation stage.   FORTRAN is such a language.

In other words, we ordinarily draw a block diagram of the method of solution; this diagram is valuable to *us* as a clear outline of what we want to do, but it cannot be "understood" by the computer. Then, using it as a guide, we write a FORTRAN program, which *will be* "understandable" to the machine after we have completed the preliminary translation phase that is discussed later.

The other goal of this book is to teach the student to write procedures in the FORTRAN language.   This necessitates learning the rules of the FORTRAN language and includes the broad question of expressing a numerical method as a series of carefully defined computational steps.

Program Checkout
There are so many chances to make mistakes in programming that most programs do not work correctly when first tried.   The mistakes must be located and the program thoroughly tested to establish that it will perform as intended.   The computer is used during this step.

Production
Now, finally, the program can be combined with problem data and run. In a typical situation many sets of data are run off at one time.   This step may take a few seconds to many hours, depending on the problem and the computer.

Interpretation
As we have noted, the results printed by the computer do not always constitute a final "answer" to the "problem."   The user of the computer must interpret the results to see what they mean in terms of the combinations of goals that the proposed system must satisfy.   Frequently it is necessary to repeat some or all of the preceding steps before the problem is really "solved."

Several conclusions may be drawn from this discussion.   First, the computer does not by itself solve problems; it only follows carefully defined computational procedures.   Second, a computer does not relieve the user of the responsibility of planning the work carefully; in fact, the computer demands much more careful planning.   The computer is faster and more accurate than a human, but it cannot decide how to proceed or what to do with the results.   Third, a computer does not in any way reduce the need for a full and detailed understanding of the problem area or for a thorough knowledge of the related mathematics.

As we have already suggested, the emphasis in this book is on the middle steps in the listing given: numerical methods and computer programming.   Problem identification, goal definition, and mathematical formulation are in the province of the technical area under consideration, whatever it is: electrical engineering, physics, chemistry, or operations research.   Program checkout is discussed briefly; production is a relatively simple matter of running the computer, and interpretation of results is once again back into the problem area.

We take it, then, that the student will approach the subject of this book with a full understanding of his problem and its mathematical formulation; we shall show him how to translate the mathematical statement into a series of arithmetic steps and from there into a correct computer program; we shall then leave him to make intelligent use of the results.

Our task for the remainder of this chapter is to master the elements of the FORTRAN language.   After a study of how procedure statements may be written in FORTRAN we shall see, in two short case studies, how a computer can be utilized to get results to simple problems.

1.3   A FORTRAN program

A procedure for solving a problem with FORTRAN consists of a series of *statements*.   These statements are of several types.   One specifies the arithmetic operations that are the heart of the procedure. A second calls for input or output, such as reading a data card, printing a line of results, or punching a card of results.   Statements of these first two types are executed in the order in which they are written; a third type alters the *flow of control* of statement execution, so that groups of statements can be executed repeatedly or the sequence otherwise changed.   The fourth provides certain information *about* the procedure without itself requiring any computation.

Taken together, all the statements that specify the problem-solving procedure constitute a *source program.*   When the source program has been written and punched onto cards, it is converted by a FORTRAN *translator* into an *object program.*   This is a set of elementary instructions that the computer can "understand": add two numbers, compare two numbers for equality, or print a line, for example.   The translation from the source program to the object program is required because the language of FORTRAN is much more sophisticated than the language of the machine's instructions.   It is the object program that is actually executed by the computer to obtain results.

The word FORTRAN thus refers both to a language for expressing problem-solving procedures and to a translator. The FORTRAN translator, which is also called a *processor* or *compiler*, is itself a large program of computer instructions. (It was the translation aspect that led to the original meaning of the word FORTRAN: FORmula TRANslation.)

We turn now to a study of the elements of which statements are composed: constants, variables, operations, expressions, and functions. After a study of these basic language units, we shall learn how to combine them into statements, and we shall then be able to write some simple programs.

1.4 Constants

We begin by considering the two kinds of numbers that can be used in FORTRAN: *fixed point* and *floating point.*

A fixed point number is just an ordinary integer (whole number). It may be zero or any positive or negative number less than 32768.* Because fixed point numbers can take on only integral values, they are ordinarily used only in special situations, as we shall see later.

Most numbers used in FORTRAN computation are in floating point form. This is a method of representation similar to scientific notation, in which a number is treated as a fraction between 0.1 and 1.0 times a power of 10.† The *magnitude* (sign not considered) of the number so represented must be zero or lie between the approximate limits of 10^{-38} and 10^{+38}.

We see that a fixed point number is always an integer, whereas a floating point number may be an integer or have a fractional part. Furthermore, FORTRAN carries out computations on floating point

---

* FORTRAN for different computers has different limits on the sizes of numbers; those stated here are for FORTRAN II for the IBM 7090 and related computers. The differences between the FORTRAN described in this book and any other system can be summarized very briefly and need not be a major concern for the reader. Before doing any actual programming for another system, however, the necessary details should be obtained. We shall not, in general, point out these differences.

† Standard scientific notation represents a number as a power of 10 times another number between 1.0 and 10.0, instead of 0.1 to 1.0. The only place in this book where it is essential to choose one form on the other is in Chapter 2 in the discussion of floating point roundoff; we use the 0.1 to 1.0 form there because it is widely established. The results of this error analysis will be completely unchanged by the form in which answers are printed, and we shall see that it is easy to transform the internal form into standard scientific notation for printing.

numbers in such a way that we do not have to be concerned with the location of decimal points.   All questions of lining up decimal points before addition or subtraction, etc., are automatically taken care of by the computer.   This is the reason for the term "floating point."

A floating point number is always a rational real number.   Irrational numbers and complex numbers are not permitted, but complex numbers can be handled by performing arithmetic on their real and imaginary parts separately.

Any number that appears in a statement in explicit form is called a *constant*, whereas a quantity that is given a name and allowed to vary is called a *variable*.   For instance, we shall see a little later that the following are *arithmetic statements:*

$$I = 2$$

$$X = A + 12.7$$

Here 2 and 12.7 are constants; I, X, and A are variables.

FORTRAN distinguishes between floating point and fixed point constants by the presence or absence of a decimal point, respectively. Thus 3 is a fixed point constant, but 3.0 (3., 3.0000, etc.) is a floating point constant.   The two forms are *not* interchangeable because they are ordinarily stored and processed within the computer in entirely different ways.

If a constant is positive, it may or may not be preceded by a plus sign, as desired.   If it is negative, it must be preceded by a minus sign. The following are acceptable fixed point constants:

0	−1234
6	10000
+400	−20000

The following are not acceptable fixed point constants:

12.78 (decimal point not allowed in fixed point)
−10,000 (comma not allowed)
12345678900 (too large)

The decimal point that characterizes a floating point constant may appear at the beginning of a number, at the end, or between any two digits.   A floating point constant may have any number of digits, but only about eight digits of significance are retained by the computer. In other words, although there is no restriction on the number of digits in a floating point constant, it makes little sense to use more than eight or nine significant digits since any additional ones will be dropped.

It is possible to follow a floating-point constant by the letter E and a one- or two-digit positive or negative integer power of 10 by which the number is to be multiplied. This simplifies the writing of very large or very small numbers. The following are acceptable floating point constants:

0.0	+15.016
6.0	$5.0E + 6$ $(= 5.0 \cdot 10^{6})$
6.	$-7.E - 12$ $(= -7.0 \cdot 10^{-12})$
$-20000.$	$6.205E12$ $(= 6.205 \cdot 10^{12})$
$-.0002784$	$-.1E7$ $(= -0.1 \cdot 10^{7})$

The following are *not* acceptable floating point constants:

12,345.6	(comma not allowed)
+234	(no decimal point)
1.6E63	(too large in most systems)
$1E - 7$	(no decimal point)
5.863E2.5	(exponent part must be an integer)
$E + 5$	(no mantissa)

Exercises

*1. Write the following numbers as FORTRAN floating point constants.

$$256, \ 2.56, \ -43{,}000, \ 10^{12}, \ 0.000000492, \ -10, \ -10^{-16}$$

2. Write the following numbers as FORTRAN floating point constants.

$$16, \ 4.59016, \ -10{,}000, \ 10^{17}, \ 0.000006, \ -1, \ -10^{-10}$$

*3. All of the following are unacceptable as floating point constants. Why?

$$12{,}345.6, \ +234, \ 1.6E63, \ 1E - 7$$

4. All of the following are unacceptable as floating point constants. Why?

$$-100{,}000, \ 1E - 55, \ 2.379427 - E12, \ 2E + 2.5$$

*5. Do the following pairs of floating point constants represent the same number in each case?

a. 16.9	+16.9
b. 23000.	2.3E4
c. 0.000007	$.7E - 5$
d. 1.0	1.
e. .906E5	$+906.0E + 2$

---

* Answers to starred exercises are given at the back of the book.

*6. Some of the following are unacceptable as fixed point constants.   Identify the errors.

$$+234, \; -234., \; 23{,}400, \; 1E12, \; +1000000000000, \; +10000$$

7. Some of the following are unacceptable as fixed point constants.   Identify the errors.

$$-16.5, \; 16000, \; 16{,}000., \; 2.E12.5, \; 2.E12, \; 0.01.$$

1.5   Variables and the names of variables

The term *variable* is used in FORTRAN to denote any quantity that is referred to by name rather than by explicit appearance and that is able to take on a number of values instead of being restricted to only one.

Variables may be either fixed point or floating point quantities.   A fixed point variable is simply one that may take on any of the values permitted of a fixed point constant, namely, zero or any positive or negative integer less than 32768.

The *name* of a fixed point variable has one to six letters or digits, the first of which is I, J, K, L, M, or N.   Examples of acceptable names of fixed point variables: I, KLM, MATRIX, L123, I6M2K, KAPPA.   Examples of unacceptable names of fixed point variables: J123456 (too many characters), ABC (does not begin with the correct letter), 5M (does not begin with a letter), $J78 (contains a character other than a letter or digit), J34.5 (contains a character other than a letter or a digit).

A floating point variable is represented inside the machine in the same form as a floating point constant, that is, as a fraction times a power of 10.   The *name* of a floating point variable has one to six letters or digits, the first of which is a letter but *not* I, J, K, L, M, or N. As one might suspect, the FORTRAN compiler uses the first letter of a variable name to determine whether the variable is fixed or floating point.   Examples of acceptable names of floating point variables: AVAR, R51TX, FRONT, G, F0009, SVECT.   Examples of unacceptable names of floating point variables: A123456 (contains too many characters), 8BOX (does not begin with a letter), KJL1 (does not begin with the correct letter), *BCD (contains a character other than a letter or a digit), A + B (contains a character other than a letter or a digit), B9.43 (contains a character other than a letter or a digit).

The assignment of names to the variables appearing in a program is entirely under the control of the programmer.   Care must be taken to observe the rule for distinguishing between the names of fixed and floating point variables, but most people learn fairly readily to avoid this pitfall. If this rule is violated, the FORTRAN compiler will generally signal the error and not compile the source program into an object program; in a few cases the error cannot be positively identified as an error, and the program will give incorrect results.

It should be noted that the compiler places no significance on names beyond inspecting the first letter to establish whether the variable is fixed or floating point. A name such as B7 specifically does *not* mean B times 7, B to the seventh power, or B_7. Many programmers choose to assign variable names that simplify recall of the meaning of the variable, but no such meaning is attached by the FORTRAN system. It should also be noted that every combination of letters and digits is a separate name. Thus the name ABC is not the same as BAC, and A, AB, and AB8 are all distinct.

Exercises

*1. Which of the following are acceptable names of fixed point variables, which acceptable as names of floating point variables, and which are unacceptable names for *any* variable? G, GAMMA, GAMMA421, I, IJK, IJK*, J79-12, LARGE, R(2)19, BTO7TH, ZSQUARED, ZCUBED, 12AT7, 2N173, CDC160, DELTA, KAPPA, EPSILON, A1.4, A1P4, FORTRAN, ALGOL.

2. Same as Exercise 1.
    K, I12G, CAT, X + 2, XP2, NEXT, 42G, LAST, MU, A*B, X1.4, (X61), GAMMA81, AI, IA, X12, 1X2, GAMMA, KAPPA, XSQUARED.

1.6   Operations and expressions

FORTRAN provides five basic operations: addition, subtraction, multiplication, division, and exponentiation. Each of these operations is represented by a distinct symbol:

Addition	+
Subtraction	−
Multiplication	*
Division	/
Exponentiation	**

Note that the combination ** is considered to be one symbol; there is no confusion between ** and *, since, as we shall see, it is never permissible to write two symbols of operation side by side. These are the only operations allowed; any other mathematical operations must be built up from the basic five or computed by using the functions we discuss later.

The term *expression* is used in its precise mathematical sense in FORTRAN. An expression is defined as a constant, variable, or function, combined with operation symbols, commas, and parentheses, which forms a meaningful mathematical expression. Some examples of expressions and their meanings are given in Table 1.1. Blank spaces may be used freely, at the discretion of the programmer, to improve readability.

In writing expressions, the programmer must observe certain rules in order to convey his intentions correctly.

1. Two symbols of operation must not appear next to each other. Thus A* − B is not a valid expression but A*(−B) is.

2. Parentheses must be used to indicate groupings just as in ordinary mathematical notation. Thus $(X + Y)^3$ must be written $(X + Y)**3$ to convey the correct meaning. Again, $A - B + C$ and $A - (B + C)$ are both legitimate expressions, but they do not mean the same thing.

3. The ambiguous expression A^{B^C} must be written as A**(B**C) or as (A**B)**C, whichever is intended, but never as A**B**C. (And there *is* a difference. For instance, $(2^2)^3 = 4^3 = 64$, but $2^{(2^3)} = 2^8 = 256$.)

4. When the hierarchy of operations in an expression is not completely specified by the use of parentheses, the sequence is as follows: all exponentiations are performed first, then all multiplications and divisions, and finally all additions and subtractions. Thus the next

Table 1.1

Expression	Meaning
K	The value of the fixed point variable K
3.14159	The value of the floating point constant 3.14159
A + 2.1828	The sum of the value of A and 2.1828
RHO − SIGMA	The difference of the values of RHO and SIGMA
X*Y	The product of the values of X and Y
OMEGA/6.2832	The quotient of the value of OMEGA and 6.2832
C**2	The value of C raised to the second power
(A + F)/(X + 2.0)	The sum of the values of A and F divided by the sum of the value of X and 2.0
1./(X**2 + Y**3)	The reciprocal of $(X^2 + Y^3)$

two expressions are equivalent:

a. A*B + C/D − E**F
b. (A*B) + (C/D) − (E**F).

As another example, X*Y**3 means $X \cdot Y^3$, not $(X \cdot Y)^3$. Note that this rule applies *only* in the absence of parentheses. Thus the expression (X*Y)**3 means $(X \cdot Y)^3$, since Rule 2 takes precedence.

5. Within a sequence of consecutive multiplications and/or divisions or additions and/or subtractions, in which the order of the operations to be performed is not completely specified by the use of parentheses, the operations are performed from left to right. Thus the expression A/B*C would be taken to mean $\dfrac{A}{B} \cdot C$, not $\dfrac{A}{B \cdot C}$, and I − J + K would mean $(I - J) + K$, not $I - (J + K)$.

6. Although any expression may be raised to a power that is a positive or negative fixed point quantity, only floating point expressions may be raised to a floating point power. An exponent itself may be any expression. Thus the expression X**(I + 2) is perfectly acceptable.

7. Fixed and floating point quantities must not be "mixed" in the same expression; however, fixed point quantities may appear in floating point expressions as exponents and as subscripts (see Chapter 7). There are exceptions also in the use of some functions, although not with any in this text (see Section 1.7).

8. Parentheses in an expression indicate only grouping. (They have other uses for entirely different purposes as we shall see.) Specifically, they never imply multiplication. Thus the expression (A + B)(C + D) is incorrect; it should be written (A + B)*(C + D).

Table 1.2 gives some examples of correct and incorrect ways of forming FORTRAN expressions.

These rules are important for a number of reasons. For one, it is necessary to convey the programmer's intention correctly. Just as in ordinary mathematical notation, the expression A*(B + C) *must* be written with parentheses. For a second reason, some things are simply impossible because of the way the computer and the compiler operate. A fixed point number cannot be raised to a floating point power because, in general, the result would have a fractional part which cannot be expressed in fixed point. Fixed and floating point quantities cannot be mixed in most FORTRAN systems because arithmetic on the two types of numbers is often done in quite different ways.

The third reason for following these rules is less obvious: arithmetic

Table 1.2

Mathematical Notation	Correct Expression	Incorrect Expression
$A \cdot B$	A*B	AB (no operation)
$A \cdot (-B)$	A*(−B) or −A*B	A* − B (two operations side by side)
$A + 2$	A + 2.	A + 2 (mixed fixed and floating point)
$-(A + B)$	−(A + B)	−A + B or − + A + B
A^{I+2}	A**(I + 2)	A**I + 2(= A^I + 2, mixed)
$A^{B+2} \cdot C$	A**(B + 2.)*C	A**B + 2.*C(= A^B + 2 · C)
$\dfrac{A \cdot B}{C \cdot D}$	A*B/(C*D) or A/C*B/D	A*B/C*D $\left(= \dfrac{ABD}{C} \right)$
$\left(\dfrac{A + B}{C} \right)^{2.5}$	((A + B)/C)**2.5	(A + B)/C**2.5 $\left(= \dfrac{A + B}{C^{2.5}} \right)$
$A[X + B(X + C)]$	A*(X + B*(X + C))	A(X + B(X + C))

operations with fractions of finite length do not obey all the normal rules of arithmetic exactly. For an example of what can happen, consider this expression:

$$0.40000000 + 12345678. - 12345677.$$

Rule 5 says that the operations will be carried out from left to right. The result of the addition, to eight figures, is just 12345678.; the 0.4 has been lost entirely. Then, when the 12345677. is subtracted, the final result is 1.0000000.

Suppose that the expression had been written this way:

$$0.40000000 + (12345678. - 12345677.)$$

The parentheses force the subtraction to be done first, giving 1.0000000. Now when the 0.40000000 is added, the result is 1.4000000. We shall return to this subject of maintaining accuracy by performing arithmetic in the proper order in Chapter 2. It is of considerable practical importance, even though the effect is not always so extreme as in this example.

The order of arithmetic operations can lead not only to loss of significance but also to a failure to get any answer, as the following example shows. Suppose we wanted to evaluate the expression A*B/C, in which the values of A, B, and C are all 10^{30}. The multiplication is done first, giving 10^{60}—which is too large for a floating point variable in most FORTRAN systems.   The final result after the division, 10^{30}, would be within allowable limits, but the intermediate result is not. Since the computer cannot represent the intermediate result, it would either stop executing the program or give a completely erroneous answer, depending on how the particular computer is built to operate.

The simple solution is to use parentheses to force the division to be done first: A*(B/C).   The result of the division is allowable and so is the final result.

Fixed point division raises a special problem of its own.   When two integers are divided, the quotient will not usually be an integer. Fixed point arithmetic is arranged to *truncate* the quotient to the next smaller integer, which means simply to ignore any fractional part. Thus the result of the fixed point division 5/3 is 1, not 2.

As it happens, most engineering calculations do not require fixed point division, but it might be well to point out the precautions that should be observed if it is needed.   Consider the fixed point expression 5/3*6.   Rule 5 says that the division will be done first; the truncated result is thus 1; this is multiplied by 6 to give 6 as the final answer. The result is *not* 10, which we would get from multiplying first and then dividing, or 12, which we would get if the quotient were rounded instead of truncated.   On the other hand, if the expression is written as 5*6/3, 6*5/3, 5*(6/3), or (6/3)*5, the result will be 10.

All of this applies only to fixed point arithmetic.   Any of the forms in the preceding paragraph, if written in floating point, would give 10.000000 (with perhaps one incorrect digit in the last place; see next paragraph).

Even in floating point, however, things can happen that might not be expected.   Suppose we were to form this sum:

$$1.0/3.0 + 1.0/3.0 + 1.0/3.0$$

The floating point representation of 1.0/3.0 is 0.33333333, to eight digits.   The result of the addition, then, is 0.99999999.   If we were to compare this sum with the expected result 1.00000000, the answer would, of course, be "not equal," which might come as something of a shock to the unsuspecting programmer.

These problems are not insuperable, and some of them are not actually so different from things that can happen when working with paper and pencil or a desk calculator.   With a computer, however, we sometimes have to take special measures to *anticipate* such difficulties, since by the time the computer is running the program we are only bystanders.

Exercises

1. Write FORTRAN expressions corresponding to each of the following mathematical expressions.

*a. $X + Y^3$

g. $\dfrac{A + B}{C + D}$

b. $(X + Y)^3$

*h. $\left(\dfrac{A + B}{C + D}\right)^2 + X^2$

c. X^4

i. $\dfrac{A + B}{C + \dfrac{D}{F + G}}$

*d. $A + \dfrac{B}{C}$

*j. $1 + X + \dfrac{X^2}{2!} + \dfrac{X^3}{3!}$

e. $\dfrac{A + B}{C}$

*k. $\left(\dfrac{X}{Y}\right)^{G-1}$

*f. $A + \dfrac{B}{C + D}$

l. $\dfrac{\dfrac{A}{B} - 1}{G\left(\dfrac{G}{D} - 1\right)}$

2. Shown below are a number of mathematical expressions and corresponding FORTRAN expressions, each of which contains at least one error. Point out the errors and write correct expressions.

a. $(X + Y)^4$ X + Y**4

*b. $\dfrac{X + 2}{Y + 4}$ X + 2.0/Y + 4.0

c. $\dfrac{A \cdot B}{C + 2}$ AB/(C + 2.)

d. $-\dfrac{(-X + Y - 16)}{Y^3}$ −(−X + Y − 16)/Y**3

*e. $\left(\dfrac{X + A + \pi}{2Z}\right)^2$ (X + A + 3.1416)/(2.0*Z)**2

f. $\left(\dfrac{X}{Y}\right)^{N-1}$ (X/Y)**N − 1

*g. $\left(\dfrac{X}{Y}\right)^{R-1}$ (X/Y)**(R − 1)

h. $\dfrac{A}{B} + \dfrac{C \cdot D}{F \cdot G \cdot H}$ A/B + CD/FGH

i. $(A + B)(C + D)$ A + B*C + D

*j. $A + BX + CX^2 + DX^3$
   $= A + X[B + X(C + DX)]$ A + X*(B + X*(C + DX))

k. $\dfrac{1,600,042X + 10^5}{4,309,992X + 10^5}$ $(1,600,042X + 1E5)/$
$(4,309,992X + 1E5)$

l. $\dfrac{1}{A^2}\left(\dfrac{R}{10}\right)^A$ $1/A**2*(R/10)**A$

1.7   Mathematical functions

FORTRAN provides for the use of certain common mathematical functions, such as square root, logarithm, exponential, sine, cosine, arctangent, and absolute value. The exact list of functions available depends on the version of FORTRAN being used and to a certain extent on the particular computer installation. All FORTRAN systems, however, make provision for computing the functions named.

Every function has a preassigned name. These names vary in general with the different versions of FORTRAN, but those of the elementary mathematical functions are fairly standard. The functions that we shall use and their names are listed in Table 1.3.

In order to make use of a mathematical function, it is necessary only to write its name and to follow it with an expression enclosed in parentheses. This directs FORTRAN to compute the named function of the value represented by the expression in parentheses.

As an example, suppose it is necessary to compute the cosine of an angle named X. This angle must be expressed in radians. Writing COSF(X) in a statement will result in the computation of the cosine of the angle. In this example the *argument* of the function is the single variable X. The argument is not limited to a single variable but may in fact be *any* expression, with the restriction that in all the mathematical functions we have mentioned the argument must be a floating point quantity, and the functional value is computed in

Table 1.3

Mathematical Function	FORTRAN Name
Square root	SQRTF
Exponential	EXPF
Sine of an angle in radians	SINF
Cosine of an angle in radians	COSF
Arctangent; angle given in radians	ATANF
Natural logarithm	LOGF
Absolute value	ABSF

floating point form.   If, for example, we wanted the square root of $B^2 - 4AC$, we would simply write SQRTF(B**2 - 4.*A*C).

1.8   Arithmetic statements

The basic FORTRAN language elements we have discussed so far have many applications in writing source programs.   The most important is computing a new value of a variable, which is done with an *arithmetic statement*.   Its general format is $a = b$, in which a is a variable name, written without a sign, and b is any expression, as described in Section 1.6.   An arithmetic statement is an order to FORTRAN to compute the value of the expression on the right and to give that value to the variable named on the left.

The equal sign in an arithmetic statement is not used as it is in ordinary mathematical notation.   We are not allowed to write statements such as Z − RHO = ALPHA + BETA, in which Z is unknown and the others are known.   The only legitimate form of arithmetic statement is one in which the left side of the statement is the name of a single variable.   The precise meaning of the equal sign is then: *replace the value of the variable named on the left with the value of the expression on the right.*   Thus the statement $A = B + C$ is an order to form the sum of the values of the variables B and C and to replace the value of the variable A with that sum.   The previous value of the variable A is lost, but the values of the variables B and C are unchanged.   It could well be that other parts of the program change the values of B and C during the execution of the program; when we say "the value of the variable B," we always mean *the value most recently assigned to the variable named B.*

Another example of an arithmetic statement brings out very forcefully the special meaning of the equal sign.   A statement such as $N = N + 1$ has the meaning: *replace the value of the variable N with its old value plus 1.*   This sort of statement, which is clearly not an equation, finds frequent use.

Although mixed arithmetic is not permitted in an expression, it is possible to convert between fixed and floating point by writing an expression of one type on the right and a variable of the other type on the left.   If we write a fixed point expression on the right and a floating point variable on the left, for instance, all the arithmetic will be done in fixed point but the result will be converted to floating point before giving the computed value to the variable on the left.   This facility is not heavily used, but it can be quite convenient when it is occasionally needed.

A few examples may help to clarify the uses of arithmetic statements. Suppose that values of A, B, C, D, and X have already been computed by previous statements and that we need to compute a new value of R from the relation

$$R = \frac{A + BX}{C + DX}$$

This statement will do what is required:

$$R = (A + B*X)/(C + D*X)$$

None of the values of variables on the right will be changed by this statement; any previous value of R will be destroyed.

Suppose we need to compute one of the roots of the quadratic equation $AX^2 + BX + C = 0$. Once again, A, B, and C would have to have been given values by previous statements or by reading in values using the READ statement described in the next section. This statement would call for the required calculation and would give the computed value to the variable ROOT1:

$$\text{ROOT1} = (-B + \text{SQRTF}(B**2 - 4.*A*C))/(2.*A)$$

It might be well to review the purpose of the parentheses here. Those enclosing B**2 − 4.*A*C are required to enclose the argument of the square-root function. The parentheses around the numerator in the expression indicate that everything before the slash is to be divided by what follows. The parentheses enclosing the 2.*A indicate that the A is in the denominator; without this final set, the action would be to divide the numerator by 2 and then multiply the entire fraction by A.

A final example shows how the argument of a function can be another function, if desired. Suppose we need to compute the value of V from

$$V = \frac{1}{\cos X} + \log \left| \tan \frac{X}{2} \right|$$

Since we have no function to compute a tangent, we must use a trigonometric identity:

$$\tan \theta = \frac{\sin \theta}{\cos \theta}$$

The statement to compute V then could be as follows:

V = 1./COSF(X) + LOGF(ABSF(SINF(X/2.)/COSF(X/2.)))

It would be perfectly permissible to use intermediate variables here, perhaps making the computation easier to follow in reading the source program:

Y = X/2.
TAN = SINF(Y)/COSF(Y)
ABSVAL = ABSF(TAN)
V = 1./COSF(X) + LOGF(ABSVAL)

The examples in Table 1.4 show acceptable arithmetic statements with equivalent mathematical forms. Variable names have been chosen arbitrarily; any other legitimate names would have been just as good. We are also assuming, of course, that previous statements have established values of all variables on the right-hand sides.

The examples in Table 1.5 are presented to emphasize the importance of writing expressions and statements in exactly the prescribed format, since FORTRAN demands exact adherence to the rules. Each of the statements in Table 1.5 contains at least one error.

Table 1.4

Arithmetic Statement	Original Formula
BETA = $-1./(2.*X) + A**2/(4.*X**2)$	$\beta = \dfrac{-1}{2X} + \dfrac{A^2}{4X^2}$
FY = $X*(X**2 - Y**2)/(X**2 + Y**2)$	$Fy = X \cdot \dfrac{X^2 - Y^2}{X^2 + Y^2}$
C = $1.112*D*R1*R2/(R1 - R2)$	$C = 1.112D \dfrac{r_1 r_2}{r_1 - r_2}$
Y = $(1.E - 6 + A*X**3)**(2./3.)$	$Y = (10^{-6} + AX^3)^{2/3}$
J = $4*K - 6*K1*K2$	$J = 4K - 6k_1 k_2$
I = $I + 1$	$I_{new} = I_{old} + 1$
K = 12	$K = 12$
PI = 3.1415927	$\pi = 3.1415927$
M = $2*M + 10*J$	$M_{new} = 2M_{old} + 10J$
R = $COSF(X) + X*SINF(X)$	$R = \cos X + X \sin X$
S = $-COSF(X)**4/4.$	$S = -(\cos^4 X)/4$
T = $ATANF(1.414214*SINF(X)/COSF(X))$	$T = \tan^{-1}(\sqrt{2} \tan X)$

Table 1.5

Incorrect Statement	Error
Y = 2.X + A	*Missing
3.14 = X − A	Left side must be a variable name
A = ((X + Y)A**2 + (R − S)**2/16.7	Not the same number of left and right parentheses; *missing
X = 1,624,009.*DELTA	Commas are not allowed in constants
−J = I**2.	Fixed point quantities may not be raised to floating point powers; variable on left must not be written with a sign
BX6 = 1./ − 2.*A**6	Two operation symbols side-by-side are not permitted, even though the minus here is not intended as indicating subtraction
DERIV = N*X**(N − 1)	"Mixing" fixed and floating point this way not permitted
A*X + B = Q	Left side must be a single variable; should be Q = A*X + B
FNC = CUBRTF(X + Y)	No such function; write FNC = (X + Y)**0.3333
SQRTF(Z) = Z**0.5	A function name cannot be used as a variable name; left side must be a variable name

Exercises

1. State the value of A or I stored as the result of each of the following arithmetic statements and whether the result is in fixed or floating point form.

*a. A = 2*6 + 1

*b. A = 2/3

c. A = 2.*6./4.

d. I = 2*10/4

e. I = 2(10/4)

f. A = 2(10/4)

g. A = 2.*(10./4.)

h. A = 2.0*(1.0E1/4.0)

i. A = 6.0*1.0/6.0

j. A = 6.0*(1.0/6.0)

*k. A = 1./3. + 1./3. + 1./3. + 1./3.

l. A = (4.0)**(3/2)

m. A = (4.0)**3./2.

*n. A = (4.0)**(3./2.)

*o. I = 19/4 + 5/4

p. A = 19/4 + 5/4

q. I = 100*(99/100)

2. Each of the arithmetic statements below contains at least one error. Identify them.

a. $-V = A + B$

b. $4 = I$

c. $V - 3.96 = X**1.67$

d. $X = (A + 6)**2$

e. $A*X**2 + B*X + C$

f. $K6 = I**A$

g. $Z2 = A* - B + C**4$

h. $X = Y + 2.0 = Z + 9.0$

3. Write arithmetic statements to do the following:

*a. Add 2 to the current value of a variable named BETA; make the sum the new value of a variable named DELTA.

b. Subtract the value of a variable named B from the value of a variable named A, square the difference, and make it the new value of W.

*c. Square A, add to the square of B, and make the new value of C the square root of the sum.

*d. A variable named R is to have its present value replaced by the square root of 2.

e. Multiply THETA by π and store the cosine of the product as the new value of RHO.

f. Add the values of F and G, divide by the sum of the values of R and S, and square the quotient; store it as the new value of P.

*g. Multiply the cosine of two times X by the square root of one half of X; set Y equal to the result.

*h. Increase the present value of G by 2 and replace the present value of G with the sum.

i. Multiply the present value of A by -0.1 and replace the present value of A with the product.

4. Write arithmetic statements to compute the values of the following formulas.   Use the letters and names shown for variable names.

*a. $\text{AREA} = 2 \cdot P \cdot R \cdot \sin\left(\dfrac{\pi}{P}\right)$

b. $\text{CHORD} = 2R \sin \dfrac{A}{2}$

*c. $\text{ARC} = 2\sqrt{Y^2 + \left(\dfrac{4X^2}{3}\right)}$

d. $S = -\dfrac{\cos^4 X}{X}$

*e. $S = -\dfrac{\cos^{P+1} X}{P + 1}$

*f. $G = \dfrac{1}{2} \log \dfrac{1 + \sin X}{1 - \sin X}$

g. $R = \dfrac{\sin^3 X \cos^2 X}{5} + \dfrac{2}{15} \sin^3 X$

h. $D = \log |\sec X + \tan X|$

*i. $E = X \arctan \dfrac{X}{A} - \dfrac{A}{2} \log (A^2 + X^2)$

j. $F = -\dfrac{\pi}{2} \log |X| + \dfrac{A}{X} - \dfrac{A^3}{9X^3}$

k. $Z = -\dfrac{1}{\sqrt{X^2 - A^2}} - \dfrac{2A^2}{3(\sqrt{X^2 - A^2})^3}$

*l. $Q = \left(\dfrac{2}{\pi X}\right)^{\frac{1}{2}} \sin X$

m. $B = \dfrac{e^{X/\sqrt{2}} \cos (\sqrt{X/2} + \pi/8)}{\sqrt{2\pi X}}$

*n. $Y = (2\pi)^{\frac{1}{2}} X^{X+1} e^{-X}$

o. $T = A \cdot e^{-\sqrt{W/2P} \cdot X}$

1.9   Input and output

If a problem is to be done only once, all data can be entered with the program in the form of constants in statements.   This is seldom done, however; programs are usually set up to read problem data from cards at the time the program is executed, with constants being used only for quantities that really are constant.   The same program can then carry out the computations on as many sets of data as desired.

Data is entered into the computer by the execution of a READ statement that lists the names of the variables for which new values are to be read from a card.   (An example of a READ statement appears on p. 36.)   The variable names must be separated by commas.   The new values must be punched on the card in the same sequence as the variable names are listed in the READ statement.   Thus there is a sort of scanning process: the first value on the card goes with the first variable name, the second value with the second variable name, and so on, for as many variable names and data values as there are.   This scanning goes from left to right and begins with the first (leftmost) data value on the card.   Furthermore, the execution of a READ statement *always* initiates the reading of a new card.   If, for instance, there are six data values punched on one card, they cannot be entered with two READ statements, the second picking up where the first left off.   The only way to enter the six numbers from one card is to provide a single READ statement that lists the names of all six variables.

The PRINT statement operates similarly: the variables for which values are to be printed are listed in the order in which they should appear on the page, from left to right. The initiation of a PRINT statement always starts a new line.*

So far we have discussed how to provide three items of information about input and output operations:

1. What data medium is to be used and whether this is an input or an output operation. READ clearly implies input and at the same time specifies reading a *card;* PRINT implies output onto a paper form.

2. What variables are to receive new values or are to have their current values printed: this is specified by listing the variable names in the READ or PRINT statement.

3. The order in which the values appear on the card or are to appear on the paper: this is specified by the order in which the variable names appear in the list of the READ or PRINT statement.

Another kind of information is also required: in what *format* are the data values punched or printed? How many card columns are allocated to each input value? How many printing positions are allocated to each output value? Is each value fixed or floating point?

This information is provided by a *FORMAT statement* that must be associated with each READ or PRINT statement.† The basic scheme is this. Each READ or PRINT statement must include, as the first thing following the word READ or PRINT, the *statement number* of a FORMAT statement. A statement number is simply a cross reference that may be written before any statement in a program. A statement number may have one to five digits. Then in the FORMAT statement there is a *field specification* for each variable in the list of the READ or PRINT statement. (A *field* is a group of card columns or printing positions.) The scanning process carries over here, too. For instance, in reading, the first value on the card is associated with the first variable name in the READ list and with the first field specification in the FORMAT statement. The complete set of field specifications in a FORMAT statement is enclosed in parentheses and the individual field specifications are separated by commas.

---

* There are other input and output statements which are useful under proper circumstances. They are discussed briefly in Appendix 1; a few examples appear in Chapters 10 and 11.

† A number of FORTRAN systems provide for some type of standardized formats for input and output, which either make the FORMAT statement unnecessary or allow it to be used in a simplified form. If available, it is strongly recommended. The reader in that case could skip the remainder of this section, coming back to it later, after the more basic ideas of programming have been learned thoroughly.

There are about half a dozen field specifications in most FORTRAN systems, the exact number depending on the availability of certain specialized functions. A great deal of flexibility is provided by these field specifications, much more, in fact, than the beginning programmer has any need for. We shall therefore consider only three of them, and even then we shall not consider all their ramifications. A more complete description appears in Appendix 1.

The simplest field specification is that used for reading or printing integers. An integer field specification consists of the letter I followed by a number that specifies how many columns there are in the field. If, for instance, we have an input field on a card that consists of eight columns, the field specification should be I8.

Integers for input must be punched without a decimal point, and no decimal point is printed with output. If an input value has fewer digits than the number of columns stated in the field specification, the number should be punched in the right-hand end of the field. On output, if there are fewer digits in a number than allowed in the field, the digits are printed at the right-hand end of the field. A positive number for input may or may not be preceded by a plus sign, as preferred; a negative number must have a minus sign before the first digit. On output most FORTRAN systems do not print a plus sign.

For floating point input and output we shall most often use the F field specification. This is slightly more complex than the I type because it is necessary to specify the handling of the decimal point.

The general form of the F field specification is Fw.d, where F may be thought of as standing for "floating point," w is an integer specifying the number of columns in the field, including space for the sign and decimal point, if any, and d is the number of digits after the decimal point. On input, an actual decimal point may be punched or not, as the programmer wishes. If an actual decimal point is punched, then the d in the field specification has no effect whatsoever; if no decimal point is punched, d gives the location of the *assumed* decimal point. If, for instance, we write F10.3, we mean that there are 10 columns allocated to the number, which is to be considered as having three decimal places if no decimal point is punched.

On output the F field specification causes the printing of an *actual* decimal point, and the printing position occupied by this symbol must be considered in determining how many positions to allot to the number. For instance, suppose that we intend to print a floating point variable, the value of which could be as large as 99999, and that we want two places after the decimal point. Counting the sign position, the five digits before the decimal point, the decimal point itself, and the two digits after it, the field would have to be at least nine columns wide.   That is, the field specification would have to be at least F9.2. If it were decided to provide more than the minimum space, for easier reading, more columns could be allowed by writing something like F12.2.   (This would leave three blank spaces before the number.)

The last example points out a problem in the F field specification. What if we do not know, as we write the program, what the maximum size of an output quantity is?   We then do not know how much space to allow.   This problem is avoided in the E field specification, which calls for the output number to be printed with a fixed number of digits in a mantissa and with an exponent.   The general form of the E field specification is Ew.d, where E may be thought of as standing for "exponent form" and w and d are as before.   This number is printed in the general form

$$\pm\ 0.\text{nn} \cdot\ \cdot\ \text{E} \pm \text{ee}$$

in which the number of places after the decimal point is specified by d. The plus signs are not ordinarily printed.   The value chosen for w must consider the sign positions as well as the positions occupied by the letter E and the two digits of the exponent.

Note that the normal form of a number printed with the E field specification is a fraction greater than or equal to 0.1 and less than 1.0, times a power of 10.   As we mentioned earlier, this form differs from standard scientific notation, which has a number greater than or equal to 1.0 and less than 10.0, times a power of 10.   To obtain more familiar form, we need only write 1P in front of an E field specification, which will cause the decimal point to appear between the first and second digits and will decrease the exponent by 1.   The 1P is called a *scale factor*.   We ordinarily employ this method in examples.

Input data may be punched in exponent form, which is sometimes useful.   However, we shall not consider the use of the E field specification for input.   The interested reader will find the necessary details in Appendix 1.

Consider an example.   We wish to read four numbers from a card. The first two are fixed point and are to become the values of two variables named J and K.   Each number could have as many as five digits and each could be negative.   The third and fourth numbers, named X and Y, are floating point; each could have as many as seven digits and will always be punched with a decimal point.   Figure 1.1 shows a data card, with illustrative numbers punched.   The vertical lines are for *our* convenience in reading the card and have no meaning to the computer, which reads only the punches.   Note that plus signs

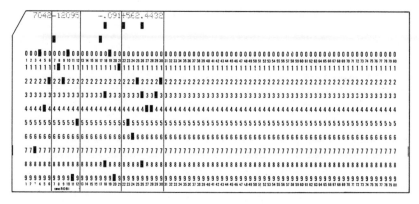

FIGURE 1.1   An illustrative data card.

may be punched or not, as desired. This card was prepared on a card punch that prints the contents of each column at the top of the column.

To read this card we need a READ statement and a FORMAT statement, as always. The READ references the FORMAT, by giving its statement number, and lists the variable names in the order in which the corresponding values appear on the card. The FORMAT statement gives the field specifications of the four fields on the card, once again in the same order as they appear on the card. The two fixed point numbers occupy six columns each: five for the digits and one for a sign. The floating point numbers occupy nine columns each: seven for the digits, one for the sign, and one for the decimal point.

The statements to read this card could be as follows:

$$\text{READ 523, J, K, X, Y}$$
$$\text{523 FORMAT (I6, I6, F9.0, F9.0)}$$

The statement number 523 was chosen arbitrarily. The only thing about the FORMAT statement that might not be clear from the preceding discussion is the zero in F9.0. It was stated that this zero represents the number of digits after the decimal point; however, if a decimal point is actually punched, this part of the specification has no effect. Since we intend to punch a decimal point, then *any* digit could be substituted.

Suppose now that we want to print these same four numbers. We would ordinarily allow a little extra space between numbers to improve readability; let us assign 10 positions to each fixed point number and

```
7042      -12095          -0.0910        562.4432

7042      -12095      -0.91000000E-01    0.56244320E 03

7042      -12095      -9.1000000E-02     5.6244320E 02
```

FIGURE 1.2   Illustrative computer output, showing three ways in which the numbers on the card in Figure 1.1 might be printed.

15 to each floating point number. We may print the floating point numbers first with the F field specification, allowing, say, four places after the decimal point. Then the statements to print the numbers should be

PRINT 609, J, K, X, Y

609 FORMAT (I10, I10, F15.4, F15.4)

The printed output would be as shown in the first line of Figure 1.2.

To print the floating point numbers with exponents, we would use the E field specification. If we wanted eight places after the decimal point and 20 spaces total, the statements would be

PRINT 781, J, K, X, Y

781 FORMAT (I10, I10, E20.8, E20.8)

The printed output would be as shown in the second line of Figure 1.2.

Whenever two or more consecutive field specifications are exactly the same, it is possible to precede one field specification with a *repetition number*, which states the number of successive fields thus described. The four numbers in the example therefore could be printed exactly as in the first line of Figure 1.2 by writing

PRINT 439, J, K, X, Y

439 FORMAT (2I10, 2F15.4)

Suppose, finally, that we want to print the floating point numbers in standard scientific notation rather than in the FORTRAN form, which starts with zero. The FORMAT statement should be

49 FORMAT (2I10, 1P2E20.7)

or, equivalently,

49 FORMAT (I10, I10, 1PE20.7, 1PE20.7)

The printed output would be as shown in the third line of Figure 1.2.

Other examples of the use of the FORMAT statement appear in the case studies.

Exercises

In each of the following exercises data values are to be read, the values used in a computation, and the results printed. The data values are to be printed with the results for easy reference. Assume that each data value is punched in 10 columns; use an F10.0 field specification for all data and an E20.8 field specification for all output. If a computer is available, the programs may be run as valuable practice.

*1. READ: A, B, C
    PRINT: A, B, C, X1, X2
    Evaluate:

$$X1 = \frac{-B + \sqrt{B^2 - 4AC}}{2A}$$

$$X2 = \frac{-B - \sqrt{B^2 - 4AC}}{2A}$$

2. READ: A, B, C, X
   PRINT: A, B, C, X, R
   Evaluate:

$$R = \frac{B \cdot C}{12}\left[6X^2\left(1 - \frac{X}{A}\right)^2 + B^2\left(1 - \frac{X}{A}\right)^4\right]$$

*3. READ: A, E, H, P
    PRINT: A, E, H, P, X
    Evaluate:

$$X = \frac{E \cdot H \cdot P}{(\sin A)\left(\dfrac{H^4}{16} + H^2 P^2\right)}$$

4. READ: HO, HF, HR, HI, ZG
   PRINT: HO, HF, HR, HI, ZG, ADMTNC
   Evaluate:

$$ADMTNC = HO - \frac{HF \cdot HR}{HI + ZG}$$

*5. READ: A, X, S
    PRINT: A, X, S, Y, Z
    Evaluate:

$$Y = \sqrt{X^2 - A^2}$$

$$Z = \frac{X \cdot S}{2} - \frac{A^2}{2}\log|X + S|$$

6. READ: ET, ES, RG, ROPT, RIN
   PRINT: ET, ES, RG, ROPT, RIN, F
   Evaluate:

$$F = \cfrac{1}{1 - \cfrac{1 + \left(\cfrac{RG}{ROPT}\right)^2}{\cfrac{ET^2}{ES^2}\left(1 + \cfrac{RG}{RIN}\right)^2}}$$

1.10 Transfer of control: GO TO and IF

The FORTRAN features we have considered provide us with the means of doing a great deal of useful computation but they leave us with a serious restriction. Nothing presented so far allows us to get out of the one-after-the-other sequence in which statements are ordinarily executed. The GO TO and IF statements offer the additional assistance we need.

The GO TO statement is a method of *transferring control* to some statement in the program other than the next one in sequence. The statement takes the form "GO TO n" in which n is the statement number of another statement somewhere else in the program. A statement number, we recall, is a number of no more than five decimal digits which may be written before any statement in a program. When a GO TO statement is encountered in the execution of a FORTRAN program, the next statement executed is the one specified by the statement number; that is, "control" (statement execution) is "transferred" to the other statement. The statement transferred to may be before or after the GO TO.

The GO TO statement alters the sequence of statement execution *unconditionally*. Besides this, however, we need a way to change the sequence of execution of statements *on the basis of what happens during the execution of the program*. In other words, we want a way of making a *conditional* transfer of control based on data or computed results.

The IF statement takes this form:

$$\text{IF (e) } n_1, n_2, n_3$$

where "e" stands for any expression, and n_1, n_2, and n_3 are statement numbers. The operation of the statement is as follows: if the value of the expression within the parentheses is negative, the statement with the number n_1 is executed next; if the value of the expression is zero, statement n_2 is executed next; and if the expression is positive, statement n_3 is executed next.

We can see the application of both statements in the following example. Suppose that at some point in a program we need to compute Y as a function of X according to one of two formulas:

$$Y = 0.5X + 0.95 \text{ if } X \leq 2.1$$

$$Y = 0.7X + 0.53 \text{ if } X > 2.1$$

The value of X has already been established by previous statements; later statements will use the value of Y. In other words, we are now required to write only a *segment* of a larger program.

The basic scheme will be to arrange two different arithmetic statements, one corresponding to each of the formulas, and then to use an IF statement to choose between the two. This arrangement is shown in the program of Figure 1.3. Which of the statements named in the IF will be executed depends on the value of the expression $X - 2.1$. If X is less than 2.1, $X - 2.1$ is negative, and we transfer to statement 40, which computes Y according to the appropriate formula for that case. If X is equal to 2.1, $X - 2.1$ is zero, and we are led again to the same statement 40, as required. If X is greater than 2.1, then $X - 2.1$ is positive, and we go to statement 30, which computes Y according to the appropriate formula. Whatever appears at statement 45—the continuation of the larger program of which this is a segment—could use the value of Y by whatever formula it was computed.

Why is the GO TO 45 necessary? Because without it the value of Y would always be computed by the second formula! Consider what would happen without the GO TO. If X were less than or equal to 2.1, we would go to statement 40 and compute Y according to the first formula, as required—but we would then immediately go on to compute Y again according to the second formula, wiping out the

```
     IF (X − 2.1) 40, 40, 30
40 Y = 0.5*X + 0.95
     GO TO 45
30 Y = 0.7*X + 0.53
45 Whatever follows
```

FIGURE 1.3 A program segment to compute Y according to one of two formulas.

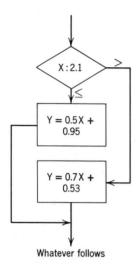

Whatever follows

FIGURE 1.4 Block diagram of the operations carried out by the program segment of Figure 1.3.

result of the first computation. The GO TO therefore is necessary to skip around statement 30 when statement 40 has been executed.

This short program is simple enough to understand by reading the program itself. We shall be faced later, however, with programs that are much easier to follow if the basic logic is first worked out in terms of a *block diagram* (see Figure 1.4). In the simple notation used in this book a diamond indicates any sort of decision. Within a decision box, a colon (:) denotes a comparison, and the actions to be taken for the possible outcomes are shown on the arrows leading out of the box. A rectangle indicates processing—in this case the two formulas. We shall see in later examples the one other block diagramming box to be used here: an oval for input and output operations.

The exercises that follow develop a number of additional methods of applying the GO TO and IF statements.

Exercises

In each of the following exercises you are asked to draw a block diagram and write a program segment to carry out the specified operations. Each segment should be thought of as a part of a larger program, and you are *not* required to write a complete program with input and output.

*1. Place whichever of the variables X and Y is algebraically larger in BIG. (For practice, do not use the special function available in some systems to do this automatically!) If $X = Y$, place *either* of them in BIG.

2. Place whichever of the variables X, Y, and Z is algebraically largest in BIG3. (This can be done with only two IF statements. Establish whether X and Y is larger, place it in a temporary location with a name of your choosing, and then compare this number with Z to find the largest of the three.)

3. The variables named R and S may be positive or negative. Place the one that is larger *in absolute value* in BIGAB. (The absolute value function, ABSF, gives the absolute value of its argument: the value of ABSF(R) is the absolute value of R, etc.)

*4. An angle named THETA is known to be positive and less than 30 radians. Subtract 2π from THETA as many times as necessary to reduce it to an angle less than 2π; leave the reduced angle in THETA.

*5. XREAL and XIMAG are the real and imaginary parts of a complex number. If they are *both* less than 1 in absolute value, transfer to statement 81; otherwise transfer to statement 82.

*6. If the square root of the sum of the squares of XREAL and XIMAG is less than 1, transfer to statement 187; otherwise transfer to statement 459.

7. If XREAL and XIMAG represent a point lying within the square of side $\sqrt{2}$ with its center at the origin and its corners on the coordinate axes, transfer to statement 12; otherwise transfer to statement 99.

8. Y1, Y2, and Y3 are the ordinates of three points on a curve. If Y2 is a *relative maximum*, that is, if Y2 > Y1 and Y2 > Y3, transfer to statement 456, otherwise to statement 567.

9. If DENOM is less than 10^{-5} in absolute value, transfer to statement 50; if it is greater than or equal to 10^{-5} in absolute value, transfer to statement 51. Write program segments to do this

    a. without using the ABSF function;

    b. using the ABSF function.

*10. If $0.999 \le X \le 1.001$, transfer to statement 63; otherwise transfer to statement 67. Write statements to do this

    a. using two IF statements without the ABSF function;

    b. using one IF statement, the expression of which contains the ABSF function.

1.11   The PAUSE, STOP, and END statements

The PAUSE or STOP statement may be written whenever it is necessary to stop executing statements in a program. There is normally a STOP (or something equivalent) at the end of every program, when the computation is finished, but there are also other useful applications of the statements. A program is often set up to do a certain amount of checking of the input data to make sure that it is consistent and that all data values are within reasonable limits. If anything is wrong, some indication can be given to the operator, by either of these statements.

The two statements are similar. Both stop the execution of the object program. Both take effect *only* when the object program is *executed;* that is, they do not cause termination of the compilation. Both may be followed by a single unsigned fixed point *octal* number (a number written with only the digits zero through seven), which will be displayed at the console when the statement is executed. The last is useful when there are numerous STOP or PAUSE statements and it is desired to inform the operator which of them caused the halt.

The difference between the two statements is this: after a STOP statement the computer cannot conveniently be made to continue with the program, whereas the PAUSE statement allows the operator to press a button on the computer console and to resume execution of the program, beginning with the statement after the PAUSE.

There are major differences in local usage of the STOP and PAUSE statements. The users of large computing systems, in particular, try to avoid the wasted machine time caused by stopping if there is any other way out. (STOP and PAUSE are sometimes actually forbidden by modifying the compiler so that they are not acceptable statements.)

Users of the large computers should also be aware that FORTRAN is often run under control of a *monitor* program, which operates the machine between jobs. A FORTRAN program to be run with a monitor should *not* have a STOP when the program is completed but rather should return control to the monitor. Methods vary on how this is done. One frequent way is to write in the FORTRAN program the statement CALL EXIT.

So far we have been talking about the termination of the execution of the *object* program. Now we turn to the question of informing the compiler that the physical end of the *source* program has been reached and that no more program statements are to follow. This is answered by the END statement, which must be the last statement of every FORTRAN program. By "last," in this case, we mean *physically* last or "geographically" last, as distinguished from the statement in the source program that is *executed* last when the compiled program is run.

To put it another way: a STOP statement may appear anywhere in the program; there may be more than one, and it is not required that the last statement executed be the last statement on the last page of the program. The END statement, on the other hand, *must* be on the very last card when the program is punched on cards.

Exercises

In the following exercises you are to read data, perform certain computations, and print results. For each exercise, draw a block diagram and write a complete program. You may assume that each data item is punched in 10 columns, in the order stated, and you may use an E20.8 field specification for each output value.

*1. Read the value of ANNERN; print ANNERN and compute and print TAX according to the following table:

ANNERN (Annual earnings)	TAX
Less than $2000.00	Zero
$2000.00 or more but less than $5000.00	2% of the amount over $2000.00
$5000.00 or more	$60.00, plus 5% of the amount over $5000.00

2. The current United States Withholding Tax on a weekly salary can be computed as follows: 14% of the difference between a man's gross pay and $13.00 times the number of dependents he claims. You may not assume that there will always be a tax: a man may not have earned more than his dependency allowance. Read the values of GROSS and DEPEND; compute and print TAX, along with GROSS and DEPEND.

*3. Y is to be computed as a function of X according to

$$Y = 16.7X + 9.2X^2 - 1.02X^3$$

There will be no data to read; compute and print both X and Y for X values from 1.0 to 9.9 in steps of 0.1. You may assume for this exercise that you are working with a decimal computer, so that adding 0.1 to X repeatedly will eventually give 9.9 *exactly*.

*4. Same as 3 but your computer is binary. Since the binary representation of decimal 0.1 is a nonterminating fraction, there is no guarantee that adding the binary representation of 0.1 to X repeatedly will give 9.9 *exactly*. Therefore, if you were to start X at 1.0, add 0.1 each time around, and each time test X against 9.9, the odds are you would not get exact equality and thus go on past 9.9—in fact, you would never get out of the "loop." Two solutions are possible, among others. Either test X for *approximate* equality with 9.9, within, say, 10^{-4}, or count the number of times around the loop with a fixed point number.

5. Y is to be computed as a function of X according to the formula

$$Y = \sqrt{1 + X} + \frac{\cos 2X}{1 + \sqrt{X}}$$

for a number of equally spaced values of X. Three numbers are to be read from a card: XINIT, XINC, and XFIN. (XINIT is less than XFIN; XINC is positive.) Y is to be computed and printed initially for $X = $ XINIT. Then X is to be incremented by XINC and Y is to be computed and printed for this new value of X, and so on, until Y has been computed and printed for the largest value of X not exceeding XFIN. (The phrase "the largest value of X *not exceeding* XFIN" lets you ignore the problem presented in the last two exercises. However, this formulation does mean that if the data is set up with the intention that the process be terminated with X exactly equal to XFIN it may not do so.)

1.12   Writing, punching, and running a program

A FORTRAN program is ordinarily written on a form similar to the one shown in Figure 1.7 in Section 1.13, with one or more lines for each statement. The information on each line is then punched into a card similar to the one shown in Figure 1.8. The complete set of cards constitutes the *source program deck*, which is compiled into an object program of machine instructions by a process that we shall outline shortly.

In order to be able to show sample programs on a standard form, it is necessary to describe the purpose of each part of the form.

The numbers shown above the first line of the coding form stand for the card columns into which the information on the form will be punched. The first field on the form, columns 1 to 5, contains the *statement number*, if any. We have seen applications of statement numbers in connection with the FORMAT, GO TO, and IF statements.

Column 1 has another function, that of indicating a *comment card*. If column 1 contains a "C," FORTRAN does not process the information on the card but only prints it on a listing of the program. Free use of comments is encouraged to make the program more easily readable by other programmers. For that matter, the original programmer will be helped by comments when he returns to a program after he has forgotten its details.

Column 6 is used to indicate a *continuation card*. If a statement can be punched entirely on one card, column 6 may be left blank or punched with a zero. If more than one card is required for a statement, the cards after the first (up to a maximum of nine continuation cards) must be punched with some nonzero character. The first card of a continued statement must still have a zero or a blank in column 6. Recommended practice is to punch a zero in the first card of a continued statement and to number the continuation cards consecutively from 1.

The statement itself is punched in columns 7 to 72. *Blanks in this field are ignored.* Blanks may thus be used freely to improve readability. The statement need not begin in column 7; some programmers, for instance, indent the continuations of a long statement to make it a little clearer that the statement is continued. Some programmers like to leave a space on both sides of each operation symbol for readability. All such conventions are at the discretion of the programmer.

Nevertheless, it is necessary to indicate clearly to the person who will punch the program exactly how many spaces are desired at each point to allow verification of the punching of the cards. It is for this reason that most FORTRAN coding forms have a box for each character or a short vertical line to indicate the character divisions.

Columns 73 to 80 are not processed by FORTRAN and may be used for any desired card or program identification.

It is essential that the coding forms be filled out with great care and attention to detail. The statements must always be written exactly in the format specified; if a comma is misplaced or omitted, the program will not be compiled or it will be compiled incorrectly. At most installations it is required that only capital letters be used and that great care be taken to write certain easily confused charac-

Zero	0	The letter O	$\emptyset$
One	/	The letter I	I
Two	2	The letter Z	$\bar{z}$

FIGURE 1.5 One acceptable way of distinguishing between easily confused pairs of characters.

ters in a distinctive manner. Various conventions are available for distinguishing between such characters as "oh" and "zero." One acceptable way to write these characters is shown in Figure 1.5.

1.13   Case study 1: The area of a triangle

To illustrate the application of some of the ideas presented in this chapter, let us take a very simple program and see how a complete FORTRAN program to solve it could be worked out.

If the lengths of the sides of a triangle are given by the values of the variables A, B, and C, then the area of the triangle can be computed from

$$\text{AREA} = \sqrt{S(S - A)(S - B)(S - C)}$$

where

$$S = \frac{A + B + C}{2}$$

We are to read the values A, B, and C from a card. The value of A is punched in columns 1 to 10, with a decimal point but without an exponent. The value of B is punched in columns 11 to 20 in the same

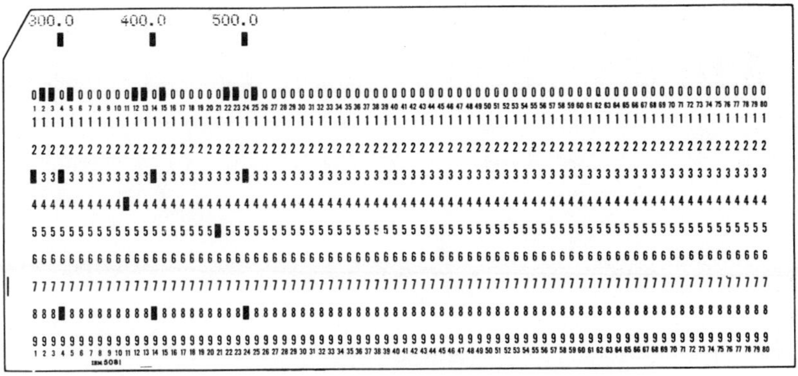

FIGURE 1.6   An illustrative data card for the program of Figure 1.7.

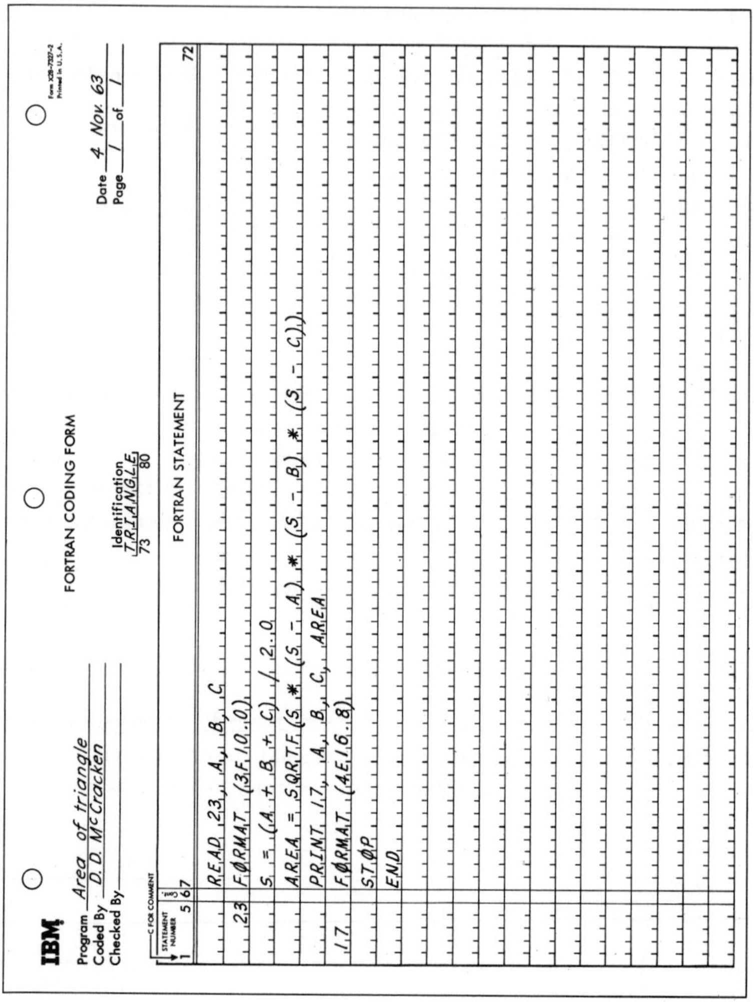

IBM

FORTRAN CODING FORM

Program __Area of triangle__
Coded By __D. D. McCracken__
Checked By _____

Identification __TRIANGLE__
73   80

Date __4 Nov 63__
Page __1__ of __1__

Form X28-7327-2
Printed in U.S.A.

STATEMENT NUMBER	FORTRAN STATEMENT
	READ 23, A, B, C
23	FORMAT (3F10.0)
	S = (A + B + C) / 2.0
	AREA = SQRTF(S * (S - A) * (S - B) * (S - C))
	PRINT 17, A, B, C, AREA
17	FORMAT (4E16.8)
	STOP
	END

FIGURE 1.7 A program to find the area of a triangle given the lengths of its sides. (Case Study 1.)

form and the value of C is punched in columns 21 to 30.   Figure 1.6 shows a typical data card on which the values of A, B, and C are 300, 400, and 500, respectively.

After the area has been computed the area and the lengths of the sides are to be printed, with the area last.   Each of the four numbers will occupy 16 printing positions and will have eight decimal places and an exponent.

A program to do the required computing is shown in Figure 1.7. We note that the statement number of the first FORMAT statement has been written in columns 4 and 5, whereas that of the second FORMAT has been written in columns 2 and 3.   This illustrates that statement numbers may be written anywhere in columns 1 to 5 if they are less than five digits long.   We see repetition numbers used in both FORMAT statements, for in this example the three numbers to be read all have the same format and the four numbers to be printed also all have the same format.   The FORMAT statements have been written immediately following their associated input and output statements; this is conventional but not required: a FORMAT statement may, in fact, be written anywhere in the program.   The statement number identifies it even if it does not immediately follow the statement that refers to it.

In the first FORMAT statement the field specification is F10.0. We recall that F means that the input data will be stored inside the machine in floating point form; the 10 means that 10 columns are allocated to the number; the 0 means that if no decimal point were punched in the card the number would be taken to have zero decimal

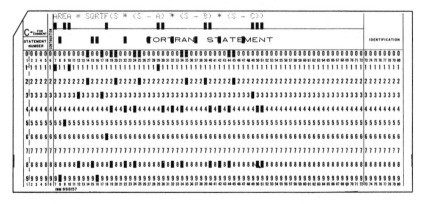

FIGURE 1.8   A source program card from the program of Figure 1.7.   (Case Study 1.)

0.30000000E 03   0.40000000E 03   0.50000000E 03   0.60000000E 05

FIGURE 1.9   A line of output from the program of Figure 1.7, using the input of Figure 1.6. (Case Study 1.)

places, but since a decimal point *is* punched the zero has no effect. In the second FORMAT statement E means that the floating point numbers will be printed with an exponent; the 16 means that 16 printing positions are allocated to each number; the 8 means that 8 decimal places will be printed.

We see that all equal signs and operation symbols have been written with spaces on both sides and that the commas in the READ and PRINT statement lists are followed by spaces.   This was done for readability; it is not required.

Figure 1.8 shows the source program card that is punched from the line for computing the area.

When all the cards are punched, the source program deck is placed in the reader of the computer, with the machine under the control of the FORTRAN compiler program.   The compiler reads the deck and produces from it an object program of machine instructions.   The data card is *not* read during this operation.

In some systems the object program is punched out on cards and must then be loaded into the computer.   In other systems the object program is left in the computer after compilation, and control can be immediately transferred to the object program.   (The second method is referred to in the trade as a "load and go" operation.)

Either way, the object program takes over.   It reads the data card, carries out the processing specified by the machine instructions created from the source program, prints the results, and stops.   Figure 1.9 shows how the line of printing produced by the program for this data would appear.

1.14   Case study 2: Current in an AC circuit

This case study is a realistic application of the GO TO and IF statements in carrying out the same basic computation on a set of data values.

Suppose that we are required to compute the current flowing in an ac circuit that contains resistance, capacitance, and inductance in series.* The current in the circuit is given by

$$I = \frac{E}{\sqrt{R^2 + \left(2\pi FL - \dfrac{1}{2\pi FC}\right)^2}}$$

where I = current, amperes
E = voltage, volts
R = resistance, ohms
L = inductance, henrys
C = capacitance, farads
F = frequency, cycles per second

We shall assume that the purpose of the computation is to provide the data for drawing a graph of the relation between current and frequency. Therefore, we shall regard the voltage, resistance, inductance, and capacitance as known and arrange to read in a series of values of frequency from cards and to print each given frequency, together with the computed value of the current for each frequency.

We wish to write a program that will process any number of frequency cards without knowing in advance how many there might be in a given run. To accomplish this, we shall specify that the last data card will be a *sentinel*, consisting of a *negative* frequency. It could never be actually necessary to compute the current for a negative frequency, so that such a sentinel may safely be used without any danger of confusion with actual data. After reading each data card, we need only use an IF to determine whether this is the sentinel. If it is not, we simply proceed with the computation. After printing each result, we return to read another frequency card, knowing that eventually a negative number will turn up and that the IF statement will then take us to a STOP to terminate the program.

In setting up the program, we immediately run into a minor difficulty. The symbols in the formula are not acceptable as variable names, since I and L would represent fixed point variables and we want all of the variables to be floating point. This is a problem that

---

* The examples used in case studies and elsewhere are taken from various areas of science and engineering. As outlined at the beginning of the book, the *complete* process of problem solution requires a full understanding of the subject matter area and of the formulation of the problem. We, however, are assuming that the preliminary steps have been completed. The reader is therefore *not* required to know how the formulas are derived or, for that matter, what they mean. The emphasis is on numerical methods and on programming; it should not matter very much if a particular example is from an unfamiliar area.

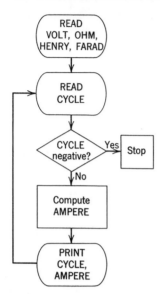

FIGURE 1.10   Block diagram of an ac circuit calculation. (Case Study 2.)

often appears; we must always be on guard to avoid inadvertently mixing fixed point and floating point computations. One solution to this problem is to prefix the unacceptable variable names with some letter that will make them floating point, which is perfectly satisfactory. However, we shall follow a different approach: the units in which the variables are expressed all happen to begin with the proper letters for floating point variables and abbreviations may be used.

The sequence of operations can be visualized more clearly with the aid of a block diagram, as shown in Figure 1.10. We first read the values of the four parameters that do not change: voltage, resistance, inductance, and capacitance. These quantities are identified in the block diagram by the symbols that have been agreed upon for use in the program, making it easier to compare the block diagram and the program.

This first step of reading the unchanging parameters will not be repeated; all the following steps will be carried out for each frequency card. In order to be able to read new frequency cards as long as more remain, without reading the fixed parameters again, we make the reading of a frequency card a separate box. Immediately after reading a frequency card we check to see whether it is a sentinel and stop the execution of the program if it is. Naturally, this would not happen after reading the *first* frequency card, and it may appear pointless to test for the possibility the first time. The point to remember is that we are now in a section of the program that will be repeated an unknown number of times; there may be one frequency card or a hundred. This being the case, we *do* need to test for a sentinel every time except the first. Arranging to avoid the test the first time would be more trouble and more time consuming in the computer than simply making the test the first time.

If the frequency card is not a sentinel, we reach the box that calls for the computation of the current (AMPERE). This will be a long statement in the program; we have not shown the formula in the box, although it would not be incorrect block diagramming practice to do so.

```
      READ 200,, VOLT,, OHM,, HENRY,, FARAD
 200  FORMAT (4F10.0)
  23  READ 200,, CYCLE
      IF (CYCLE) 600,, 601,, 601
 600  STOP
 601  AMPERE = VOLT/SQRTF (OHM**2 + (6..2832*CYCLE*
     1 HENRY - 1../(6..2832*CYCLE*FARAD))**2)
      PRINT 201,, CYCLE, AMPERE
 201  FORMAT (1P2E16.6)
      GO TO 23
      END
```

FIGURE 1.11   A program to carry out an ac circuit calculation.   (Case Study 2.)

After computing the current we print the frequency and the corresponding current and return to read another frequency card.

The program, as diagrammed here, will continue reading frequency cards, computing and printing the current, and returning to read

```
1.000000E 03      3.644963E-03
1.100000E 03      4.134031E-03
1.200000E 03      4.660168E-03
1.300000E 03      5.225302E-03
1.400000E 03      5.828942E-03
1.500000E 03      6.466553E-03
1.600000E 03      7.127432E-03
1.700000E 03      7.792458E-03
1.800000E 03      8.432623E-03
1.900000E 03      9.009940E-03
2.000000E 03      9.482350E-03
2.100000E 03      9.812753E-03
2.200000E 03      9.979228E-03
2.300000E 03      9.981335E-03
2.400000E 03      9.838939E-03
2.500000E 03      9.584666E-03
2.600000E 03      9.254577E-03
2.700000E 03      8.881089E-03
2.800000E 03      8.489593E-03
2.900000E 03      8.097989E-03
3.000000E 03      7.717787E-03
3.100000E 03      7.355687E-03
3.200000E 03      7.015050E-03
3.300000E 03      6.697064E-03
3.400000E 03      6.401578E-03
3.500000E 03      6.127667E-03
```

FIGURE 1.12   Output of the program of Figure 1.11, using the parameter values stated in text. (Case Study 2.)

another card, until it "gets out of the loop" by discovering a sentinel card.

With the process precisely defined by a well-understood block diagram, the program in Figure 1.11 is fairly easy to write and to understand. Statement numbers have been given to the FORMAT statements and to the three statements that are referred to by the IF and GO TO statements. A word about the IF statement might be in order. If the frequency just read is negative, we go to a STOP statement which has been placed immediately after the IF. (The STOP could just as well have been placed elsewhere, for instance, immediately before the END.) If the frequency is zero or positive, we go to compute the current. It is doubtful if there would ever be any real need to be able to process a frequency of zero, but *some* action must be specified for this possibility. There is no provision for writing an IF statement with only two statement numbers.

Note that the arithmetic statement has been written on two lines, by use of a continuation card.

The GO TO statement specifies that after the frequency and the computed value of the current have been printed control should return to the second READ statement, which has been given the statement number 23, to repeat the whole process.

In the second FORMAT statement note the use of a scale factor (the 1P) to shift the decimal point to a position between the first and second digits of the mantissa rather than at the beginning. The exponent is automatically adjusted to reflect the change.

This program was run with a data card that gave the parameters as 10 volts, 1000 ohms, 0.1 henry, and 0.00000005 farad ($=$ 0.05 mfd). The frequency cards ranged from 1000 cps to 3500 cps in steps of 100 cps. The output is shown in Figure 1.12.

When $2\pi FL = 1/(2\pi FC)$, the term in parentheses in the radical is zero and the circuit is said to be *resonant*. In the printout a broad resonance peak around the resonant frequency of about 2250 cps is clearly evident.

—2

Errors

2.1 Introduction

Analysis of the error in a numerical result is fundamental to any intelligent computation, whether done manually or with a computer. The input data is seldom exact, since it is often based on experiments or estimates, and the numerical processes themselves introduce errors of various types. Before beginning our study of the subject of errors let us observe in a few examples how important it is.

Exercise 18 at the end of this chapter asks you to find one of the roots of the equation $x^2 + 0.4002x + 0.00008 = 0$, using four-digit floating point arithmetic. By employing the familiar formula

$$x = \frac{-b + \sqrt{b^2 - 4ac}}{2a}$$

we get an answer of -0.00015. This formula is usually presented in algebra courses without any qualification of its accuracy, yet errors are introduced by the four-digit floating point arithmetic that make the result wrong by 25%; the true root, found with eight-digit arithmetic, is -0.0002.

The culprit there was the four-digit arithmetic, but do not think that eight-digit floating point numbers will solve all problems. Consider the Taylor series for the sine:

$$\sin x = x - \frac{x^3}{3!} + \frac{x^5}{5!} - \frac{x^7}{7!} + \cdots$$

This series is usually described as valid for any finite angle, and the truncation error committed by stopping the summation after a finite

43

number of terms is said to be less in absolute value than the first term neglected. These statements would be true *if there were some way to keep an infinite number of digits in each arithmetic result.* We shall see in Case Study 3 in Chapter 3 that the series is, in fact, totally useless for large angles. Suppose, for instance, that we try to evaluate the sine of 1470° (= 25.7 radians, approximately), using eight-digit floating point arithmetic and computing terms until we find one that is less than 10^{-8} in absolute value. The computed result will be 24.25401855, which has the appearance of great precision but is, of course, meaningless. Even if we use 16-digit floating point numbers, the sine of 2550° is computed as 29.5.

The difficulties in these examples were created by the finite representation of numbers. This is by no means the only problem. Consider the following two simultaneous equations:

$$5x - 331y = 3.5$$

$$6x - 397y = 5.2$$

An "exact" answer is readily found, with no problems of the type encountered above: $x = 331.7$, $y = 5.000$. These results have the appearance of containing four significant digits. Do they? Let us first see what happens to the answers if the constant in the second equation is changed to 5.1, a variation of about 2%. We now compute $x = 298.6$, $y = 4.5$. This is disturbing: a change of 2% in one data item changed the results by about 10%. Even more disturbing is that if we substitute $x = 358.173$, $y = 5.4$ into the equations the computed left-hand sides round off to exactly the same right-hand sides! We conclude that the computed values of x and y have at best one significant digit.

This was no fault of the arithmetic; all results were exact. The trouble lies in the nature of the data; the determinant of the system is small or, stated geometrically, the two lines represented by the equations are very nearly parallel.

For a final example, the integral

$$\int_{e^{-4}}^{1} \frac{dx}{x}$$

is easily found to have the exact value 4. Yet integration with the familiar trapezoidal rule, using 10 intervals, gives a result of 5.3. Even using 40 intervals we get 4.13, off by 3%.

The difficulty this time is in the nature of the integrand, which is very large for small x, and in the numerical process. With exact data and exact calculations we still get a large error from the nature of the function and of the numerical technique employed.

Without multiplying the examples further, it should be clear that without an analysis of the errors in a calculation we really do not know very much about the results. It will sometimes happen, of course, that we can tell by a careful inspection of the calculations that no special problems will occur; in the first two case studies in Chapter 4, for instance, we rather blithely observe that there is no problem with accuracy in the computations. This is distinctly *not* always true, however.

The material in this chapter should be interesting and useful in itself in analyzing the results of simple arithmetic computations. It is also fundamental to the development of the error analysis in the numerical procedures to be discussed in subsequent chapters. Error analysis is a proper starting point for our study of numerical methods.

2.2   Relative and absolute errors

We begin by distinguishing between relative and absolute errors. The *absolute error* in a number is the difference between the true value, assuming it to be known, and an approximation to the true value. Common notation is to write a bar over a symbol to indicate an approximation and to write an e with a subscript to stand for the error. Thus, if x is the true value, we would write

$$x = \bar{x} + e_x$$

Here e_x is the absolute error, which, to repeat, is defined as the difference between the true value and the approximation:

$$e_x = x - \bar{x}$$

The *relative error* is the absolute error divided by the approximation. It might seem more reasonable to define it as the absolute error divided by the *true* value, but we usually do not know the true value. All we have is the approximate value and an *estimate* of the error or a *bound* on the maximum size of the error. If the error is small, the difference in definition has no sizable bearing on the numerical value of the relative error.

For numbers close to 1 the absolute error and the relative error are nearly equal. For numbers not close to 1 there can be a great difference. For example, if we have a true value of 0.00006 and an approximation of 0.00005, the absolute error is only 10^{-5} but the relative error is 0.2, or 20%. On the other hand, if we have a true value of 100,500 and an approximation of 100,000, the absolute error is 500 but the relative error is only 0.005, or 0.5%.

It is obviously essential to state in all cases whether we mean absolute or relative error, unless the meaning is clear from the notation or the context.

2.3   Inherent errors

There are three basic types of errors in a numerical computation: inherent, truncation, and roundoff.   Each can be expressed in absolute or relative form.

Inherent errors are errors in the values of data, caused by uncertainty in measurements, by outright blunders, or by the necessarily approximate nature of representing in some finite number of digits a number that cannot be represented exactly in the number of digits available.

A physical measurement, such as a distance, a voltage, or a time period, cannot be exact.   If the measurement is given to many digits, such as a voltage of 6.4837569, we can be certain that at least some of the rightmost digits are not meaningful, since voltages cannot be measured to this accuracy.   If the measurement is given to only a few digits, such as a time interval of 2.3 sec, we can be quite certain that there is some inherent error because only by accident would the time interval be *exactly* 2.3 sec.*   In such cases we may know some reasonable limits on the inherent error, such as the time is 2.3 within ±0.1 sec.

It is sometimes assumed that when a physical measurement is stated without any qualification on the significance of the digits it is understood to be accurate within a half a unit in the last place.   Thus a distance stated as 5.63 cm. would be understood to be not less than 5.625 and not greater than 5.635.   This convention is not universally observed, however.   When the limits on accuracy are important, it is much better to state explicitly what they are, for example, by writing 5.63 ± 0.005.

Regardless of the number of digits used to represent a quantity, it may contain an outright mistake of some kind.   These mistakes may range from simple blunders, such as miscopying data or misreading a scale, to "sophisticated" errors based on incomplete understanding of physical laws.

Many numbers cannot be represented exactly in a given number of

---

* As a matter of fact, it is not even meaningful to speak of an "exact" measurement; no workable definition of the term can be given.

decimal digits.   If we need π in a calculation, we may write it as 3.14, 3.14159265, or 3.141592653589793.   In any case, we have no *exact* representation of π, which is an irrational number and therefore has no exact finite decimal representation.   Even a simple fraction in many cases has no exact decimal representation, such as $\frac{1}{3}$, which can be written only as a succession of 3's.

It also happens that many fractions which have terminating representations in one number base have no such representations in another base.   The number $\frac{1}{10}$, for instance, obviously has the simple representation 0.1 in decimal, but the binary representation is 0.0001100-11001100 . . . , a nonterminating repeating binary fraction.   Thus, forming the sum of 10 numbers, each of which is a binary approximation to decimal 0.1, will not give exactly 1.0.   Beginners in work with binary computers have been known to become frustrated by their first encounter with this perversity of nature.   The problem is unavoidable; its solution is not difficult, once it is recognized, as we shall see in some of the case studies.

2.4   Truncation errors

Inherent errors refer to errors in the data operated on by a computer with some numerical procedure.   The other two types of errors, truncation and roundoff, refer to errors that are introduced by the way the numerical procedures are done.

The familiar infinite Taylor series

$$\sin x = x - \frac{x^3}{3!} + \frac{x^5}{5!} - \frac{x^7}{7!} + \cdots$$

may be used to calculate the sine of any angle x in radians.*   We cannot, of course, use all the terms in the series in a computation, since the series is infinite; we terminate after calculating some finite number of terms up to, say, x^7 or x^9.   The terms omitted (which are infinite in number) introduce an error into calculated results.   This error is called the *truncation error*, since it is caused by truncating an infinite mathematical process.

Many of the procedures used in numerical calculations are infinite, so that this subject of truncation error assumes major importance. We shall discuss it in detail in later chapters in connection with the topics to which it applies.

---

* We shall see in Chapter 3, however, that this is seldom the best way to compute a sine.

2.5   Roundoff errors

Even if we assume input data that has no inherent error and apply computational processes that are finite and therefore have no truncation error, we can introduce another kind of error in doing simple arithmetic: roundoff error.   Suppose for the moment that we have a computer in which each number contains five digits and that we wish to add 9.2654 and 7.1625, both of which we take to be exact.   The sum is 16.4279, which has six digits and therefore cannot be stored in one location in our hypothetical computer.   The computer must therefore *round off* the six-digit result to 16.428 and in so doing introduces a *roundoff error*.   Since computer work is done with numbers of some fixed number of digits, this requirement for rounding occurs frequently.

In FORTRAN roundoff is of concern only in connection with floating point numbers.   Fixed point numbers, as the term is used in FORTRAN, are integers.   The sum, difference, or product of two integers is always an integer; if a result is too large to fit in one computer location, the program is considered to be in error; the result is *not* rounded and shifted to make it fit.   The quotient of two integers is not always an integer, so that rounding might be thought to be a problem, but in practice fixed point arithmetic is not applied in a way that we ordinarily want to round a quotient.   (In a large majority of engineering calculations fixed point division is not used at all.)

Since floating point roundoff is our primary concern, we shall review the form of representation of a floating point number and establish a notation.   We recall that each number is represented as a fraction often called the mantissa, which is multiplied by a power of the number base, usually called the exponent.   Thus we have numbers such as

$$.7392 \cdot 10^4 \qquad (= 7392.)$$
$$.3246 \cdot 10^2 \qquad (= 32.46)$$
$$.1627 \cdot 10^{-3} \qquad (= .0001627)$$

A floating point number is said to be *normalized* if the leading digit of the mantissa is nonzero.   We shall assume throughout that all floating point numbers are normalized.

If we denote the mantissa of a floating point number x by f and its exponent by e, the generalized form of a floating point number (in decimal) is

$$x = f \cdot 10^e$$

The value of f cannot be less than $\frac{1}{10}$, since we assume normalized numbers; it cannot be so great as 1, since the mantissa is a proper fraction.

The result of an arithmetic operation in general consists of two parts, a more significant half and a less significant half. For instance, suppose we were to add the following two floating point numbers and that we assume for the moment a computer in which the mantissa is four digits and the exponent is one digit.

$$.1624 \cdot 10^3 \quad (= 162.4)$$
$$.1769 \cdot 10^1 \quad (= 1.769)$$

We have said that the computer automatically takes care of decimal-point location problems in doing floating point arithmetic. What this means, in adding, is that the exponents of the two numbers are compared to see how far the mantissa of the number with the smaller exponent should be shifted to the right to "line up" the assumed decimal points. In the illustrative numbers the result would be

$$.1624 \qquad \cdot 10^3$$
$$.001769 \qquad \cdot 10^3$$

In other words, the mantissa of the number with the smaller exponent is shifted to the right as many places as the difference between the exponents. Now, the two mantissas may be added directly.

The sum, obviously, has more than four digits in its mantissa. The result, before rounding, can be shown as two floating point numbers:

$$.1624 \quad \cdot 10^3$$
$$+ \ .001769 \cdot 10^3$$
$$\overline{.164169 \cdot 10^3} = .1641 \cdot 10^3 + .6900 \cdot 10^{-1}$$

Any of the four arithmetic operations will produce a result in two halves. In general, we may denote it (before rounding) by

$$y = f_y \cdot 10^e + g_y \cdot 10^{e-t}$$

where f_y has t digits. The range of possible values of f_y, as we have seen, is $\frac{1}{10} \le |f_y| < 1$. For g_y it is different, since we cannot guarantee that g_y will be normalized; as a matter of fact, g_y can be zero. The range is $0 \le |g_y| < 1$.

We now reach the two questions of primary importance in this discussion: how is g_y to be taken into account in modifying f_y, and for each such rule what is the maximum error in $\bar{y}$ as a result?

"Rounding" usually implies that something is done to f_y, depending on the value of g_y. Under a more general definition of rounding, however, we must include the approach to ignoring g_y entirely, which means that f_y is never modified. This as a rule is called *truncating* the result; we prefer to call it *chopping*, which is acceptable alternative terminology, to avoid confusion with the truncation error in taking only a part of an infinite process—which is not the same thing at all.

A large number of the FORTRAN compilers in operation at the time of writing do in fact set up the object program to use chopping. This kind of rounding introduces more error than the familiar rule, as we shall see. On the other hand, the use of a familiar rounding rule wastes computer time if it is used on *every* arithmetic operation, including the many places in a program in which it is not really essential. Many compiler designers have evidently made the economic decision that chopping does not cause enough trouble to justify the cost of a more sophisticated rule.

A bound on the maximum relative error in a chopped arithmetic result is easily found. The maximum relative error occurs when g_y is large and f_y is small. The maximum possible value of g_y is less than 1.0; the minimum value of f_y is 0.1. The absolute value of the relative error is therefore

$$\left| \frac{e_y}{\bar{y}} \right| = \left| \frac{g_y \cdot 10^{e-t}}{f_y \cdot 10^e} \right| \leq \frac{1 \cdot 10^{e-t}}{0.1 \cdot 10^e} = 10^{-t+1}$$

Remembering that t is the number of digits in the mantissa of *any* floating point number, we have a very interesting result: the maximum relative rounding error in the result of a floating point arithmetic operation does not depend in any way on the sizes of the numbers. This gives us a firm hold on the relative error in floating point calculations.

The more familiar type of rounding, which is usually called *symmetric rounding*, can be expressed as follows: given the two parts of a result, as before, let the rounded approximation to y be given by

$$|\bar{y}| = \begin{cases} |f_y| \cdot 10^e & \text{if } |g_y| < \frac{1}{2} \\ |f_y| \cdot 10^e + 10^{e-t} & \text{if } |g_y| \geq \frac{1}{2} \end{cases}$$

where $\bar{y}$ has the same sign as f_y. The addition of 10^{e-t} in the second line of the equation corresponds to adding 1 in the last digit retained if the first digit dropped is 5 or greater. The absolute value signs are written so that the same formulas apply to positive and negative numbers.

If $|g_y| < \frac{1}{2}$, the absolute error is

$$|e_y| = |g_y| \cdot 10^{e-t}$$

If $|g_y| \geq \frac{1}{2}$, the absolute error is

$$|e_y| = |1 - g_y| \cdot 10^{e-t}$$

Either way, we have 10^{e-t} multiplied by a factor whose absolute value is no greater than $\frac{1}{2}$. The absolute value of the absolute error, therefore, is

$$|e_y| \leq \frac{1}{2} \cdot 10^{e-t}$$

and the absolute value of the relative error is then

$$\left| \frac{e_y}{\bar{y}} \right| \leq \left| \frac{\frac{1}{2} \cdot 10^{e-t}}{f_y \cdot 10^e} \right| \leq \left| \frac{\frac{1}{2} \cdot 10^{e-t}}{0.1 \cdot 10^e} \right| = 5 \cdot 10^{-t} = \frac{1}{2} \cdot 10^{-t+1}$$

Sometimes a slightly more refined rule is used to take into account the case in which g_y is exactly one half: f_y is left unchanged if its last digit is even and rounded up if its last digit is odd. This complicates the design and operation of the computer somewhat and is seldom done.

We shall assume henceforth that the proper rule for rounding is the familiar one, with no special provision for $g_y = \frac{1}{2}$.

For an example of the difference between the two rounding rules, suppose that the result of some arithmetic operation is as follows:

$$y = .7324 \cdot 10^3 + .8261 \cdot 10^{-1}$$

For "chopping"

$$\bar{y} = .7324 \cdot 10^3$$

and

$$\left| \frac{e_y}{\bar{y}} \right| = \frac{.8261 \cdot 10^{-1}}{.7324 \cdot 10^3} \simeq 1.1 \cdot 10^{-4}$$

($\simeq$ means "is approximately equal to.")

For what we have called symmetric rounding,

$$\bar{y} = .7325 \cdot 10^3$$

$$e_y = -.1739 \cdot 10^{-1}$$

and

$$\left| \frac{e_y}{\bar{y}} \right| = \frac{.1739 \cdot 10^{-1}}{.7325 \cdot 10^3} \simeq .24 \cdot 10^{-4}$$

The error from rounding is thus considerably less than the error from chopping in this example. The rounding error never exceeds the chopping error and is less than the chopping error about half the time.

Neither error is nearly so large as the corresponding bound, which is $10 \cdot 10^{-4}$ for chopping and $5 \cdot 10^{-4}$ for symmetric rounding. And it can happen, by good luck or special circumstances, that the roundoff error will be zero. The typical situation is that we know a *bound* on the error in a calculation but not the *actual* error. To be completely safe, we shall always assume the worst, that is, that the error could be as large as the bound. A more satisfactory approach would be to take some kind of "average" error and use statistical techniques to find a most probable value for the total error in a computation. However, such techniques are beyond the scope of this book.

These results have been stated in terms of floating *decimal* numbers. Many computers for scientific calculation operate in floating *binary*, that is, base 2 instead of base 10 numbers. Here, each floating point number is represented as a fraction (expressed in binary, of course) times a power of 2:

$$\bar{x} = f \cdot 2^e \qquad \tfrac{1}{2} \leq |f| < 1$$

An analysis similar to that above leads to a bound on the relative error of $2 \cdot 2^{-t}$ for chopping and 2^{-t} for symmetric rounding.

Some computers are *hexadecimal*, or base 16, in which case the bounds become $16 \cdot 16^{-t}$ for chopping and $8 \cdot 16^{-t}$ for symmetric rounding.

We shall discuss floating point roundoff in later material entirely in terms of floating decimal, to stay with a familiar number system. It should be realized, however, that the results will be slightly different in other number systems.

2.6 Error propagation

A major concern in numerical analysis is the question how an error at one point in a calculation *propagates*, that is, whether its effect becomes greater or smaller as subsequent operations are carried out. The subtraction of two nearly equal numbers is an extreme case: even though the two numbers have small errors, the relative error in the difference may be quite large. This large relative error will be propagated by any succeeding arithmetic operations.

Our first step in this very important study is to find expressions for the absolute and relative error in the result of each of the four arithmetic operations as functions of the operands and their errors. Then in the next section we shall develop a technique for finding a bound on the total error in a calculation containing any number of arithmetic operations.

Addition

We have two approximations, $\bar{x}$ and $\bar{y}$, to two true values, x and y, together with respective errors, e_x and e_y. Then we have

$$x + y = \bar{x} + e_x + \bar{y} + e_y = (\bar{x} + \bar{y}) + (e_x + e_y)$$

The error in the sum, which we shall denote by e_{x+y}, is therefore

$$e_{x+y} = e_x + e_y$$

Subtraction
In a similar manner we get

$$e_{x-y} = e_x - e_y$$

Multiplication
Here we have

$$x \cdot y = (\bar{x} + e_x) \cdot (\bar{y} + e_y)$$
$$= \bar{x}\bar{y} + \bar{x}e_y + \bar{y}e_x + e_xe_y$$

We assume that the errors are much smaller than the approximations, and we shall ignore the product of the errors. Thus

$$x \cdot y \simeq \bar{x}\bar{y} + \bar{x}e_y + \bar{y}e_x$$

and

$$e_{x \cdot y} \simeq \bar{x}e_y + \bar{y}e_x$$

Division
We have

$$\frac{x}{y} = \frac{\bar{x} + e_x}{\bar{y} + e_y}$$

Multiply the denominator by $\bar{y}/\bar{y}$ and rearrange to get

$$\frac{x}{y} = \frac{\bar{x} + e_x}{\bar{y}} \left(\frac{1}{1 + e_y/\bar{y}} \right)$$

The factor in parentheses can be expanded in a series by long division:

$$\frac{x}{y} = \frac{\bar{x} + e_x}{\bar{y}} \cdot \left(1 - \frac{e_y}{\bar{y}} + \left(\frac{e_y}{\bar{y}} \right)^2 - \cdots \right)$$

Multiplying out and dropping all terms that involve products or powers greater than 1 of e_x and e_y, we have

$$\frac{x}{y} \simeq \frac{\bar{x}}{\bar{y}} + \frac{e_x}{\bar{y}} - \frac{\bar{x}}{\bar{y}^2} e_y$$

Therefore

$$e_{x/y} \simeq \frac{1}{\bar{y}} e_x - \frac{\bar{x}}{\bar{y}^2} e_y$$

For a simple example of the meaning of these formulas, consider the addition of two four-place logarithms. Since we may assume that the logarithms are both correct to four places, we know that the error in each is no greater than 0.00005.   The error in the sum can be no greater than 0.0001.   Naturally, we do not know that it *is* that great but only that it *could* be that large.

It must be realized that we seldom know the sign of an error.   It should not be inferred, for instance, that addition always increases the error and subtraction always decreases it just because the errors add in addition and subtract in subtraction.   This will not be true, of course, if the errors have different signs.

Since we now have formulas for the propagation of absolute errors in the four arithmetic operations, it is a simple matter to divide and get the relative errors.   For addition and subtraction the results have been rearranged to display explicitly the effect of errors in the operands.

Addition

$$\frac{e_{x+y}}{\bar{x} + \bar{y}} = \frac{\bar{x}}{\bar{x} + \bar{y}}\left(\frac{e_x}{\bar{x}}\right) + \frac{\bar{y}}{\bar{x} + \bar{y}}\left(\frac{e_y}{\bar{y}}\right)$$

Subtraction

$$\frac{e_{x-y}}{\bar{x} - \bar{y}} = \frac{\bar{x}}{\bar{x} - \bar{y}}\left(\frac{e_x}{\bar{x}}\right) - \frac{\bar{y}}{\bar{x} - \bar{y}}\left(\frac{e_y}{\bar{y}}\right)$$

Multiplication

$$\frac{e_{x \cdot y}}{\bar{x} \cdot \bar{y}} = \frac{e_x}{\bar{x}} + \frac{e_y}{\bar{y}}$$

Division

$$\frac{e_{x/y}}{\bar{x}/\bar{y}} = \frac{e_x}{\bar{x}} - \frac{e_y}{\bar{y}}$$

It is important to understand clearly what these error propagation formulas mean.   We start with two approximate values, $\bar{x}$ and $\bar{y}$, containing errors e_x and e_y.   The errors may be of any type.   The values of $\bar{x}$ and $\bar{y}$ may be experimental results containing inherent errors; they may be the results of some prior calculation by an infinite process and therefore may contain truncation errors; they may be the results of prior arithmetic operations and therefore may contain roundoff errors.   They may also easily be some combination of the three.

The formulas, then, give the error in the result of each of the four arithmetic operations as functions of $\bar{x}$ and $\bar{y}$, e_x, and e_y, *assuming no roundoff error*.   If, as is often the case, we now want to know how the error in this result propagates in still other arithmetic operations, *we must add in the roundoff error explicitly*.

We will often write x without the bar, even though to be completely

precise the bar should be written.   It will be clear from the context
that an approximation is represented and not the true value.

The situation can be made much clearer with an example.   Suppose we start a calculation with three numbers, x, y, and z, and to
make matters simpler let us assume that they are exact, that is, that
they have no errors of any kind.   Suppose we calculate

$$u = (x + y) \cdot z$$

As the expression is written, the addition must be done first.   Both
operands are assumed to have no error, so that the error *propagated*
by the addition is zero; however, a roundoff error is introduced in
doing the addition.   This roundoff error can be viewed as an inherent
error in the sum as we now go on to do the multiplication.   Let us
agree to understand by e_{x+y} the total error in the sum, including any
propagated error and roundoff.   Then

$$\left| \frac{e_{x+y}}{x + y} \right| \leq 5 \cdot 10^{-t}$$

which is simply the bound on the roundoff error in any arithmetic
operation, always assuming symmetric rounding.   Here again we are
assuming a computer in which a floating point number has a fractional
part consisting of t decimal digits.

We know that the relative error in a product is the sum of the relative errors in the two factors, plus the rounding error in the multiplication.   Since the result of the multiplication is just $\bar{u}$, our approximation of u, we can write

$$\frac{e_u}{\bar{u}} = \frac{e_{x+y}}{x + y} + \frac{e_z}{z} + r_m$$

where e_z/z is the relative error in z and r_m is the rounding error in the
multiplication.   But we took the error in z to be zero, and

$$\left| \frac{e_u}{\bar{u}} \right| = \left| \frac{e_{x+y}}{x + y} + r_m \right| \leq \left| \frac{e_{x+y}}{x + y} \right| + |r_m|$$

(The last inequality is called the *triangle inequality*: the equality applies
if $e_{x+y}/(x + y)$ and r_m have the same signs, and the inequality if they
have different signs.)   We thus have

$$\left| \frac{e_u}{\bar{u}} \right| \leq 5 \cdot 10^{-t} + 5 \cdot 10^{-t}$$

Since we know $\bar{u}$ at the end of the calculation, we can easily get the bound on the absolute error:

$$|e_u| \le |\bar{u}| \cdot 10^{-t+1}$$

2.7   Process graphs

We now have expressions for the propagation of the errors in the operands of arithmetic operations, and we have seen in an example how to find the total error in a calculation.   What we need now is a more convenient way to handle the error propagation in a complete calculation.

A *process graph** is a pictorial representation of the sequence in which the arithmetic operations in a calculation are carried out and a scheme for labeling the arrows that appear in the graph so that the total error in the final result is more easily found.   The method also makes it quite easy to determine the contribution of any one error, anywhere in the sequence, to the total error.

Figure 2.1 is the process graph for the example in the preceding section, $u = (x + y) \cdot z$.   A process graph is read from the bottom up, following the arrows.   All operations at any one horizontal level are done first, then all operations at the next higher level, and so on. Figure 2.1 makes it explicit, for instance, that x and y are first added, and the result is multiplied by z.

So far we have only a picture of the order of arithmetic operations, which is interesting but not the main purpose.   Now we add labels to each of the arrows, according to the following rules, to show how the errors propagate.

Addition
Let the two arrows leading to an addition circle come from two circles whose results are a_1 and a_2.   (These "results" may actually be those of other operations or, as here, input data.)   The arrow from a_1 to $\oplus$ is labeled $a_1/(a_1 + a_2)$ and the arrow from a_2 to $\oplus$ is labeled $a_2/(a_1 + a_2)$.

Subtraction
If the operation is $a_1 - a_2$, the appropriate arrows may be labeled $a_1/(a_1 - a_2)$ and $-a_2/(a_1 - a_2)$.

Multiplication
The two arrows leading to a multiplication are both labeled $+1$.

---

* The use of the process graph for this purpose was first suggested to the authors by Dr. Kenneth M. King of Columbia University.

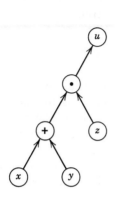

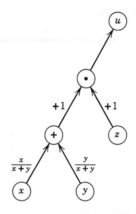

FIGURE 2.1   Process graph of the operation $u = (x + y) \cdot z$.

FIGURE 2.2   The process graph of Figure 2.1,
with the arrows labeled to show the propagation of errors.

Division

If the division is a_1/a_2, the arrow from a_1 to $\oslash$ is labeled $+1$, and the arrow from a_2 to $\oslash$ is labeled -1.

The point of all this is contained in the following rule: *The relative error in the result of any operation (circle) appears in the result of the next operation multiplied by the term on the arrow connecting the operations.*

For example, consider Figure 2.2, which is the same as Figure 2.1 except that the arrows have been labeled properly.

Let us now assume that the three numbers in Figure 2.1 have relative inherent roundoff errors of i_x, i_y, and i_z and see how the rule is applied.   Consider first the addition.   We have a relative error of i_x in x; this appears in the result of the next operation (the addition) multiplied by the term on the arrow connecting $\widehat{x}$ and $\oplus$:

$$\frac{x}{x + y}\, i_x$$

We have omitted the bars from x and y but it should be understood that these are approximations to the true values.   Likewise, the error in y, i_y, appears in the result of the next operation multiplied by the term on the arrow connecting $\widehat{y}$ and $\oplus$:

$$\frac{y}{x + y}\, i_y$$

There is, finally, a roundoff error in the addition, which we call r_1, and the total relative error in the result of the addition is

$$\frac{e_{x+y}}{x+y} = \frac{x}{x+y}\, i_x + \frac{y}{x+y}\, i_y + r_1$$

The rule may now be applied to the multiplication. One of the inputs is the sum of x and y, which has an error as just stated; this becomes an inherent error in the input to the multiplication, which appears in the result of the multiplication, according to the rule, multiplied by $+1$. The inherent roundoff error in z, i_z, shows in the result of the multiplication, also multiplied by $+1$. The multiplication will have a roundoff error that we call r_2, and the total error after the multiplication, which is the total error in u, is

$$\frac{e_u}{u} = \frac{x}{x+y}\, i_x \cdot 1 + \frac{y}{x+y}\, i_y \cdot 1 + r_1 \cdot 1 + i_z \cdot 1 + r_2$$

If all results are properly rounded (according to the agreed-on rounding method), none of the roundoff errors will exceed $5 \cdot 10^{-t}$. Thus we have

$$\left| \frac{e_u}{u} \right| \le \left(\left| \frac{x}{x+y} \right| + \left| \frac{y}{x+y} \right| + 3 \right) \cdot 5 \cdot 10^{-t}$$

Now if x and y are both non-negative, then

$$\left| \frac{x}{x+y} \right| + \left| \frac{y}{x+y} \right|$$

cannot exceed 1, and we finally have

$$\left| \frac{e_u}{u} \right| \le 20 \cdot 10^{-t} = 2 \cdot 10^{-t+1}$$

2.8   Examples

Let us now apply the process graph technique to three examples, to see what error propagation means in terms of practical computations. The conclusions we draw will be directly usable in a number of situations in later chapters. These examples also nicely illustrate the special problems in working with a digital computer; the first two results, in particular, are not what our training in classical mathematics would lead us to expect.

Example 1

Addition of positive numbers that are sorted into ascending order.

Consider the problem of adding four positive numbers:

$$y = x_1 + x_2 + x_3 + x_4$$

where

$$0 < x_1 < x_2 < x_3 < x_4$$

A process graph is shown in Figure 2.3. Let us suppose that there are no inherent errors in the x_i, and let r_1, r_2, and r_3 be the relative roundoff errors, reading from the bottom. A systematic application of the rule for the total error in a process graph gives

$$\frac{e_y}{y} = r_1 \frac{x_1 + x_2}{x_1 + x_2 + x_3} \cdot \frac{x_1 + x_2 + x_3}{x_1 + x_2 + x_3 + x_4} + r_2 \frac{x_1 + x_2 + x_3}{x_1 + x_2 + x_3 + x_4} + r_3$$

Cancelling the $x_1 + x_2 + x_3$ in the first term and multiplying through by $y = x_1 + x_2 + x_3 + x_4$ gives us

$$e_y = r_1(x_1 + x_2) + r_2(x_1 + x_2 + x_3) + r_3(x_1 + x_2 + x_3 + x_4)$$

Multiplying out and rearranging gives

$$|e_y| \le (3x_1 + 3x_2 + 2x_3 + x_4) \cdot 5 \cdot 10^{-t}$$

It is clear that the bound on the total error (absolute or relative) due to roundoff is minimized by arranging the numbers so that the smallest numbers are added first.

This result is somewhat on the surprising side, when one's whole mathematical training has been based on the assumption—often unstated—that addition is commutative and associative. The difference, if it is not obvious, is that we are not dealing with infinite precision, which is tacitly assumed in classical mathematics. Every result in a computer must be expressed in some finite number of digits, and this simple-appearing restriction completely changes many of the "standard" mathematical ideas.

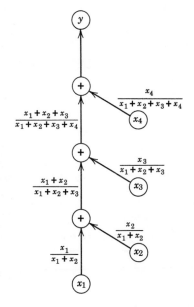

FIGURE 2.3 Process graph for the addition $y = x_1 + x_2 + x_3 + x_4$, where $0 < x_1 < x_2 < x_3 < x_4$.

For n numbers having no inherent errors the formula for the total error bound due to roundoff is

$$|e_y| \le [(n-1)x_1 + (n-1)x_2 + (n-2)x_3 + \cdots + 2x_{n-1} + x_n] \cdot 5 \cdot 10^{-t}$$

For a numerical example suppose we need to form the sums of the following numbers:

$$0.2897 \cdot 10^0$$
$$0.4976 \cdot 10^0$$
$$0.2488 \cdot 10^1$$
$$0.7259 \cdot 10^1$$
$$0.1638 \cdot 10^2$$
$$0.6249 \cdot 10^2$$
$$0.2162 \cdot 10^3$$
$$0.5233 \cdot 10^3$$
$$0.1403 \cdot 10^4$$
$$0.5291 \cdot 10^4$$

If we add in ascending order, the successive partial sums are as follows. (The first partial sum is the sum of the first two numbers; the second partial sum is the sum of the first partial sum and the third number; etc.)   Bear in mind that we are assuming a computer in which each mantissa is four digits; every partial sum that exceeds four digits must be rounded off.   This fact, of course, is basic to the entire discussion, although eight digits would be more typical of computer numbers.

$$0.7873 \cdot 10^0$$
$$0.3275 \cdot 10^1$$
$$0.1053 \cdot 10^2$$
$$0.2691 \cdot 10^2$$
$$0.8940 \cdot 10^2$$
$$0.3056 \cdot 10^3$$
$$0.8289 \cdot 10^3$$
$$0.2232 \cdot 10^4$$
$$0.7523 \cdot 10^4$$

If, on the other hand, we add the 10 numbers in reverse order, from largest to smallest, the partial sums are

$$0.6694 \cdot 10^4$$
$$0.7217 \cdot 10^4$$
$$0.7433 \cdot 10^4$$
$$0.7495 \cdot 10^4$$
$$0.7511 \cdot 10^4$$

$$0.7518 \cdot 10^4$$
$$0.7520 \cdot 10^4$$
$$0.7520 \cdot 10^4$$
$$0.7520 \cdot 10^4$$

The correct sum to eight figures can be found by keeping all digits at each addition. It is $0.75229043 \cdot 10^4$. The error in the ascending sum is thus $-0.1 \cdot 10^0$, whereas the error in the descending sum is $2.9 \cdot 10^0$, about 30 times greater.

The bounds on the errors are about $5.5 \cdot 10^0$ for the ascending sum and $33 \cdot 10^0$ for the descending sum. In both cases the actual errors are considerably less than the maximum possible. The maximum error, as given by the bounds, occurs when rounding every partial sum requires dropping a less significant half that is nearly $\frac{1}{2}$, which is seldom the case.

Notice that if the two smallest numbers are discarded the ascending sum becomes $0.7522 \cdot 10^4$, which is slightly different, but that the descending sum is unchanged at $0.7520 \cdot 10^4$. What happens is that the two smallest numbers in the descending sum are both too small to affect the last digit of the partial sum when they are added separately. In the ascending sum, on the other hand, they are added first, and their sum is large enough to have effect on the last digit of the larger partial sums.

Example 2

Addition of nearly equal positive numbers. Suppose that we are adding four positive numbers, but now they are nearly equal. We may write

$$x_i = x_0 + \delta_i, \qquad i = 1, 2, 3, 4$$

where

$$|\delta_i| \ll x_0$$

(The symbol $\ll$ means "is *much* less than.") A straightforward application of the result for adding four numbers gives

$$|e_y| \leq (9x_0 + 3|\delta_1| + 3|\delta_2| + 2|\delta_3| + |\delta_4|) \cdot 5 \cdot 10^{-t}$$

Since $|\delta_i|$ is small compared with x_0, we have approximately

$$|e_y| \leq 4.5 \cdot 10^{-t+1} \cdot x_0$$

This result is based on computing partial sums as expressed by the process graph of Figure 2.3. Consider an alternative way of forming the sum, as in the process graph of Figure 2.4. Here $y = (x_1 + x_2) + (x_3 + x_4)$, where the operations in parentheses are carried out first.

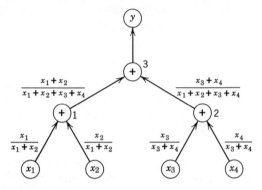

FIGURE 2.4 A different process graph for adding four numbers. The numbers next to the addition circles give the sequence of the additions.

If we call the relative roundoff errors in the three additions r_1, r_2, and r_3, with the subscripts corresponding to the order of the additions, we have

$$\frac{e_y}{y} = r_1 \cdot \frac{x_1 + x_2}{x_1 + x_2 + x_3 + x_4} + r_2 \cdot \frac{x_3 + x_4}{x_1 + x_2 + x_3 + x_4} + r_3$$

Rearranging, we get

$$|e_y| \leq (2x_1 + 2x_2 + 2x_3 + 2x_4) \cdot 5 \cdot 10^{-t}$$

Again setting $x_i = x_0 + \delta_i$ and neglecting terms in $|\delta_i|$ compared with x_0, we get finally

$$|e_y| \leq 4 \cdot 10^{-t+1} \cdot x_0$$

Comparing with the error bound for the process graph of Figure 2.3, we see that this arrangement of the additions yields a slightly lower bound, a result that is not intuitively obvious.

In general, if we wish to add n^2 positive numbers of approximately the same magnitude, the total roundoff error is reduced if they are added in n groups of n each and the n partial sums are added. For large n the bound on the error is only $1/n$ as large as it is for simple addition of all n^2 in a single "stream" (see Figure 2.3).

For a numerical example, consider these four numbers:

$$x_1 = 0.5243 \cdot 10^0$$
$$x_2 = 0.5262 \cdot 10^0$$
$$x_3 = 0.5226 \cdot 10^0$$
$$x_4 = 0.5278 \cdot 10^0$$

We can let $x_0 = 0.5200$ and $t = 4$ as usual. Adding them one after the other and rounding properly at each addition, we get $y = 0.2102 \cdot 10^1$. By forming $x_1 + x_2 = 0.1051 \cdot 10^1$ and $x_3 + x_4 = 0.1050 \cdot 10^1$, we get $y = 0.2101 \cdot 10^1$. The exact sum is $0.21009 \cdot 10^1$.

It may occur to the inexperienced reader to wonder whether these small improvements are worth the trouble. It should always be kept in mind that we are working with examples that need only a few operations. Later on we will see processes that require hundreds or frequently even thousands of arithmetic operations; in these more realistic situations a small error can be greatly multiplied by the later operations. The things we are discussing are definitely of practical importance.

Example 3

Subtraction of two nearly equal numbers. Suppose we have $z = x - y$. Then from the formulas on p. 54

$$\frac{e_z}{z} = \frac{x}{x - y}\left(\frac{e_x}{x}\right) - \frac{y}{x - y}\left(\frac{e_y}{y}\right)$$

Now suppose x and y are properly rounded positive numbers, so that

$$\left|\frac{e_x}{x}\right| \le 5 \cdot 10^{-t} \quad \text{and} \quad \left|\frac{e_y}{y}\right| \le 5 \cdot 10^{-t}$$

If $x - y$ is small, the relative error in z may be large, even though the absolute error is small. Since it is relative errors that are propagated in floating point computation, this can have a drastic effect on the final results.

For a simple example suppose that we have

$$x = 0.5628 \cdot 10^4$$

$$y = 0.5631 \cdot 10^4$$

Then

$$z = -0.0003 \cdot 10^4$$

Since we know x and y, we know

$$\left|\frac{e_x}{x}\right| \le 0.5 \cdot 10^{-4} = 0.005\%$$

$$\left|\frac{e_y}{y}\right| \le 0.5 \cdot 10^{-4} = 0.005\%$$

which are small relative errors.   Yet

$$\left| \frac{e_z}{z} \right| \le \frac{10^4}{3} \cdot 10^{-4} = \frac{1}{3} = 33\%$$

which is large.   This large relative error in $x - y$ is then propagated through all following computations.   If the next operation were to multiply by $0.7259 \cdot 10^4$, the result, if we printed it, would be $0.2178 \cdot 10^5$, which has four digits of precision; the beginner is tempted to believe them.   Yet there is only one digit that is significant.

2.9   An accuracy checklist

Some of the ideas presented in this chapter can be summarized in a short list of suggestions for practical computation.   Some of the exercises that follow illustrate these points, and are referenced accordingly.

1. When numbers are to be added and/or subtracted, work with the smallest numbers first (Exercise 13).

2. If possible, avoid subtraction of two nearly equal numbers.   An expression containing such a subtraction can often be rewritten to avoid it (Exercises 12, 14, and 18).

3. An expression such as $a(b - c)$ can be rewritten as $ab - ac$, and $(a - b)/c$ can be rewritten as $a/c - b/c$.   If there are nearly equal numbers, *do the subtraction before multiplying*.   This will avoid compounding the problem with additional roundoff errors (Exercises 16 and 17).

4. When none of the above applies, minimize the number of arithmetic operations (Exercises 6 and 7).

Exercises

*1. Current flows through a 10-ohm resistance that is accurate within 10%.
The current is measured as 2.0 amp, within ±0.1 amp.   From Ohm's law, the voltage drop across the resistance is the product of the resistance and the current.   What are the absolute and relative errors in the computed voltage?   Neglect roundoff errors.

2. The average airline route distance from New York to San Francisco is 2700 miles, but may be 200 miles shorter or longer because of route variations.   The cruising speed of a certain airliner is 580 mph, but may vary as much as 60 mph either way because of winds.   What are the bounds on the time of the flight?

3. The reactance of a capacitor is given by

$$X_c = \frac{1}{2\pi fC}$$

where X_c = capacitive reactance, ohms
   f = frequency, cycles per second
   C = capacitance, farads

What are the bounds on X_c for $f = 400 \pm 1$ cps and $C = 10^{-7}$ farads $\pm 10\%$?

4. The position S of a body falling freely in a vacuum is given by

$$S = \tfrac{1}{2}gt^2$$

where g = acceleration of gravity, feet/second^2
   t = time since release, seconds.

Assume that $g = 32.2$ ft/sec^2, exactly, but that t can be measured to only ± 0.1 sec. Show that, as t increases, the absolute error of the computed value of S increases but that the relative error decreases.

*5. Assume that a is a positive, properly rounded number, and that the number 2 can be represented in a computer exactly. Draw process graphs and derive bounds on maximum relative errors to show that the bounds are the same for $u = a + a$ and $v = 2a$.

*6. With the same assumptions as in Exercise 5, show that the bound on the maximum relative error for $u = a + a + a$ is greater than that for $v = 3a$. Illustrate with $a = 0.6992$, keeping only four digits after each arithmetic operation.

7. Assume that a and b are properly rounded positive numbers. Draw process graphs and derive error-bound expressions to show that the bound on the relative error of $u = 3(ab)$ is less than that for $v = (a + a + a)b$. Illustrate with $a = 0.4299$ and $b = 0.6824$.

*8. Assume that x is a properly rounded number. Draw process graphs and derive error-bound expressions to show that $u = x \cdot (x \cdot (x \cdot x))$ and $v = (x^2)^2$ have the same error bounds.

9. Assume that x is a properly rounded number. Draw process graphs and derive error-bound expressions to show that $u = x \cdot (x \cdot (x \cdot (x \cdot (x \cdot (x \cdot (x \cdot x))))))$ and $v = ((x^2)^2)^2$ have the same error bounds.

10. Show that in floating decimal $10./10. = 10.*(1./10.)$ and $2./2. = 2.*(1./2.)$ but $3./3. \neq 3.*(1./3.)$.

*11. Assume that a, b, and x are positive and exact. Draw process graphs and derive error-bound expressions to show that the relative roundoff error bounds for $u = ax + bx^2$ and $v = x(a + bx)$ are the same. Use $a = 0.7625$, $b = 0.6947$, and $x = 0.4302$ to show that although the bounds are the same the actual errors, which are usually smaller than the bounds, need not be the same.

12. Assume that a and b are positive and exact and that $a > b$. Show that although in infinite precision it is true that $a + b = (a^2 - b^2)/(a - b)$,

roundoff errors may make the value of the right-hand expression considerably different from that of the left-hand. Show that the worst case
occurs when the roundoff errors made in forming a^2 and b^2 are near
the maximum but of opposite signs. Illustrate with $a = 0.3525$ and
$b = 0.3411$, using four-digit floating point arithmetic.

13. Assume that a is a properly rounded positive number and that 1 can be
represented exactly. Consider the expressions $u = (1 + a)^2$ and $v = 1 + (2a + a^2)$. Show that as a becomes very large the relative error
bounds for u and v approach equality but that as a becomes very small
the relative error bound for u approaches three times the relative error
bound for v. Illustrate with $a = 0.2635$.

14. Draw a process graph and derive an expression for the bound on the
relative error for $(a + b) - b$. Illustrate with $a = 0.8614 \cdot 10^{-2}$ and
$b = 0.9949$ and with $a = 0.3204$ and $b = 0.5837$.

15. Consider the expression $5a + b$. Show that in the result the relative
inherent error in a is weighted five times as heavily as the relative
inherent error in b.

*16. Consider the expressions $u = (a - b)/c$ and $v = a/c - b/c$. Assume
that a, b, and c are all positive and have no inherent errors and that
$a \simeq b$. Show that the relative roundoff error in v can be much greater
than the relative roundoff error in u. Illustrate with $a = 0.41, b = 0.36$,
and $c = 0.70$, using two-digit floating point arithmetic.

17. Consider the expressions $u = a \cdot (b - c)$ and $v = ab - ac$, in which we
assume that $a > 0$, $b > 0$, $c > 0$, $b > c$, and $b \simeq c$. Show that u has
much better relative accuracy under the conditions stated. Show that,
with $a = 0.9364$, $b = 0.6392$, and $c = 0.6375$, $u = 0.1592 \cdot 10^{-2}$, which
is properly rounded from the exact answer, but $v = 0.1500 \cdot 10^{-2}$.

*18. In the quadratic equation $ax^2 + bx + c = 0$, assume that the coefficients
are all positive and exact and that $b^2 \gg 4ac$. Show first that in infinite
precision the smaller in absolute value of the two roots is given either by

$$x_1 = \frac{-b + \sqrt{b^2 - 4ac}}{2a}$$

or

$$x_1' = \frac{-2c}{b + \sqrt{b^2 - 4ac}}$$

Then show that for the conditions stated x_1' gives much better relative
accuracy. Show that, with $a = 0.1000 \cdot 10^1$, $b = 0.4002 \cdot 10^0$, and $c = 0.8000 \cdot 10^{-4}$, $x_1 = -0.1500 \cdot 10^{-3}$ and $x_1' = -0.2000 \cdot 10^{-3}$. The last
is the exact root. (You may show the square root operation in a process
graph as a circle with only one operand leading to it. The inherent
relative error in the operand appears in the square root multiplied by $\frac{1}{2}$,
and the arrow leading from the operand to the square root circle may be
so labeled. The square root contains an additional relative roundoff
error that in most FORTRAN systems will not exceed 10^{-t+1}.)

19. Consider the simultaneous equations

$$ax + by = c$$

$$dx + ey = f$$

and the solution by Cramer's rule

$$x = \frac{ce - bf}{ae - bd}$$

$$y = \frac{af - cd}{ae - bd}$$

Show that if $ae - bd$ is small the accuracy of the solution may be poor, even if the coefficients have no inherent errors. Illustrate by showing that the solution of the system

$$0.2038x + 0.1218y = 0.2014$$

$$0.4071x + 0.2436y = 0.4038$$

obtained with four-digit floating point arithmetic is $x = -1.714$, $y = 4.286$, whereas the exact solution, which can be obtained with eight-digit floating point arithmetic, is $x = -2.000$, $y = 5.000$. If the coefficients themselves are inexact, as they almost always are, the "solution" of this system can be totally meaningless.

20. The following problem, suggested by Richard V. Andree, demonstrates effectively that roundoff is not the only problem in numerical computation. Consider the system

$$x + 5.0y = 17.0$$

$$1.5x + 7.501y = 25.503$$

Show that if enough digits are carried to make all roundoff "errors" zero the system will have a unique solution, $x = 2$, $y = 3$. Now show that if the constant term in the second equation is changed to 25.501, a modification of one part in about 12,000, a greatly different solution will be obtained.

If the coefficients and constant terms were experimental results, with a corresponding doubt about their exact values, the "solution" would be meaningless.

—3

Practical Evaluation of Functions

3.1 Introduction

We have seen in Chapter 1 that the common elementary functions—sine, cosine, logarithm, etc.—are available in FORTRAN simply by writing the appropriate names. For many purposes these automatically supplied functions are completely adequate. At other times, however, they may not be fast enough; they may compute the function to much more accuracy than is needed, and thereby waste time, or a function may be needed that is not available in the standard list.

For these reasons we begin our study of actual methods of numerical computation with the subject of function evaluation. The presentation is in terms of a familiar function, the sine, but it should be realized that the same methods apply to any function that can be expressed as a Taylor series. The Taylor series for a function, with which we assume the reader is familiar from calculus, is the starting point in evaluating any function by the methods that are discussed.

Besides presenting methods by which functions can be evaluated, this chapter considers the important topic of how best to evaluate a polynomial and continues the development of the fundamental idea of error analysis.

3.2 Power series

The first thing to do in working with any series expression for a function, if possible, is to reduce the range of the argument for which computation is required. This will greatly reduce roundoff error. The "mathematical" definition of the sine in terms of the familiar

68

power (Taylor) series is completely valid for *all* values of the argument, that is, if it were possible to keep an infinite number of digits in each arithmetic operation. *Computationally*, the simple sine series becomes useless for large angles and gives results that have no significant figures at all.

Fortunately, in the case of the sine series this is no problem. Recall that if n is an integer

$$\sin (n\pi + y) = \sin n\pi \cos y + \cos n\pi \sin y = (-1)^n \sin y,$$

$$-\frac{\pi}{2} \leq y \leq \frac{\pi}{2}$$

Thus by subtracting a suitable multiple of π we can reduce the problem of finding the sine of any angle to that of finding the sine of an angle between $-\pi/2$ and $\pi/2$. Finally, if we make the substitution

$$y = \frac{\pi x}{2}, \qquad \sin y = \sin \frac{\pi x}{2}$$

it is sufficient to consider $\sin \pi x/2$ for $-1 \leq x \leq 1$.

The reduction is not actually done by repeated subtraction. The original angle is instead divided by π, with the division arranged within the machine so that the quotient is an integer. The remainder must then be an angle between 0 and π. If the remainder is between $\pi/2$ and π, one final subtraction of π gives an angle between $-\pi/2$ and $\pi/2$. The integer quotient is used only to determine whether the sign of the final result should be changed.

These preliminary operations on the angle modify its inherent error. The value of π used in the division contains an inherent roundoff error since π is an irrational number; reducing the size of the angle increases its relative error even though the absolute error is the same; the substitution $y = \pi x/2$ introduces a further roundoff error. A thorough error analysis must consider all of these factors. In practice, however, such effects will be overshadowed by the uncertainty in the value of the original angle and by the error committed in truncating the series used to compute the value of the function. It is the last point that is our primary concern.

The first five terms of the Taylor series for the sine are

$$(3.1) \quad \sin \frac{\pi x}{2} \simeq \frac{\pi x}{2} - \frac{1}{3!}\left(\frac{\pi x}{2}\right)^3 + \frac{1}{5!}\left(\frac{\pi x}{2}\right)^5 - \frac{1}{7!}\left(\frac{\pi x}{2}\right)^7 + \frac{1}{9!}\left(\frac{\pi x}{2}\right)^9$$

$$= 1.5707963x - 0.64596410x^3 + 0.079692626x^5$$
$$- 0.0046817541x^7 + 0.00016044118x^9$$

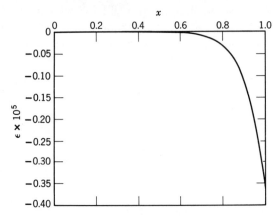

FIGURE 3.1   The error curve for the truncated Taylor series (3.1).

The full series, of course, has an infinite number of terms, so we have introduced a truncation error. It can be shown that for any alternating convergent series this truncation error is no greater than the first term neglected:

$$(3.2) \qquad |e_T| \leq \frac{1}{11!}\left(\frac{\pi x}{2}\right)^{11} \leq 0.0000035988 \simeq 3.6 \cdot 10^{-6}$$

(x is, at most, 1.)

Figure 3.1 is a plot of the total error committed by using (3.1). This total error includes both roundoff and truncation error, but the truncation error predominates in this case. Notice that although the error is essentially zero for $|x| < \frac{1}{2}$ it rapidly becomes large for x near 1. The maximum error is $3.54 \cdot 10^{-6}$, which agrees with the bound given in (3.2).

3.3   Chebyshev series

It is of interest to see whether there is some way to reduce the size of the error near $x = 1$. As it happens, we can do so, but only at the expense of increasing the error somewhere else. The technique to be explored now, the Chebyshev series, spreads the error over the entire interval.

Toward this end we define the Chebyshev polynomials $T_n(x)$ as follows:

$$(3.3) \qquad T_n(x) = \cos n\theta$$

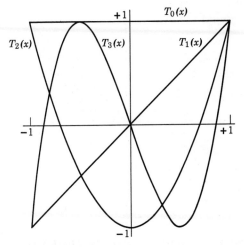

FIGURE 3.2   Graphs of the Chebyshev polynomials $T_0(x)$, $T_1(x)$, $T_2(x)$, and $T_3(x)$.

where $x = \cos \theta$.   In other words,

$$T_n(x) = \cos (n \arccos x)$$

For example,

(3.4) $T_0(x) = \cos 0 = 1$

(3.5) $T_1(x) = \cos \theta = x$

(3.6) $T_2(x) = \cos 2\theta = \cos^2 \theta - \sin^2 \theta = x^2 - (1 - x^2) = 2x^2 - 1$

We could go on using trigonometric identities to find as many of the $T_n(x)$ as we wished, but instead let us establish a recurrence relation that will define *any* $T_{n+1}(x)$ in terms of $T_n(x)$ and $T_{n-1}(x)$.

$$T_{n+1}(x) = \cos (n\theta + \theta) = \cos n\theta \cos \theta - \sin n\theta \sin \theta$$

$$T_{n-1}(x) = \cos (n\theta - \theta) = \cos n\theta \cos \theta + \sin n\theta \sin \theta$$

By adding these two equations, we get

$$T_{n+1}(x) + T_{n-1}(x) = 2 \cos n\theta \cos \theta = 2x T_n(x)$$

and

(3.7) $$T_{n+1}(x) = 2x T_n(x) - T_{n-1}(x)$$

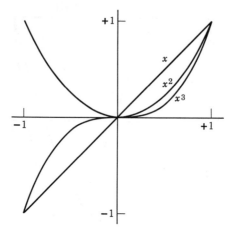

FIGURE 3.3 Graphs of the first three powers of x.

From (3.4), (3.5), (3.6), and (3.7) we can find any Chebyshev polynomial. For instance, by letting $n = 2$ in (3.7) we have

$$T_3(x) = 2xT_2(x) - T_1(x)$$

and by using (3.5) and (3.6)

$$T_3(x) = 2x(2x^2 - 1) - x = 4x^3 - 3x$$

A list of the first 12 Chebyshev polynomials is given in Appendix 2, Part A, together with the first 11 powers of x expressed in terms of Chebyshev polynomials.

The first four Chebyshev polynomials are plotted in Figure 3.2. Succeeding $T_n(x)$ continue to oscillate between ± 1, with the oscillations becoming more frequent as n gets larger.

By way of contrast, and to show why we are interested in Chebyshev polynomials, the first three powers of x are plotted in Figure 3.3. Comparing the two figures, we see that a change in the coefficients of the functions used in a Taylor series $(1, x, x^2, x^3, \ldots)$ will have a much larger effect near $x = 1$ than at zero, whereas the effect of a change in the coefficients of a series whose terms are the Chebyshev polynomials will be spread out over the whole interval ± 1.

The problem of finding the coefficients of the Chebyshev series is

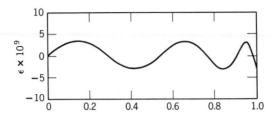

FIGURE 3.4 The error curve for the approximation (3.8). Note the change of scale from Figure 3.1.

somewhat complex and is not discussed here.* The result for a sine series that uses Chebyshev polynomials up to degree 9 and therefore results in an expression of odd powers of x up to degree 9 is as follows:†

$$(3.8) \quad \sin\left(\frac{\pi x}{2}\right) = 1.5707963x - 0.64596336x^3 + 0.079688475x^5$$
$$- 0.0046722203x^7 + 0.00015081716x^9$$

The error curve for this approximation is shown in Figure 3.4. It should be compared with the Taylor series of Figure 3.1, which contains the same powers of x, but with different coefficients. (Note the change in scale.) We see here the characteristics of the expansion in Chebyshev polynomials: the maximum error is smaller than with the Taylor series, the points of maximum error are spaced along the interval, and the signs of the maximum errors alternate.

The difference between the two types of approximation is perhaps made clearer in Figure 3.5, in which we have shown the sine function with the two approximations. The error, of course, is greatly exaggerated.

The "best" approximation, in the sense that the maximum error for $-1 \leq x \leq 1$ is a minimum, is called the *Chebyshev approximation*. This is *not* the same as what we have done, which is an expansion in Chebyshev polynomials. Methods for obtaining the Chebyshev

---

* The interested reader may consult "Mathematical Tables, Chebyshev Series for Mathematical Functions," C. W. Clenshaw, *Nat. Phys. Lab.* (*G. Brit.*), 1962, for a detailed explanation of the process.

† Table 9 of "Chebyshev Approximations of Some Transcendental Functions for Use in Digital Computing," A. W. Duijvestijn and A. J. Dekkers, *Philips Res. Rept.*, **16** (April, 1961). This report also contains Chebyshev series for many elementary functions (log, sine, arctan, exp, etc.).

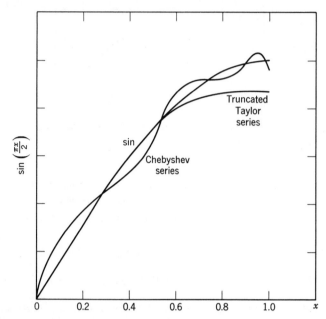

FIGURE 3.5   The sine function, the Chebyshev approximation, and the truncated Taylor series approximation.   The errors are greatly exaggerated.

approximations are available, of course, but the additional work required to obtain them is seldom worth the relatively small reduction in the error.*   (Many computer installations have programs that find the Chebyshev approximation of a function.   Finding the approximation is then an almost routine process.)

3.4   Telescoping power series

Chebyshev polynomials provide a good approximation to a function, in the sense that the maximum error is small, but the approximations are a bit of work to compute.   They are often worth the trouble in a computer routine that is to be heavily used by many programmers, but for one programmer to derive an expansion in Chebyshev polynomials for his own use is usually more effort than it is worth.

A relatively easy method for improving a Taylor series is available.

---

* See, for instance, F. D. Murnaghon and J. D. Wrench, "The Determination of the Chebyshev Approximating Polynomial for a Differentiable Function," *Math. Tables*, **13**, 185–193 (1959).

Finding the improved coefficients is not difficult, so that the method, *economizing* or *telescoping* a power series, is within the range of practicality for day-to-day computation.

Consider again the Taylor series for the sine, but now with terms through x^{11}.

$$\sin \frac{\pi x}{2} = 1.5707963x - 0.64596410x^3 + 0.079692626x^5$$
$$- 0.0046817541x^7 + 0.00016044118x^9 - 0.0000035988432x^{11}$$

From Appendix 2, Part B, we have

$$x^{11} = \frac{1}{1024} (462T_1 + 330T_3 + 165T_5 + 55T_7 + 11T_9 + T_{11})$$

Now replacing T_1, T_3, T_5, T_7, and T_9 with the expressions given in Appendix 2, Part A, it follows that

$$x^{11} = \frac{1}{1024} (11x - 220x^3 + 1232x^5 - 2816x^7 + 2816x^9 + T_{11})$$

By using this equation to replace x^{11} in the Taylor series, we get

$$(3.9) \quad \sin\left(\frac{\pi x}{2}\right) = 1.5707962x - 0.64596332x^3 + 0.079688296x^5$$
$$- 0.0046718573x^7 + 0.00015054436x^9 - 0.00000000351T_{11}$$

Now, since $T_{11}(x)$ never exceeds 1 in absolute value, the last term is

$$|e_T| < 3.51 \cdot 10^{-9}$$

provided we determined the coefficients in (3.9) with infinite accuracy. Since this is not the case, the error using (3.9) is considerably larger. In fact, if (3.9) is evaluated for various values of x, the maximum error is found to be

$$\max |e_T| = 8.0 \cdot 10^{-9}$$

This is less than the truncation error in the Taylor series of the same degree [see (3.2)].

The error curve for (3.9) is shown in Figure 3.6.   Notice that it is "better" than that of the uneconomized Taylor series (Figure 3.1, noting change of scale) but not so good as that of the Chebyshev series (Figure 3.4), especially for $0.7 \leq |x| \leq 1.0$.

The telescoping process can be continued: x^9 could be replaced by a polynomial of degree 7 and T_9.   Naturally, the truncation error would then be larger.   The telescoping process may be continued as long as

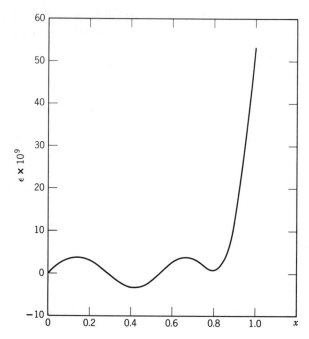

FIGURE 3.6   The error curve for the telescoped series for the sine (3.9).

the error is acceptable.   Formulas for telescoping all powers of x up to x^{11} are given in Appendix 2, Part C.

3.5   Evaluation of series

No matter what type of series is used to evaluate a function—Taylor, Chebyshev, or telescoped—the analyst is faced eventually with finding the numerical value of a polynomial of the form

$$(3.10) \quad p(x) = a_0 + a_1 x + a_2 x^2 + \cdots + a_{n-1} x^{n-1} + a_n x^n$$

This polynomial can be rearranged to a form that is not only faster to compute but also, in many practical cases of interest, more accurate. We shall work through a detailed derivation of the computational technique, even though the result is intuitively obvious, in order to lay the groundwork for later applications, particularly in Chapter 5. Suppose we divide $p(x)$ by $(x - x_0)$.   We will get a quotient that is a polynomial of degree $n - 1$ and a constant remainder:

$$(3.11) \quad p(x) = (x - x_0)(b_1 + b_2 x + \cdots + b_n x^{n-1}) + b_0$$

Notice that $p(x_0) = b_0$, so that if we can find b_0 we will have a way of evaluating $p(x_0)$. This can easily be done. We multiply out the right-hand side of (3.11) and equate like powers of x:

$$a_n \quad = b_n$$
$$a_{n-1} = b_{n-1} - x_0 b_n$$

$$\cdot$$
$$\cdot$$
$$\cdot$$

$$a_j \quad = b_j - x_0 b_{j+1}$$

$$\cdot$$
$$\cdot$$
$$\cdot$$

$$a_0 \quad = b_0 - x_0 b_1$$

or

$$b_n \quad = a_n$$
$$b_j \quad = a_j + x_0 b_{j+1} \qquad j = n - 1, \ldots, 0$$

Therefore, we can calculate $b_n, b_{n-1}, b_{n-2}, \ldots$ and finally b_0, in that order.

For instance, let $n = 5$ and observe that the successive b's are as follows.

$$b_5 = a_5$$
$$b_4 = a_4 + x_0 a_5$$
$$b_3 = a_3 + x_0(a_4 + x_0 a_5)$$
$$b_2 = a_2 + x_0(a_3 + x_0(a_4 + x_0 a_5))$$
$$b_1 = a_1 + x_0(a_2 + x_0(a_3 + x_0(a_4 + x_0 a_5)))$$
$$b_0 = a_0 + x_0(a_1 + x_0(a_2 + x_0(a_3 + x_0(a_4 + x_0 a_5))))$$

Since we placed no restriction on x_0, it can be *any* x, and we can drop the zero subscript.

This method of evaluating the polynomial (3.10) is known as *Horner's rule* and may be represented in general by

$$p(x) = a_0 + x(a_1 + x(a_2 + \cdots + x(a_{n-1} + x(a_n)) \cdots))$$

The a's here are the same ones as in (3.10). It is understood that the innermost parentheses are removed first in the calculation; indeed,

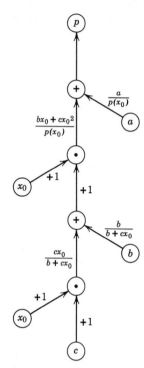

FIGURE 3.7   The process graph
for evaluating $p(x) = a + bx$
$+ cx^2$ by Horner's rule, $p(x) =$
$a + x \cdot (b + x \cdot c)$.

there is no other way to do the calculation without, in effect, rewriting it. Because of the appearance of the formula, Horner's rule is often referred to as the *nesting procedure*.

To evaluate a general polynomial by Horner's rule requires n multiplications and n additions. The number of multiplications in evaluating (3.10) is $n(n + 1)/2$, if each power of x is obtained by successive multiplications by x, that is, $x^k = x \cdot x^{k-1}$, etc.

For most applications, Horner's rule is sufficient, and it is in wide use. For special polynomials that are evaluated a large number of times for different arguments, methods have been devised that reduce the total number of arithmetic operations considerably.*

The method of evaluating a polynomial naturally has a considerable influence on the propagation of inherent and roundoff errors. For an example, suppose we need to evaluate the second-degree polynomial

$$p(x) = a + bx + cx^2$$

The process graph for Horner's rule is shown in Figure 3.7. The arrows are labeled as described in Chapter 2, p. 56.

We can now determine the effect of inherent and roundoff errors in $p(x)$. Let m_1 and m_2 be the relative errors in the first and second multiplications, respectively. Similarly, let α_1 and α_2 be the relative roundoff errors in the two additions. Finally let Δ be the inherent error in x_0 and let δ_a, δ_b, δ_c be the respective inherent errors in a, b, and c. Then

$$\frac{e_p}{p(x_0)} = \delta_c \frac{cx_0{}^2}{p(x_0)} + \delta_b \frac{bx_0}{p(x_0)} + \delta_a \frac{a}{p(x_0)} + \Delta \left(\frac{cx_0{}^2}{p(x_0)} + \frac{bx_0 + cx_0{}^2}{p(x_0)} \right)$$

$$+ m_1 \frac{cx_0{}^2}{p(x_0)} + m_2 \frac{bx_0 + cx_0{}^2}{p(x_0)} + \alpha_1 \frac{bx_0 + cx_0{}^2}{p(x_0)} + \alpha_2$$

---

* See "Evaluation of Polynomials by Computer," Donald E. Knuth, *Communications* of the Association for Computing Machinery, **5**, No. 12 (December 1962).

The absolute error in $p(x_0)$ is

$$e_p = cx_0{}^2(\delta_c + 2\Delta + m_1 + m_2 + \alpha_1 + \alpha_2)$$
$$+ bx_0(\delta_b + \Delta + m_2 + \alpha_1 + \alpha_2) + a(\delta_a + \alpha_2)$$

For a computer with t decimal digits in the mantissa of each floating point number and for $|x_0| \leq 1$ we have

$$|e_p| \leq 5 \cdot 10^{-t}(7|c| + 5|b| + 2|a|) = E_H$$

Consider now another way of evaluating the polynomial, namely a straightforward evaluation of the polynomial as written. We can represent the sequence of operations by regrouping the terms as follows; operations in parentheses are performed first, then the operation in brackets, and finally the operation in braces.

$$p(x_0) = \{[a + (b \cdot x_0)] + c \cdot (x_0 \cdot x_0)\}$$

The process graph is shown in Figure 3.8. Let α_1 and α_2 be the relative roundoff errors in the two additions as numbered, and let m_1, m_2, and m_3 be the relative roundoff errors in the three numbered multiplications. Then

$$e_p = cx_0{}^2(\delta_c + 2\Delta + m_2 + m_3 + \alpha_2)$$
$$+ bx_0(\delta_b + \Delta + m_1 + \alpha_1 + \alpha_2) + a(\delta_a + \alpha_1 + \alpha_2)$$

and again for $|x_0| \leq 1$

$$|e_p| \leq 5 \cdot 10^{-t}(6|c| + 5|b| + 3|a|) = E_*$$

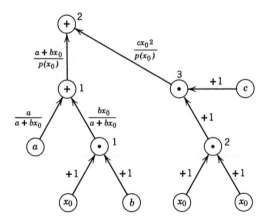

FIGURE 3.8 The process graph for $p(x_0) = \{[a + (b \cdot x_0)] + c \cdot (x_0 \cdot x_0)\}$.

Therefore

$$E_* - E_H = 5 \cdot 10^{-t}(|a| - |c|)$$

If $|a| > |c|$, Horner's rule produces a smaller bound for the effect of roundoff and inherent error. In the cases of interest in this chapter this condition is satisfied: the series are truncated convergent series, and the coefficients become smaller for higher powers of x.

Thus here and in many other practical situations Horner's rule not only saves computing time by requiring fewer arithmetic operations but it also produces a smaller absolute roundoff error.

For a general polynomial, as given in (3.10), the error arising from Horner's rule is bounded by

$$\text{error} \leq 5 \cdot 10^{-t} \left[\sum_{j=0}^{n} (3j + 2)|a_j| - |a_n| \right]$$

For convergent series the a_j decrease with j, and in the error-bound expression the larger coefficients are multiplied by the smaller numbers.

It is worth noting again that these are upper bounds to the roundoff and inherent error. The actual error is usually considerably smaller.

3.6 Rational approximations and continued fractions

Some functions cannot conveniently be expressed in terms of polynomials. In other cases the polynomial form is available and accurate but converges too slowly. For these reasons we turn to another form of representation: *rational approximation*, in which we work with the ratio of two polynomials.

Again we start from a Taylor series expansion

$$(3.12) \quad f(x) = a_0 + a_1x + a_2x^2 + a_3x^3 + a_4x^4 + a_5x^5 + a_6x^6 + a_7x^7 + \cdots$$

Now we write $f(x)$ as the ratio of two third-degree polynomials

$$(3.13) \qquad f(x) = \frac{b_0 + b_1x + b_2x^2 + b_3x^3}{1 + c_1x + c_2x^2 + c_3x^3}$$

The constant $+1$ in the denominator is no loss of generality, since any other constant that appeared there could be divided out of both numerator and denominator. By equating the right-hand sides of (3.12) and (3.13) and clearing the fractions we have

$$b_0 + b_1x + b_2x^2 + b_3x^3$$
$$= (1 + c_1x + c_2x^2 + c_3x^3)(a_0 + a_1x + \cdots + a_7x^7)$$

By multiplying out and equating like powers of x,

$$b_0 = a_0$$
$$b_1 = a_1 + a_0c_1$$
$$b_2 = a_2 + a_1c_1 + a_0c_2$$
$$b_3 = a_3 + a_2c_1 + a_1c_2 + a_0c_3$$
$$0 = a_4 + a_3c_1 + a_2c_2 + a_1c_3$$
$$0 = a_5 + a_4c_1 + a_3c_2 + a_2c_3$$
$$0 = a_6 + a_5c_1 + a_4c_2 + a_3c_3$$

(The last three result from the fact that we assumed a form of representation in which the coefficients of powers of x higher than 3 in the numerator are zero.)

Now we have seven equations in the seven unknowns b_0, b_1, b_2, b_3, c_1, c_2, and c_3. These seven simultaneous equations can be solved by the methods of Chapter 8.

We estimate the error in this formulation by considering the size of what the coefficient of b_7 would be, if it were included, divided by the value of the denominator:

$$\frac{(a_7 + a_6c_1 + a_5c_2 + a_4c_3)x^7}{1 + c_1x + c_2x^2 + c_3x^3}$$

This is an approximation to the truncation error only and does not include roundoff error, but the truncation error will ordinarily be much larger than the roundoff error.

Rational approximations are not usually evaluated as expressed in (3.13) but by the use of an equivalent *continued fraction*. We may see how this is done by considering the sine function one last time.

$$(3.14) \qquad \sin\left(\frac{\pi x}{2}\right) = \frac{\pi x}{2} - \frac{1}{3!}\left(\frac{\pi x}{2}\right)^3 + \frac{1}{5!}\left(\frac{\pi x}{2}\right)^5 - + \cdots$$

We look for a rational approximation of the form*

$$(3.15) \qquad \sin\left(\frac{\pi x}{2}\right) = \frac{ax + bx^3}{1 + cx^2}$$

and

$$(1 + cx^2)\left(\frac{\pi}{2}x - \left(\frac{\pi}{2}\right)^3 \frac{1}{3!}x^3 + \left(\frac{\pi}{2}\right)^5 \frac{1}{5!}x^5 - \left(\frac{\pi}{2}\right)^7 \frac{1}{7!}x^7\right) = ax + bx^3$$

Therefore

$$a = \frac{\pi}{2} \qquad \text{(powers of } x\text{)}$$

$$c \cdot \frac{\pi}{2} - \left(\frac{\pi}{2}\right)^3 \frac{1}{3!} = b \qquad \text{(powers of } x^3\text{)}$$

$$-c\left(\frac{\pi}{2}\right)^3 \frac{1}{3!} + \left(\frac{\pi}{2}\right)^5 \frac{1}{5!} = 0 \qquad \text{(powers of } x^5\text{)}$$

By solving the last equation for c, we have

$$(3.16) \quad \begin{cases} & c = \frac{1}{20}\left(\frac{\pi}{2}\right)^2 \quad = 0.12337\ 0055 \\ \text{Then} & \\ & b = -\frac{7}{60}\left(\frac{\pi}{2}\right)^3 \quad = -0.45217\ 4868 \\ \text{and} & \\ & a = \frac{\pi}{2} \quad\qquad = 1.57079\ 633 \end{cases}$$

The *approximate* truncation error is

$$e_T = \frac{\left(\frac{\pi}{2}\right)^7 \frac{1}{7!}x^7}{1 + \frac{1}{20}\left(\frac{\pi}{2}\right)^2 x^2} = \frac{0.0046815 x^7}{1 + 0.12337 x^2}$$

---

* Picking an appropriate form for a rational approximation is partly science, partly art, and partly judgment guided by experience. We cannot give explicit rules, but we can at least justify the general features of this example. We need no constant term in the numerator; if we included one, it would turn out to be zero because the sine of zero is zero. The reader can verify that the absence of a term in x^2 in the numerator and a term in x in the denominator is reasonable, since the sine is an odd function; that is, $\sin(-x) = -\sin(x)$. The decision to have three independent parameters is consistent with the presence of three independent coefficients in the truncated sine series being approximated.

Notice that (3.15) is approximately equivalent to a three-term power series, as in (3.14).

This rational approximation has the same order of accuracy as a fifth-degree Taylor series:

$$\sin\left(\frac{\pi x}{2}\right) \simeq \frac{\pi x}{2} - \frac{1}{3!}\left(\frac{\pi x}{2}\right)^3 + \frac{1}{5!}\left(\frac{\pi x}{2}\right)^5$$

If this expression is evaluated by Horner's rule, with a preliminary evaluation of x^2, four multiplications and two additions are required:

$$\sin\left(\frac{\pi x}{2}\right) = x(a - x^2(b - cx^2))$$

If the rational function (3.15) is evaluated by using Horner's rule for both numerator and denominator, four multiplications, two additions, and one division are required. This is no economy over the Taylor series.

Therefore we convert (3.15) into an equivalent continued fraction. We first rewrite (3.15) as

$$\sin\left(\frac{\pi x}{2}\right) = -\frac{7\pi}{6}\left[\frac{x^3 - \frac{60}{7}\left(\frac{2}{\pi}\right)^2 x}{x^2 + 20\left(\frac{2}{\pi}\right)^2}\right]$$

and divide the numerator by the denominator to get a quotient of x and a remainder of $-\dfrac{200}{7}\left(\dfrac{2}{\pi}\right)^2 x$:

$$\sin\left(\frac{\pi x}{2}\right) = -\frac{7\pi}{6}\left[x - \frac{\frac{200}{7}\left(\frac{2}{\pi}\right)^2 x}{x^2 + 20\left(\frac{2}{\pi}\right)^2}\right]$$

or

$$\sin\left(\frac{\pi x}{2}\right) = -\frac{7\pi}{6}\left\{x - \frac{\frac{200}{7}\left(\frac{2}{\pi}\right)^2}{\left[\frac{x^2 + 20\left(\frac{2}{\pi}\right)^2}{x}\right]}\right\}$$

Now we take the fraction in brackets and again divide the numerator by the denominator to get

$$\frac{x^2 + 20 \left(\dfrac{2}{\pi}\right)^2}{x} = x + \frac{20 \left(\dfrac{2}{\pi}\right)^2}{x}$$

and finally

$$\sin\left(\frac{\pi x}{2}\right) = -\frac{7\pi}{6}\left[x - \frac{\dfrac{200}{7}\left(\dfrac{2}{\pi}\right)^2}{x + \dfrac{20\left(\dfrac{2}{\pi}\right)^2}{x}} \right]$$

or

$$(3.17) \qquad \sin\frac{\pi x}{2} = -3.66519143 \left(x - \frac{11.47221432}{x + \dfrac{8.03055026}{x}} \right)$$

The evaluation of (3.17) requires two divisions, two additions, and one multiplication, which is a considerable saving over the rational function (3.15) and the polynomial (3.14). In this example, if the computer's division time is less than $\frac{3}{2}$ the multiplication time, the continued fraction (3.17) is faster than the polynomial (3.14). (In quite a number of widely used computers this timing condition is satisfied; in some machines multiplication and division take the same time.)

Continued fractions may be telescoped in an analogous way to power series. See, for instance, Hans J. Maehly, "Methods for Fitting Rational Approximations, Part I: Telescoping Procedures for Continued Fractions," *Communications* of the Association of Computing Machinery, **7**, 150–162 (April 1960).

3.7 Elementary functions

We have already seen in Section 3.1 that it is not necessary to be able to evaluate a sine for an arbitrary argument: a reduction to $-\pi/2 \le x \le \pi/2$ is possible. This is one example of how the computation of elementary functions can often be simplified. We may now consider similar practical techniques for some other common functions.

Cosine
A separate program to compute a cosine is never required because we can employ the identity

$$\sin(x + \pi/2) = \sin x \cos \pi/2 + \cos x \sin \pi/2 = \cos x$$

All that is required is to add $\pi/2$ to the angle and use the sine routine.

Hyperbolic functions

Assuming that a routine to compute an exponential is available, the hyperbolic sine and cosine can be found from

$$\sinh x = \tfrac{1}{2}(e^x - e^{-x})$$

$$\cosh x = \tfrac{1}{2}(e^x + e^{-x})$$

Notice, however, that for x near zero e^x and e^{-x} are approximately equal. Thus in forming sinh (x) we are subtracting two nearly equal numbers, and we have already seen in Section 2.8 how the relative accuracy deteriorates. If the relative accuracy for small x is important, it is much better to use a power series:

$$\sinh x = x + \frac{x^3}{3!} + \frac{x^5}{5!} + \frac{x^7}{7!} + \cdots$$

For small x a few terms will be sufficient.

Logarithms

The logarithm routine that is called into operation when we write LOGF in a FORTRAN program was classified in Chapter 1 as a natural logarithm, that is, a logarithm to the base e. Some systems also provide a separate function to give the common logarithm (base 10) where it is heavily used, but this is done only to simplify program writing and is not essential.

Given a logarithm to the base e and requiring the logarithm of the same number to some other base b, we proceed as follows. We recall that if

$$\log_e x = k$$

then

$$e^k = x$$

by definition. Therefore

$$\log_b x = \log_b (e^k) = k \log_b e = (\log_b e)(\log_e x)$$

Thus, to get the logarithm of a number to some base other than e, we need only multiply by the logarithm of e to the new base; this is a fixed constant. In particular, $\log_{10} e = 0.43429448$.

Approximations for some of the elementary functions (sin, exp, log, tan, arctan) are given in Appendix 2, Part D.

3.8 Case study 3: Errors in the direct evaluation of the sine series

The Taylor series for the sine

$$\sin x = x - \frac{x^3}{3!} + \frac{x^5}{5!} - \frac{x^7}{7!} + \cdots$$

is, as we have noted, theoretically valid for all values of x. In actual fact it is almost useless for large values of x. It will be instructive to investigate why this is so.

We shall write a program that evaluates the series directly, that is, starting with the first term and continuing to compute terms until we find one that is less in absolute value than, say, 10^{-8}. We know that the truncation error is then less than the first term neglected, so that it ought to be possible to compute the sine within 10^{-8} simply by taking enough terms. We shall see that it is not practically possible because of extreme roundoff problems.

The program will require an interesting stratagem to avoid producing intermediate results too large for a floating point variable. The largest angle we shall consider will be about 50 radians; if we were to try to raise 50 to the large powers that will be required, we would greatly exceed the sizes permitted of floating variables in all but a few FORTRAN systems. Therefore we shall take another approach, that of computing each new term from the preceding term. The recursion relation is not complicated. Having the first term x, we can get the next term by multiplying by $-x^2$ and dividing by $2 \cdot 3$. Having the second term, we can get the third by multiplying by $-x^2$ and dividing by $4 \cdot 5$. In short, given the preceding term, we can get the next one by multiplying by $-x^2$ and dividing by the product of the next two integers.

A block diagram is shown in Figure 3.9. It is set up to read cards, each containing an angle in degrees, until it reaches a "sentinel card" with an angle of zero. The angle in degrees is first converted to radians by dividing by $180/\pi$; the result is called X. Now we need to get the recursion process started. We shall continually be adding a new term to a sum which eventually becomes the sine when enough terms have been computed. To get started, we set this sum equal to X; the first term computed by the recursion method will be $-x^3/3!$. Thus the preceding term is also X. To get the successive integers, we start a variable named DENOM at 3. To save recomputing x^2 repeatedly, we compute it once before entering the loop and give it the name XSQ.

Getting a new term is now a simple matter of multiplying the preceding term by $-$XSQ and dividing by the product of DENOM and DENOM $-$ 1.0. This new term replaces the preceding term and is added to the sum. We are now ready to find out whether enough terms have been computed. We ask if the absolute value of the term just computed is less than or equal to 10^{-8}. If it is, we are ready to print the result and to go back to read another card. If not, the value

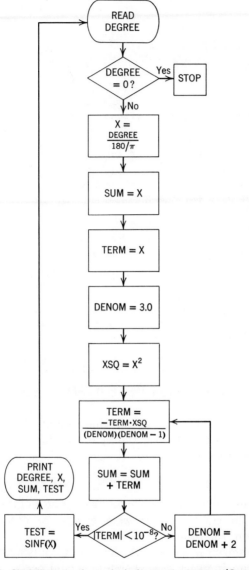

FIGURE 3.9 Block diagram of a method of computing a sine. (Case Study 3.)

C FOR COMMENT		
STATEMENT NUMBER 1 5	6 7	FORTRAN STATEMENT
62		READ 100, DEGREE
100		FORMAT (F10.0)
		IF (DEGREE) 150, 200, 150
200		STOP
150		X = DEGREE / 57.29577795
		SUM = X
		TERM = X
		DENOM = 3..0
		XSQ = X * X
25		TERM = - TERM * XSQ / (DENOM * (DENOM - 1.0))
		SUM = SUM + TERM
		IF (ABSF(TERM) - 1.E-8) 16, 16, 12
12		DENOM = DENOM + 2.0
		GO TO 25
16		TEST = SINF(X)
		PRINT 30, DEGREE, X, SUM, TEST
30		FORMAT (F10.0, F15.8, F20.8, F15.8)
		GO TO 62
		END

FIGURE 3.10   Program for computing a sine.   (Case Study 3.)

of DENOM must be increased by 2.0 before returning to compute another term.

Besides printing the value of the sine computed by this method, it might be interesting to use the sine function supplied with the FORTRAN system to compute it also. This is done just before printing.

The program shown in Figure 3.10 follows the block diagram closely and presents no new FORTRAN concepts. The lengths of the F-field specifications in statement 30 were chosen to accommodate the expected sizes of the results.

The results shown in Figure 3.11 are for 30° plus multiples of 360°. The exact result in every case therefore should be $\frac{1}{2}$. The entry for 30° is as close as we could reasonably expect, the error being just the tolerance of 10^{-8}. The error builds with larger angles. For 390° the value is acceptable; at 750° and 1110° the values are deteriorating; and at 1470° the system disintegrates. Larger angles lead to values of the sine that are likewise complete nonsense.

Let us consider the first entry in which the method fails completely (1470°) to see if we can determine what happened. Using a separate program, not shown, the values of the individual terms were printed. The first term is just the value of x, 25.656340 radians. The second term is -2789.0484, to eight digits; when these two terms are added, keeping only eight digits, the sum is -2763.3921. In the addition the last two digits of the first term were dropped. Obviously they can never re-enter the computation later, when the sum should have been reduced to a number less than 1. The third term is 89849.610; in the addition to get a new sum of 87086.218, the last digit of the preceding sum is dropped. Thus three digits of the first term are now lost. The fourth term is -1362035.9; the addition to get a new sum of -1274949.7 drops two digits of the preceding sum. The last five digits of the first term are now lost, and the pattern should be clear. The largest term in the series is $55037680 \cdot 10^2$; after adding it to the preceding sum, all digits of the first term have left the scene, along with some of the digits of the other terms. In the next entry of Figure 3.10, that of 1830°, the largest term is about $2.7 \cdot 10^{12}$, which causes the loss of all digits in the first and second terms.

The most serious problem here, clearly, is that the additions are being done in a sequence far from ideal. We noted in Chapter 2 that it is much better to start with the smallest terms or, more generally, to keep the partial sums as small as possible.

But this is not the only problem. This example was run on a binary computer in which floating point variables are represented with the equivalent of about eight decimal digits. Consider a term such as $0.26553689 \cdot 10^{13}$. Writing this out, we have 2,655,368,900,000, in which the zeros, of course, are not significant: they merely locate the decimal point in this form of writing the number. Obviously, the eight significant digits are an approximation, and the zeros stand for digits that we cannot keep in the computing system. In other words, this approximation could differ from the true term by as much as

30.	0.52359878	0.49999999	0.49999999
390.	6.80678415	0.49999993	0.50000005
750.	13.08996952	0.50013507	0.50000010
1110.	19.37315488	0.51658490	0.50000016
1470.	25.65634012	24.25401855	0.50000010
1830.	31.93952560	14380.23767090	0.50000025
2190.	38.22271109	25902480.00000000	0.50000040
2550.	44.50589609	-130402508.00000000	0.50000013
2910.	50.78908157	-83272283.00000000	0.50000029

FIGURE 3.11   Output of the program of Figure 3.10. (Case Study 3.)

30.	0.52359878	0.49999999	0.49999999
390.	6.80678415	0.50000006	0.50000005
750.	13.08996952	0.50000011	0.50000010
1110.	19.37315488	0.50000016	0.50000016
1470.	25.65634012	0.50000143	0.50000010
1830.	31.93952560	0.49953845	0.50000025
2190.	38.22271109	0.79868912	0.50000040
2550.	44.50589609	29.53991437	0.50000013
2910.	50.78908157	-142982.02734375	0.50000029

FIGURE 3.12   Output of the program of Figure 3.10, modified to do the calculation in double precision. (Case Study 3.)

50,000. This kind of error makes it hopeless to expect any significance at all in computing a final value that is properly never greater than 1.

We can demonstrate that the trouble here really is the limited significance of the floating point variables by turning to *double precision*. This is a method of representing each variable by twice as many digits as we would normally and arranging the arithmetic operations to take all the digits into account. In the version of FORTRAN used for this example placing a D in column 1 of an arithmetic statement forces all arithmetic in that statement to be done in double precision. The results of running the same program with this change are shown in Figure 3.12. We see that they are now somewhere in the right neighborhood out through 1830°, by which point the single-precision program had failed completely. With very large angles, however, even double precision is not enough.

We may note briefly how the sine function supplied with the system fared. In all cases there are at least six good digits. The decreased accuracy for the larger angles is caused by a loss of significance in reducing the original angle to an angle less than $\pi/2$. For instance, when we convert 2190° to radians, we get 38.22271109. The computer has printed 10 digits as the decimal equivalent of the floating binary value, but there simply cannot be more than eight meaningful digits there. When this eight-digit approximation is reduced to an angle less than $\pi/2$, we have in effect subtracted two nearly equal numbers, which we have seen before leads to reduced relative accuracy. In other words, we did not really compute the sine of 2190° but of some slightly different angle.

For large angles sines are literally never computed by the method of this case study for obvious reasons. It is hoped that the reader has gained some appreciation of the problems that are faced in working with a computer, which inevitably involves approximations.

Naïve computer users have a tendency to assume that if the "giant brain" prints eight digits they must mean something. We trust that this case study shows the lack of wisdom of this assumption.

Exercises

1. Shown below are a number of functions and corresponding Taylor series. For the value of x shown estimate the number of terms required to produce a function value with a truncation error less than $5 \cdot 10^{-5}$. For each also estimate the number of terms required for a truncation error less than $5 \cdot 10^{-9}$.

*a. $\sin x = x - \dfrac{x^3}{3!} + \dfrac{x^5}{5!} - \dfrac{x^7}{7!} + \cdots \qquad x = 1$

b. $\sin x = x - \dfrac{x^3}{3!} + \dfrac{x^5}{5!} - \dfrac{x^7}{7!} + \cdots \qquad x = 3$

*c. $\arctan x = \dfrac{\pi}{2} - \dfrac{1}{x} + \dfrac{1}{3x^3} - \dfrac{1}{5x^5} + \dfrac{1}{7x^7} + \cdots \qquad x = 2$

(Series valid for $x > 1$.)

d. $\log_e x = (x - 1) - \dfrac{(x-1)^2}{2} + \dfrac{(x-1)^3}{3} - \dfrac{(x-1)^4}{4} + \cdots \qquad x = 2$

(Series valid for $0 < x \le 2$.)

e. $e^{-x} = 1 - x + \dfrac{x^2}{2!} - \dfrac{x^3}{3!} + \dfrac{x^4}{4!} + \cdots \qquad x = 1$

2. Show that for $|x| \le 1$ the Chebyshev polynomials satisfy $|T_n(x)| \le 1$.
3. Show that

$$\int_{-1}^{1} \frac{T_m(x)\, T_n(x)\, dx}{\sqrt{1 - x^2}} = 0 \qquad m \ne n$$

Because the Chebyshev polynomials have this property they are said to be *orthogonal* over the interval $(-1, 1)$ with weighting $1/\sqrt{1 - x^2}$. (*Hint.* Use the definition of $T_m(x)$ and replace x by θ.)

4. Show that

$$\int_{-1}^{1} \frac{[T_m(x)]^2\, dx}{\sqrt{1 - x^2}} = \begin{cases} \pi & m = 0 \\ \dfrac{\pi}{2} & m = 1, 2, \ldots \end{cases}$$

5. Based on the results of Exercises 3 and 4, show that the coefficients a_i in a Chebyshev series for $f(x)$

$$f(x) = \sum_{i=0}^{\infty} a_i\, T_i(x)$$

can be obtained from

$$a_0 = \frac{1}{\pi} \int_{-1}^{1} \frac{f(x)\, dx}{\sqrt{1 - x^2}}$$

$$a_n = \frac{2}{\pi} \int_{-1}^{1} \frac{f(x)\, T_n(x)\, dx}{\sqrt{1 - x^2}} \qquad n \neq 0$$

In practice these formulas are seldom used to compute the coefficients, a_i, because of the difficulty in evaluating the integrals.

*6. From the result of Exercise 5 find the first five coefficients in the Chebyshev series for

$$f(x) = x$$

You may use the following definite integrals:

$$\int_{-1}^{1} \frac{dx}{\sqrt{1 - x^2}} = \pi \qquad \int_{-1}^{1} \frac{x^2\, dx}{\sqrt{1 - x^2}} = \frac{\pi}{2} \qquad \int_{-1}^{1} \frac{x^4\, dx}{\sqrt{1 - x^2}} = \frac{3\pi}{8}$$

$$\int_{-1}^{1} \frac{x\, dx}{\sqrt{1 - x^2}} = 0 \qquad \int_{-1}^{1} \frac{x^3\, dx}{\sqrt{1 - x^2}} = 0 \qquad \int_{-1}^{1} \frac{x^5\, dx}{\sqrt{1 - x^2}} = 0$$

7. From the fact that the sixth coefficient, a_5, in the Chebyshev series for $f(x) = x$ must vanish deduce that

$$\int_{-1}^{1} \frac{x^6\, dx}{\sqrt{1 - x^2}} = \frac{5\pi}{16}$$

Use the integrals given in Exercise 6.

*8. a. Find the first five coefficients of the Chebyshev series for

$$f(x) = \sqrt{1 - x^2}$$

b. Write out the five terms of the series in powers of x.

c. Evaluate the five-term series in x at $x = 0.5$; compare the result with the correct value and with the value given by the five-term Taylor series about $x = 0$.

9. a. Using the integrals in Exercises 6 and 7, find the first five coefficients of the Chebyshev series for

$$f(x) = |x|$$

b. Write out the five terms of the Chebyshev series in powers of x.

c. Evaluate the result of part b at $x = +0.5$.

*10. The *shifted Chebyshev polynomials* may be defined as

$$T_n{}^*(x) = T_n(2x - 1)$$

The shifted polynomials, $T_n{}^*$, are used over the interval $0 \leq x \leq 1$ just as the T_n are used for $-1 \leq x \leq 1$. Find the first four shifted Chebyshev polynomials.

11. Show that the shifted Chebyshev polynomials are orthogonal over the interval, $(0, 1)$ with a weighting $(x - x^2)^{-\frac{1}{2}}$; that is,

$$\int_0^1 \frac{T_n^*(x)\, T_m^*(x)\, dx}{\sqrt{x - x^2}} = 0 \qquad m \neq n$$

*12. Telescope the approximation

$$e^x \simeq 1 + x + \frac{x^2}{2!} + \frac{x^3}{3!} + \frac{x^4}{4!} + \frac{x^5}{5!} + \frac{x^6}{6!} + \frac{x^7}{7!}$$

to an approximation through x^6.

13. Telescope the result of Exercise 12 to an approximation through x^5.

14. a. Find the first five coefficients of the Chebyshev expansion for

$$f(x) = 6x^4 - 2x^3 + x^2 - x + 4 \qquad |x| \leq 1$$

   b. Use the telescoping procedure twice to approximate $f(x)$ by a second-degree polynomial.

15. Show that the approximation

$$e^x \simeq 1 + \frac{x}{1!} + \frac{x^2}{2!} + \frac{x^3}{3!} + \frac{x^4}{4!} + \frac{x^5}{5!}$$

may be rewritten

$$e^x \simeq 1 + x\left(1 + \frac{x}{2}\left(1 + \frac{x}{3}\left(1 + \frac{x}{4}\left(1 + \frac{x}{5}\right)\right)\right)\right)$$

16. Show that the approximation

$$\tan^{-1} x \simeq x - \frac{x^3}{3} + \frac{x^5}{5} - \frac{x^7}{7} + \frac{x^9}{9}$$

may be rewritten

$$\tan^{-1} x \simeq x(1 - x^2(\tfrac{1}{3} - x^2(\tfrac{1}{5} - x^2(\tfrac{1}{7} - x^2(\tfrac{1}{9})))))$$

17. Find a factorization similar to those in Exercises 15 and 16 for

$$\sin^{-1} x \simeq x + \frac{x^3}{2 \cdot 3} + \frac{1 \cdot 3 \cdot x^5}{2 \cdot 4 \cdot 5} + \frac{1 \cdot 3 \cdot 5 \cdot x^7}{2 \cdot 4 \cdot 6 \cdot 7} + \frac{1 \cdot 3 \cdot 5 \cdot 7 \cdot x^9}{2 \cdot 4 \cdot 6 \cdot 8 \cdot 9}$$

18. Find a factorization similar to those in Exercises 15 and 16 for

$$J_0(x) \simeq 1 - \frac{(x/2)^2}{1^2} + \frac{(x/2)^4}{1^2 \cdot 2^2} - \frac{(x/2)^6}{1^2 \cdot 2^2 \cdot 3^2} + \frac{(x/2)^8}{1^2 \cdot 2^2 \cdot 3^2 \cdot 4^2}$$

*19. If the number of terms to be retained in a truncated convergent infinite series is known in advance, the best computational procedure is Horner's rule. Write a statement using Horner's rule to evaluate the Taylor series for e^x through x^6:

a. Using the values of the coefficients in decimal form, that is,

$$e^x \simeq 1 + x + 0.5x^2 + 0.166667x^3 + 0.0416667x^4$$
$$+ 0.00833333x^5 + 0.00138889x^6$$

b. Using no constants except the integers 1 through 6, following the method of Exercise 15.

*20. Consider the following computational sequence:

1. Set a variable named E equal to 1.
2. Set a variable named D equal to 5.
3. Replace E with $1 + (EX/D)$.
4. If D equals 1, stop; otherwise subtract 1 from D and go back to step 3.

Show that when the procedure stops

$$E = 1 + x + \frac{x^2}{2} + \frac{x^3}{2 \cdot 3} + \frac{x^4}{2 \cdot 3 \cdot 4} + \frac{x^5}{2 \cdot 3 \cdot 4 \cdot 5} \simeq e^x$$

Draw a block diagram of the procedure and write a program segment in which it is assumed that X has been given a value by a previous statement.

21. Following the method of Exercise 20, draw a block diagram and write a program segment to evaluate the Taylor series for $\sin^{-1} x$ through x^{15}. (See Exercise 17.)

22. Write a routine to evaluate $\sin x$ for $-3 \le x \le 3$ with a truncation error less than $5 \cdot 10^{-9}$, using a suitable modification of the method in Exercise 20. If $|x| \le 1$, set $D = 7$ before entering the computing loop; if $|x| > 1$, set D equal to the result of Exercise 1b.

23. If the number of terms to be retained *cannot* be determined in advance, Horner's rule cannot be used; the series must be evaluated "from the front." However, if x is large, say in the range of 10 to 20, raising x to a large power may exceed the size permitted of a floating point number even though the complete term is not too large. One solution is to do the divisions by the numbers in the denominator as x is raised to the power. (See Case Study 3.) Write a routine to evaluate e^{-x}, starting from the front and continuing until a term that is less than 10^{-7} in absolute value is found.

24. Write a routine to evaluate the following functions by the method of Case Study 3, starting from the front and continuing until a term that is less than 10^{-7} in absolute value is found.

a. $I_0(r) = 1 - \frac{(x/2)^2}{1^2} + \frac{(x/2)^4}{1^2 \cdot 2^2} + \cdots$

b. $\tan^{-1} x = \frac{\pi}{2} - \frac{1}{x} + \frac{1}{3x^3} - \frac{1}{5x^5} + \cdots \qquad x > 1$

c. $J_2(x) = \frac{x^2}{2^2 \cdot 2!} - \frac{x^4}{2^4 \cdot 1! \cdot 3!} + \frac{x^6}{2^6 \cdot 2! \cdot 4!} - \frac{x^8}{2^8 \cdot 3! \cdot 5!} + \cdots$

25. Recall that if $p(x)$ is a polynomial of degree n then

$$p(x) = (x - x_0) q(x) + b_0$$

where

$$q(x) = b_1 + b_2 x + \cdots + b_n x^{n-1}$$

and the b_j may be calculated recursively from

$$b_n = a_n$$

$$b_j = a_j + x_0 b_{j+1}, \qquad j = n - 1, \ldots, 0$$

a. Show that

$$\left. \frac{dp}{dx} \right|_{x=x_0} = q(x_0)$$

b. Find a simple recursion formula in terms of the b_j for the derivative of $p(x)$ at $x = x_0$. (*Hint.* Notice that $q(x)$ is a polynomial in x of degree $n - 1$.)

*26. Write an arithmetic statement to carry out the operations of (3.17).

27. Write arithmetic statements to carry out the operations in the five approximations of Appendix 2, Part·D.

*28. Write

$$\sin\left(\frac{\pi x}{2}\right) \simeq \frac{\pi}{2} x - \left(\frac{\pi}{2}\right)^3 \frac{x^3}{6} + \left(\frac{\pi}{2}\right)^5 \frac{x^5}{120} - \left(\frac{\pi}{2}\right)^7 \frac{x^7}{5040}$$

Find the coefficients of a rational approximation of the form

$$\sin\left(\frac{\pi x}{2}\right) \simeq \frac{b_1 x + b_3 x^3}{1 + c_2 x^2 + c_4 x^4}$$

Use the fact that the sine is an odd function $[\sin(-x) = -\sin(x)]$ to explain why we may set $b_0 = b_2 = c_1 = c_3 = 0$ in the assumed form of the rational approximation.

29. Find the coefficients in a rational approximation of $\cos(\pi x/2)$ of the form

$$\cos\left(\frac{\pi x}{2}\right) \simeq \frac{b_0 + b_2 x^2}{1 + c_2 x^2}$$

30. Given that

$$\tan x \simeq x + \tfrac{1}{3} x^3 + \tfrac{2}{15} x^5 + \tfrac{17}{315} x^7$$

find the coefficients of a rational approximation of the form

$$\tan x \simeq \frac{b_1 x + b_3 x^3}{1 + c_2 x^2 + c_4 x^4}$$

*31. Given a rational approximation of the form

$$f(x) = \frac{a + bx + cx^2}{1 + dx}$$

find a corresponding continued fraction of the form

$$f(x) = k_1 + \cfrac{x}{k_2 + \cfrac{x}{k_3 + \cfrac{x}{k_4}}}$$

32. Given a rational approximation of the form

$$f(x) = \frac{a + bx + cx^2}{1 + dx + ex^2}$$

find a corresponding continued fraction of the form

$$f(x) = k_1 + \cfrac{x}{k_2 + \cfrac{x}{k_3 + \cfrac{x}{k_4 + \cfrac{x}{k_5}}}}$$

33. Given a rational approximation of the form

$$f(x) = \frac{a + bx}{1 + dx + ex^2}$$

find a corresponding continued fraction of the form

$$f(x) = \cfrac{1}{k_1 + \cfrac{x}{k_2 + \cfrac{x}{k_3 + \cfrac{x}{k_4}}}}$$

34. From the binomial theorem

$$(1 - x)^{\frac{1}{2}} \simeq 1 - \tfrac{1}{2}x - \tfrac{1}{8}x^2 - \tfrac{3}{24}x^3 - \tfrac{15}{384}x^4 - \tfrac{105}{3840}x^5$$

a. Telescope to a series in terms through x^3.
b. From the telescoped series, find a rational approximation of the form

$$(1 - x)^{\frac{1}{2}} \simeq \frac{a + bx + cx^2}{1 + dx}$$

c. From the rational approximation find a continued fraction of the form

$$(1 - x)^{\frac{1}{2}} \simeq k_1 + \cfrac{x}{k_2 + \cfrac{x}{k_3 + \cfrac{x}{k_4}}}$$

35. Show that the logarithm of any finite positive number may be obtained from the logarithm of another number y where $0 < y < 1$. To compute logarithms, therefore, we need only to provide a polynomial or rational approximation for arguments less than 1.

36. Show that the tangent of any finite number may be obtained from the tangent of another number y where $-\pi/4 \le y \le \pi/4$.

—4

Program Development

4.1 Introduction

The reader is by now about ready to begin some fairly interesting work with a computer. In this chapter we present three case studies that will help to clarify the process of developing a program to solve a given problem. We show all the steps in sequence: how to get started, the error analysis, a little of what to do when trouble appears, how to plan for input and output, and so on.

The emphasis is thus on a question that most students find troublesome at this point: how to integrate all the bits and pieces of knowledge that have been accumulated. The applications through which this is done are realistic. They are typical of the size of job that the reader should be able to handle without too much difficulty but, of course, somewhat smaller than the normal run of practical computer applications.

4.2 Case study 4: Column design

An engineer wishes to obtain data for plotting a curve of the safe loading of a certain type of load-bearing column as a function of the slimness ratio of the column. He has selected from a handbook two empirical formulas that give the safe loading in two ranges of the slimness ratio,

$$S = \begin{cases} 17{,}000 - 0.485R^2 & \text{for } R < 120 \\ \dfrac{18{,}000}{1 + \dfrac{R^2}{18{,}000}} & \text{for } R \geq 120 \end{cases}$$

where S = safe load, pounds per square inch

R = slimness ratio

The safe loading is to be calculated for slimness ratios of 20 to 200 in steps of five.

Planning a program to get the output desired can be approached by breaking it down into three questions:

1. How to choose between the two formulas, given a value of R. This is fairly easy: use an IF statement to compare the size of R against 120 and branch to one of two arithmetic statements to apply the appropriate formula.

2. How to run through the required values of R. This can be handled in a number of ways. Perhaps the easiest is to start R at 20, compute S, then add 5 to R, compute a new S, etc., each time around testing to see whether R is yet 200. This method will not require the reading of data cards, which makes the program a bit simpler, but it does mean that to run the program for any values of R other than those "built into" the program would mean a program change. We are buying simplicity at the cost of inflexibility—a common trade off, by the way.

3. How to present the results, taking into account the accuracy expected. *Computationally*, given a value of R, there are no accuracy problems in computing S: we are not subtracting two nearly equal numbers, roundoff errors will be completely overshadowed by the inaccuracy of the approximation formulas, and there is no process by which errors can build up. In fact, the accuracy of the computed results is almost completely dominated by the question of the accuracy of the approximation formulas. The handbook from which they were taken is silent on accuracy (a not uncommon situation), but we can draw some conclusions from the fact that the constants are given to only two or three significant figures. Furthermore, mechanical design formulas of this kind usually include a safety factor, so that extreme precision is clearly not indicated.

We shall see, however, that there *is* an accuracy problem in getting the successive values of R for other values of the increment in R than the one stated. We shall return to this question later.

It appears that if we presented the results as integers we should be providing more significant figures than could possibly mean anything. In fact, we should probably be much closer to reality if we printed about three significant figures, multiplied by a power of 10—which is exactly what we can do in floating point by using the E field specification.

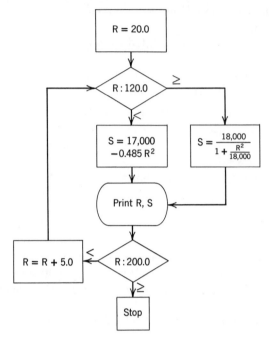

FIGURE 4.1   Block diagram of a column design calculation.   (Case Study 4.)

A block diagram is shown in Figure 4.1.   We begin by setting R equal to 20 to get our starting value; this step will never be repeated. Then we must test to see whether R is more or less than 120—which seems pointless, since we just made it 20.   The point, of course, is that we are now in the part of the program that will be repeated many times as R increases.   There is simply no way to say to a computer, "Be sensible: use the first formula until R reaches 120."   *We* must provide an *explicit* test on the value of R *every time.*

The decision box takes us to one of the two formulas to compute S, after either of which we print the values of R and S.   (It is a good idea, incidentally, to print the computed value *and* the argument.   If we were to print only the computed result, anyone using the output would have to figure out for himself the R value going with each value of S.)

Now we ask whether R is equal to 200.   If it is less, we add five to it and go around again.   If it is equal, we have just computed the last line of the output and we are ready to stop.   One would think that R could never be greater than 200 at this point; if it were, we should already have left the loop the time before.   This is indeed true in infinite precision and, *as it happens,* would be true even in the real world of finite precision *with these numbers.*   We shall return to this question shortly.

The FORTRAN program is shown in Figure 4.2.   If the block diagram is clearly understood, it should not be much trouble to follow the program (which demonstrates the value of block diagrams).   The FORMAT statement provides a review of the two most common field specifications.   In F10.0 the F means that the number will be printed in fixed format (without an exponent), the 10 means that 10 printing positions will be allotted to the number, and the zero means that there will be no decimals.   In 1PE15.3 the 1P means to shift the decimal point to the more familiar position between the first and second digits, the E means floating point form (with an exponent), the 15 means 15 printing positions, and the 3 means three decimal places.

The output is shown in Figure 4.3.

Let us now return to the question of comparing R against 200 to determine the end of the loop.   Suppose we were to ask that S be printed for all values of R from 20 to 200 in steps of 0.1.   To do this we simply change the constant at line 50.   While we are changing the program, let us also change the FORMAT statement so that we get seven digits in each number.   The last few lines of the output this time are shown in Figure 4.4.

What has happened?   Why is the last value of R not 200?   The

```
      C FOR COMMENT
STATEMENT
 NUMBER                                    FORTRAN STATEMENT
1        5 6 7

         R = 20.
   10    IF (R - 120.) 20, 30, 30
   20    S = 1..7E4 - .485 * R * R
         GO TO 40
   30    S = 1..8E4/((1. + R * R / 1..8E4))
   40    PRINT 70, R, S
   70    FORMAT (F10.0, 1PE15.3)
         IF (R - 200.) 50, 60, 60
   50    R = R + 5.
         GO TO 10
   60    STOP
         END
```

FIGURE 4.2   Program for a column design calculation.   (Case Study 4.)

20.	1.681E 04
25.	1.670E 04
30.	1.656E 04
35.	1.641E 04
40.	1.622E 04
45.	1.602E 04
50.	1.579E 04
55.	1.553E 04
60.	1.525E 04
65.	1.495E 04
70.	1.462E 04
75.	1.427E 04
80.	1.390E 04
85.	1.350E 04
90.	1.307E 04
95.	1.262E 04
100.	1.215E 04
105.	1.165E 04
110.	1.113E 04
115.	1.059E 04
120.	1.000E 04
125.	9.636E 03
130.	9.284E 03
135.	8.944E 03
140.	8.617E 03
145.	8.302E 03
150.	8.000E 03
155.	7.710E 03
160.	7.431E 03
165.	7.164E 03
170.	6.908E 03
175.	6.663E 03
180.	6.429E 03
185.	6.204E 03
190.	5.989E 03
195.	5.783E 03
200.	5.586E 03

FIGURE 4.3   Output of the program of Figure 4.2. (Case Study 4.)

answer, as suggested in passing in Chapter 2, is that the program was run on a binary computer, and there is no exact binary representation of decimal 0.1. In the computer used, the IBM 7094, the floating binary approximation of decimal 0.1 differs from the true value by about 2^{-33}. This is far too small an error to make any difference in the accuracy of the output, but it does build up when the floating binary approximation of 0.1 is added to R many hundreds of times, as it is in this version of the program.

If we had required R to be *exactly* 200 to terminate the loop, we should naturally never have achieved the equality.

This particular problem would not arise in a decimal computer, since decimal 0.1 obviously has an exact representation in such a machine. The problem, nevertheless, is general: suppose we had wanted to increment R in steps of 1/7, which has no exact representation in decimal or binary. (There are no base seven computers!)

The solution is to make the test for "equality" of R with 200 a little more sophisticated. Instead of comparing R directly with 200, we can test the *difference* between R and 200 to see whether it is less than some tolerance. For instance, we could write

$$IF(ABSF(R - 200.) - 0.001)\ 60,\ 60,\ 50$$

Now, if the absolute value of the difference between R and 200 is less than or equal to .001, we go to the STOP, because R must be very close to 200. The absolute-value function is necessary because, in general, we do not know whether the accumulated roundoff error will be positive or negative. The tolerance used must be less than 0.1, the increment, but greater than the expected accumulated roundoff error. If the tolerance were taken as 0.2, we would obviously stop too soon; if it were taken as 10^{-8}, we would never stop.

If we make this change in the program and also modify the FORMAT statement so that S is printed to tenths and R is printed with four digits, everything will be handled smoothly. We will always stop pre-

198.0985	5.660078E 03	198.0	5.664E 03
198.1985	5.656163E 03	198.1	5.660E 03
198.2985	5.652250E 03	198.2	5.656E 03
198.3985	5.648341E 03	198.3	5.652E 03
198.4985	5.644436E 03	198.4	5.648E 03
198.5985	5.640534E 03	198.5	5.644E 03
198.6985	5.636635E 03	198.6	5.641E 03
198.7985	5.632740E 03	198.7	5.637E 03
198.8985	5.628849E 03	198.8	5.633E 03
198.9985	5.624960E 03	198.9	5.629E 03
199.0985	5.621075E 03	199.0	5.625E 03
199.1985	5.617194E 03	199.1	5.621E 03
199.2985	5.613316E 03	199.2	5.617E 03
199.3985	5.609441E 03	199.3	5.613E 03
199.4985	5.605570E 03	199.4	5.609E 03
199.5985	5.601702E 03	199.5	5.606E 03
199.6985	5.597838E 03	199.6	5.602E 03
199.7985	5.593977E 03	199.7	5.598E 03
199.8985	5.590119E 03	199.8	5.594E 03
199.9985	5.586265E 03	199.9	5.590E 03
200.0985	5.582414E 03	200.0	5.586E 03

FIGURE 4.4   Output of the program of Figure 4.2, modified to take more intervals and then print more figures. (Case Study 4.)

FIGURE 4.5   Output of the program of Figure 4.2, modified to take an interval of 0.1 and with the method of testing changed as described in the text. (Case Study 4.)

cisely when we want to, and the accumulated roundoff error will not be great enough to appear in the rounded value of R.

The last few lines of output for this final version of the program, in which the increment is still 0.1, are shown in Figure 4.5.

Another method of handling this roundoff problem in running through a set of values is mentioned in Section 7.7.

4.3   Case study 5: A servomechanism frequency response plot; program checkout

The transfer function of a certain servomechanism is given by

$$T(j\omega) = \frac{K}{j\omega(1 + jT_1\omega)(1 + jT_2\omega)}$$

where ω = angular frequency, radians/second

$j = \sqrt{-1}$*

T = transfer function

K = amplification factor

T_1, T_2 = time constants, seconds

---

* In mathematics the symbol for $\sqrt{-1}$ is, of course, i.   In electrical engineering i is used to represent current; j is written for $\sqrt{-1}$.

Without attempting to show the complete theory, we characterize a transfer function as follows.   We have a "black box" with two input terminals and two output terminals.   An input signal with a given frequency is applied to the input; the signal appears at the output with its amplitude multiplied by the magnitude (absolute value, or modulus, in the complex variables sense) of the transfer function and its phase shifted by the phase angle (amplitude) of the transfer function.

The transfer function will in general be a complex number.   The simplest way to handle the complex arithmetic in this case is to rewrite the formula so that the real and imaginary parts are separated.   All arithmetic will then require only real quantities—which are all we can deal with.*   The formula for the function now becomes

$$T(j\omega) = \frac{-K(T_1 + T_2)}{(1 + T_1{}^2\omega^2)(1 + T_2{}^2\omega^2)} - \frac{K(1 - T_1 T_2\omega^2)}{(1 + T_1{}^2\omega^2)(1 + T_2{}^2\omega^2)\omega} \cdot j$$

If we now write this form of the transfer function as $T(j\omega) = a + bj$, the situation can be restated a little more clearly.   The magnitude of the input signal appears at the output multiplied by $\sqrt{a^2 + b^2}$ and with its phase shifted by an angle $\theta = \arctan b/a$.

The computational problem is as follows.   An electrical engineer wishes to be able to read in values of K, T_1, and T_2 and to compute the transfer function for a number of values of ω.   He wishes also to be able to read in starting and final values of ω, an increment for ω, called OMGINC, and a number L.   If L is zero, OMGINC is to be *added* to ω between repetitions, but if L is not zero ω is to be *multiplied* by OMGINC.   In either case the computation is to be continued until T has been computed for the largest value of ω that does not exceed the specified final value of ω.

For each value of ω and the given values of K, T_1, and T_2 we are to print the real and imaginary parts of the transfer function, the modulus, and the phase angle in degrees.

Further discussion will be simplified if we now agree on the variable names to be used in the program.

AMP   amplification factor, K in formula
OMEGA ω

---

* A number of versions of FORTRAN permit direct complex arithmetic, in which each complex quantity is represented within the machine as two (real) numbers, one for the real part and one for the imaginary part.   When the source program calls for arithmetic operations on complex numbers, the compiler sets up the necessary actions with the real and imaginary parts of the two complex numbers.

T1, T2	time constants
OMGFST	starting value of ω
OMGLST	final value of ω
OMGINC	increment of ω
L	add OMGINC (L = 0) or multiply by OMGINC (L $\neq$ 0)
TREAL	real part of transfer function
TIMAG	imaginary part of transfer function
ABSVAL	absolute value, or modulus, of transfer function
PHASE	phase angle of transfer function, degrees
DENOM	intermediate variable: denominator of expressions for real and imaginary parts
OMGSQ	intermediate variable: ω^2

Note the measures taken to avoid giving floating point variables improper names: K could not be used for the amplification factor or MODULS for the modulus. L is properly named, since it will be read and used as a fixed point variable.

A block diagram is shown in Figure 4.6. We begin by reading the data and immediately print the three parameters; assuming that the program would normally be used to run through values of ω for many different sets of values of K, T_1, and T_2, it is essential that the output be identified with these parameters. Then we set ω equal to the starting value that has been read, compute the four output numbers, and print them. After incrementing ω by whatever method the value of L specifies, we ask whether the new value is greater than the specified final value of ω and stop if it is; otherwise we return to compute the new point. In order to follow the problem specifications exactly, it is necessary to increment ω *before* testing it; if it were tested first, we might get the signal to go around once more and increment ω to a value greater than the final.

The program shown in Figure 4.7 contains quite a number of deliberate errors. After noting a few of the features of the program, we shall trace through the steps we might follow in discovering and correcting the various kinds of errors. To simplify the discussion, all statements have been given statement numbers.

The printing of the amplification factor and the two time constants is done with a field specification of 1P3E14.5; this is somewhat arbitrary, since there is no compelling reason for any particular number of digits in these parameters. In the second print statement the field specification is 1P7E12.4; these numbers are printed with fewer digits and less space between numbers in order to hold down the total width

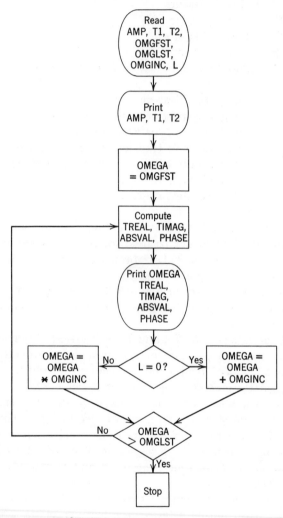

FIGURE 4.6 Block diagram of a servomechanism frequency response plot calculation. (Case Study 5.)

of the printing to a size suitable for reproduction. We have also arranged to print two intermediate variables, OMGSQ and DENOM, for possible assistance in hunting down programming errors. In other respects the program follows the logic of the block diagram quite closely (except for the errors, of course).

There are a great many ways to make mistakes in a program. One

of the easiest is in punching the program cards.   If the programmer
punches them himself, he may make mistakes because he is not experienced at operating the card punch.   If they are punched by a card-
punch operator, there is the danger of misreading handwriting.   Either
way, much time can be saved in the long run by checking the deck
carefully before trying to compile it.

One common way to check the accuracy of punching is to *verify* the
deck with a *verifier*.   This machine has the same general appearance
as a card punch but only checks the punching.   A second operator
goes through the same motions of punching but all that happens is
that the holes in the deck are checked to see if they correspond to the
keys struck by the verifier operator.   If not, a red light signals the
discrepancy.

A second way to check the accuracy of the punching of the program
deck is to *list* it with a *tabulator*.   Figure 4.8 shows the listing of the
deck punched from Figure 4.7.   Careful study discloses three errors
in punching.   In statement 3 PRINT has been punched as PR1NT,

STATEMENT NUMBER 1 5	C FOR COMMENT / 6	7 FORTRAN STATEMENT
1		READ 2, AMP, T1, T2, OMGFST, OMGLST, OMGINC, L
2		FORMAT (6F10.0, I1)
3		PRINT 4, AMP, T1, T2
4		FORMAT (1P3E14.5)
5		OMEGA = OMGFST
6		OMGSQ = OMEGA * OMEGA
7		DENOM = (1. + T1**2 * OMGSQ) * (1. + T2**2 * OMGSQ)
8		TREAL = -AMP*(T1 + T2)/DENOM
9		TIMAG = -AMP*(1. - T1*T2*OMGSQ)/DENOM*OMEGA
10		ABSVAL = SQRTF(TREAL**2 + TIMAG**2)
11		PHASE = ATANF(TIMAG/TREAL)
12		PRINT 13, OMEGA, OMGSQ, DENOM, TREAL, TIMAG,
1		ABSVAL, PHASE
13		FORMAT (1P7E12.4)
14		IF (L) 17, 16, 17
15		OMEGA = OMEGA + OMGINC
16		GO TO 18
17		OMEGA = OMEGA * OMGINC
18		IF (OMEGA - OMGLST) 5, 5, 9
19		STOP
		END

FIGURE 4.7   Program for a servomechanism frequency response plot calculation.   (Case Study 5.)
This program contains deliberate errors.

```
 1 READ 2, AMP,.T1, T2, OMGFST, OMGLST, OMGINC, L
 2 FORMAT (6F10.0,· I1)
 3 PRINT 4, AMP, T1, T2
 4 FORMAT (1P3E14.5)
 5 OMEGA = OMGFST
 6 OMGSQ = OMEGA * OMEGA
 7 DENOM = (1. + T1**2 * OMGSQ)*(1. + T2**2 * OMGSQ)
 8 TREAL = -AMP$(T1 + T2)/DENOM
 9 TIMAG = -AMP*(1 - T1*T2*OMGSQ)/DENOM*OMEGA
10 ABSVAL = SQRTF(TREAL**2 + TIMAG**2)
11 PHASE = ATANF(TIMAG/TREAL)
12 PRINT 13 OMEGA, OMGSQ, DENOM, TREAL, TIMAG,
 1        ABSVAL, PHASE
13 FORMAT (1P7E12.4)
UJ IF (L) 17, 16, 17
15 OMEGA = OMEGA + OMGINC
16 GO TO 18
17 OMEGA, = OMEGA * OMGINC
18 IF (OMEGA - OMGLST) 5, 5, 19
19 STOP
   END
```

FIGURE 4.8 Listing of the deck punched from the program of Figure 4.7. (Case Study 5.)

an easy slip. The FORTRAN compiler would reject the statement. In statement 8 there is a dollar sign where there should be an asterisk; this happens to be easy to do because of the way the card punch works. The same explanation applies to the UJ where statement number 14 should appear.

A careful study of this listing will no doubt reveal to the careful reader many of the deliberate errors. This is generally true. *Desk checking* of the program or the program listing before compiling is a good investment of the programmer's time as well as saving wasted computer time. Let us pretend that we have not seen these errors in order to learn how they can be detected later in the process.

Now we try to compile. All FORTRAN compilers include some degree of diagnostic checking for statements that are *syntactically illegal*; that is, statements that do not follow the rules for forming a statement, no matter what they may mean. FORTRAN cannot determine whether you wrote what you meant to, in general, but it can sometimes establish without question that a statement is illegal. The degree of checking in the various FORTRAN systems varies widely.

In our case the compiler detected two errors the first time, as shown in Figure 4.9. The first line gives the statement and the second the diagnostic comment on that statement. "Mixed" refers to combining fixed and floating point variables or constants in some illegal way. Clearly, the trouble here is a missing decimal point in the constant 1.

```
    9        TIMAG = -AMP*(1 - T1*T2*OMGSQ)/DENOM*OMEGA

 11252       MIXED EXPRESSION.

   12        PRINT 13 OMEGA, OMGSQ, DENOM, TREAL, TIMAG,

 04336       MORE THAN SIX CHARACTERS IN SOME SYMBOL.
```

FIGURE 4.9   Error listing produced by the compiler from the program of Figure 4.7.   (Case Study 5.)

The third line gives the second error statement and the fourth the diagnosis. The comment this time is a little less specific; given a statement with an error, it is often quite difficult to establish precisely what the error was in terms of what the programmer meant to do. In this case the error is the absence of a comma after the 13, the FORMAT statement number.

The compiler used for this program consists of a number of phases. If an error is detected in the first phase, the program is rejected and nothing more is done with it. After we correct the two errors found in the first phase, we try again. This time the compiler rejects the program with the diagnostic: "A PART OF THE PROGRAM CANNOT BE REACHED. IT IS LOCATED AT OR NEAR THE STATEMENT NUMBER 15." This means that there is some section of the program that can never be executed; no flow of statement execution ever leads to it. The error is not in statement 15; it could be anywhere in the program, in principle. A study of the surrounding statements discloses an error in statement number 14, which should be

$$14 \text{ IF (L) } 17, 15, 17$$

With this corrected, the program compiles. There may still be errors! (And there are.) There is a limit to the amount of checking that can economically be designed into a compiler, and there are certain types of errors that the compiler simply cannot detect in any case.

The object program was run with a data card that specified $K = 100, T_1 = 0.25, T_2 = 0.0625, \text{OMGFST} = 0.01, \text{OMGLST} = 100,$ $\text{OMGINC} = 1.3,$ and L = 1. The object program read the data card, began printing, and continued to print the same line over and over until the program was removed from the computer. The values printed on all lines were

OMEGA	0.01
OMGSQ	0.0001

DENOM	1.0000
TREAL	−31.250
TIMAG	−0.99999
ABSVAL	31.266
PHASE	0.031989

The immediate question is, why was the one line repeated indefinitely? We note first of all that it is the line for the proper first value of OMEGA; this is a clue. Could the program have transferred back to the statement that gives OMEGA its starting value? This is indeed the trouble: statement 18 returns control to statement 5 if OMEGA has not yet reached OMGLST. Thus, after modifying the value of OMEGA at statement 15 or 17, it is always set back to its initial value at statement 5. Statement 18 clearly should be

$$18 \text{ IF (OMEGA } - \text{ OMGLST) } 6, 6, 19$$

The beginning programmer is strongly tempted at this point to correct the error and try again. Even though these errors admittedly are contrived, they illustrate a sound piece of advice nicely: try to correct *all* the trouble you can locate with each attempt. Let us see what else we can learn from these output values before correcting the one known error and rerunning.

There is no difficulty with OMGSQ. DENOM looks reasonable; OMGSQ is quite small, so we do not expect the denominator to be much larger than 1.0. Since DENOM is 1.0000, it easy to check that TREAL is also right. TIMAG, however, looks suspicious. K is 100; with OMGSQ small, the factor in parentheses ought to be close to 1.0; DENOM is 1.0; with OMEGA equal to 0.01, the entire expression ought to be approximately 100/0.01, or 10,000. Instead, it is about 1.0. What happened?

Since OMGSQ and DENOM appear to be correct, the trouble is presumably in the expression for TIMAG itself. Inspection reveals the difficulty: parentheses were not written around DENOM*OMEGA, so that OMEGA was in effect in the numerator. This completely explains the discrepancy in the value of TIMAG, and we are once again tempted to correct and rerun.

But what about ABSVAL and PHASE? ABSVAL is just slightly larger than TREAL, which seems reasonable. PHASE is another matter. Is 0.03 degrees a reasonable angle for a complex number with a real part of −31 and an imaginary part of −1? Hardly. In the first place it is in the wrong quadrant; with real and imaginary parts both negative, the angle should be between 180 and 270°.

This is no fault of FORTRAN or of the mathematics. The arctangent is a multiple-valued function: an infinite number of angles have the same tangent. The arctangent routine supplied with the version of FORTRAN used here selects the branch of the arctangent function between $-\pi/2$ and $+\pi/2$.

In other words, the value of 0.03 is based on the assumption that the angle is in the first quadrant. But even with this assumption, is the result what we would expect? Approximately what is the angle in the first quadrant whose tangent is about $\frac{1}{31}$? A little slide-rule work or a glance at a handbook shows that it is not 0.03°.

The trouble this time is that the angle was computed in radians and we expected degrees.

So here we have two problems: getting into the proper quadrant and converting from radians to degrees. The conversion is easily done by multiplying by $180/\pi$, or 57.29578. Finding the quadrant would be somewhat more work if we were required to handle an angle that could be in *any* of the four. But consider the formulas. The real part is always negative; the imaginary part can be positive or negative. Thus our complex number will always be in the second or third quadrant. If both parts are negative, the arctangent function will produce an angle in the first quadrant; we can convert to the third by adding 180°. If the real part is negative and the imaginary part positive, the arctangent function will produce an angle in the fourth quadrant; we can convert to the second here also by adding 180°.

It appears that we can solve our problems by making statement 11 read

11 PHASE = ATANF(TIMAG/TREAL)*57.29578 + 180.0

It now appears that we have an explanation for all the troubles in the program. Let us make the necessary corrections and try again. The corrected program, with all changes to date incorporated, is shown in Figure 4.10. We have removed OMGSQ and DENOM from the second PRINT statement, since no difficulties were found in them.

The object program this time produced the output of Figure 4.11, which looks altogether better. Are we done? Not at all. We now know that the FORTRAN compiler cannot detect any errors and the errors in one line of output have been explained away, but we do not know that the results are actually correct. In other words, we have *hopefully* removed all the errors from the program, but we have not *proved* that the results are correct.

The next step is to compute, with a desk calculator if possible, the proper results for several different sets of values of the various param-

STATEMENT NUMBER 1 5	6 7	FORTRAN STATEMENT
1		READ 2, AMP, T1, T2, OMGFST, OMGLST, OMGINC, L
2		FORMAT (6F10.0, I1)
3		PRINT 4, AMP, T1, T2
4		FORMAT (1P3E14.5)
5		OMEGA = OMGFST
6		OMGSQ = OMEGA * OMEGA
7		DENOM = (1. + T1**2 * OMGSQ)*(1. + T2**2 * OMGSQ)
8		TREAL = -AMP*(T1 + T2)/DENOM
9		TIMAG = -AMP*(1. - T1*T2*OMGSQ)/(DENOM*OMEGA)
10		ABSVAL = SQRTF(TREAL**2 + TIMAG**2)
11		PHASE = ATANF(TIMAG/TREAL) * 57..2957.8 + 180..0
12		PRINT 13, OMEGA, TREAL, TIMAG, ABSVAL, PHASE
13		FORMAT (1P5E12.4)
14		IF (L) 17, 15, 17
15		OMEGA = OMEGA + OMGINC
16		GO TO 18
17		OMEGA = OMEGA * OMGINC
18		IF (OMEGA - OMGLST) 6, 6, 19
19		STOP
		END

FIGURE 4.10   Final corrected version of the program of Figure 4.7.   (Case Study 5.)

eters, being very careful not to introduce any special conditions. For an example of special conditions suppose we calculated ABSVAL and PHASE for an OMEGA of 1.0; the missing parentheses in statement 9 would not have been detected. Or suppose we made the two time constants equal; certain types of errors in computing DENOM could go undetected.

Hand calculation of several values shows agreement with the computer's values, and we conclude that the program is probably correct.

A majority of programs either do not compile the first time or, if they do, they produce incorrect answers. Experienced programmers expect to have to spend time on checkout and they plan accordingly. We may conclude this brief introduction to the subject of program checkout with a few suggestions on how to go about it.

1. Checkout is usually much simpler if intermediate variable values are available. In common practice we insert extra PRINT statements to get the values, then simply remove the cards and recompile when checkout is completed.

2. Time spent in desk checking a program will shorten the total time the programmer must spend on checkout and it will also save computer time.   This should be done both before and after the program cards are punched.

3. Never assume that a program is correct just because the compiler detects no errors.

4. Accomplish as much as you can with each computer run.   Resist the almost overpowering temptation to hurry back to the machine after finding each error.

5. The final test of a program is comparison with hand calculations whenever possible.   In choosing test cases, try to select values that bring all parts of the program into operation and avoid special cases unless they are specifically needed to test some section of the program.

```
1.00000E 02   2.50000E-01   6.25000E-02
10.0000E-03 -3.1250E 01 -9.9999E 03 10.0000E 03 2.6982E 02
1.3000E-02 -3.1250E 01 -7.6922E 03 7.6923E 03 2.6977E 02
1.6900E-02 -3.1249E 01 -5.9170E 03 5.9171E 03 2.6970E 02
2.1970E-02 -3.1249E 01 -4.5515E 03 4.5516E 03 2.6961E 02
2.8561E-02 -3.1248E 01 -3.5010E 03 3.5012E 03 2.6949E 02
3.7129E-02 -3.1247E 01 -2.6930E 03 2.6932E 03 2.6934E 02
4.8268E-02 -3.1245E 01 -2.0714E 03 2.0716E 03 2.6914E 02
6.2749E-02 -3.1242E 01 -1.5931E 03 1.5935E 03 2.6888E 02
8.1573E-02 -3.1236E 01 -1.2252E 03 1.2256E 03 2.6854E 02
1.0604E-01 -3.1227E 01 -9.4213E 02 9.4264E 02 2.6810E 02
1.3786E-01 -3.1211E 01 -7.2425E 02 7.2492E 02 2.6753E 02
1.7922E-01 -3.1183E 01 -5.5652E 02 5.5739E 02 2.6679E 02
2.3298E-01 -3.1138E 01 -4.2732E 02 4.2845E 02 2.6583E 02
3.0288E-01 -3.1061E 01 -3.2770E 02 3.2917E 02 2.6459E 02
3.9374E-01 -3.0931E 01 -2.5078E 02 2.5268E 02 2.6297E 02
5.1186E-01 -3.0715E 01 -1.9124E 02 1.9369E 02 2.6088E 02
6.6542E-01 -3.0356E 01 -1.4497E 02 1.4812E 02 2.5817E 02
8.6504E-01 -2.9767E 01 -1.0883E 02 1.1282E 02 2.5470E 02
1.1246E 00 -2.8819E 01 -8.0385E 01 8.5395E 01 2.5028E 02
1.4619E 00 -2.7339E 01 -5.7845E 01 6.3980E 01 2.4470E 02
1.9005E 00 -2.5140E 01 -3.9941E 01 4.7194E 01 2.3781E 02
2.4706E 00 -2.2093E 01 -2.5886E 01 3.4033E 01 2.2952E 02
3.2118E 00 -1.8264E 01 -1.5264E 01 2.3802E 01 2.1989E 02
4.1754E 00 -1.4001E 01 -7.8075E 00 1.6031E 01 2.0915E 02
5.4280E 00 -9.8628E 00 -3.1377E 00 1.0350E 01 1.9765E 02
7.0564E 00 -6.3621E 00 -6.4046E-01 6.3943E 00 1.8575E 02
9.1733E 00 -3.7574E 00 4.1267E-01 3.7800E 00 1.7373E 02
1.1925E 01 -2.0317E 00 6.6624E-01 2.1381E 00 1.6184E 02
1.5503E 01 -1.0060E 00 5.7217E-01 1.1574E 00 1.5037E 02
2.0154E 01 -4.5787E-01 3.8869E-01 6.0061E-01 1.3967E 02
2.6200E 01 -1.9335E-01 2.2968E-01 3.0023E-01 1.3009E 02
3.4060E 01 -7.6857E-02 1.2367E-01 1.4560E-01 1.2186E 02
4.4278E 01 -2.9217E-02 6.2571E-02 6.9056E-02 1.1503E 02
5.7561E 01 -1.0771E-02 3.0402E-02 3.2254E-02 1.0951E 02
7.4830E 01 -3.8928E-03 1.4398E-02 1.4915E-02 1.0513E 02
9.7279E 01 -1.3894E-03 6.7120E-03 6.8543E-03 1.0169E 02
```

FIGURE 4.11   Output from the corrected program of Figure 4.10.   (Case Study 5.)

4.4   Case study 6: The normal probability integral

A statistician is writing a program in which he will frequently need the value of the normal probability integral:

$$P(x) = \frac{1}{\sqrt{2\pi}} \int_{-x}^{x} e^{-t^2/2} \, dt$$

This integral gives the area between $-x$ and x of the familiar normal probability curve shown in Figure 4.12. The total area of the curve, that is, from $-\infty$ to ∞, is 1. Table 4.1 lists the values of the integral for a few values of x.

Table 4.1

x	Integral
0.0	0.0000
0.1	0.0797
0.2	0.1585
0.3	0.2358
1.0	0.6827
2.0	0.9545
3.0	0.9973
4.0	0.9999

We shall not consider what the usage of the integral may be but only explore a program to compute its value, given a value of x. The program we shall write is required to accept any value of x from 0.0 to 4.0. It must provide a value of the integral accurate to four decimal

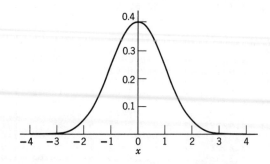

FIGURE 4.12   The normal probability curve. (Case Study 6.)

places. It will be used fairly heavily and should be reasonably fast. We may assume that the x values will themselves be normally distributed, which means that small values of x are much more likely than large ones. Looking at Table 4.1, we conclude, for instance, that x will be less than 1.0 better than two thirds of the time [since $P(1) = 0.6827$]. It is reasonable, therefore, to concentrate on speed for small x and not worry too much about speed for large x.

The value of $P(x)$ is calculated from a power series. (Direct numerical integration of the integral is entirely possible with methods presented in Chapter 6, but it would be hopelessly slow compared to working with the series.) The derivation of the series is not our primary interest; we state it without proof:

$$P(x) = x \left(\frac{2}{\pi}\right)^{1/2} \left[1 - \frac{x^2}{2 \cdot 1! \cdot 3} + \frac{x^4}{2^2 \cdot 2! \cdot 5} - \frac{x^6}{2^3 \cdot 3! \cdot 7} + \cdots \right]$$

As with any convergent alternating series, the truncation error is less than the first term neglected. We begin to decide how to proceed by determining how many terms of this series will be needed to get the accuracy required. Four decimal digits mean absolute accuracy, not relative; $P(0.1) = 0.0797$ will be acceptable, even though the relative accuracy drops off for small x. What this means to us is that the value of $P(x)$ we compute must be correct within 0.00005. In other words, the first term neglected, multiplied by $x(2/\pi)^{1/2}$, must be less than 0.00005 in absolute value.

Let's try a few x values to see how many terms are required. (Slide-rule accuracy, approximately 0.1%, is good enough for this purpose.)

$$P(x) = x \left(\frac{2}{\pi}\right)^{1/2} \left(1 - \frac{x^2}{6} + \frac{x^4}{40} - \frac{x^6}{336} + \frac{x^8}{3456} - \frac{x^{10}}{42{,}240} \right.$$
$$\left. + \frac{x^{12}}{599{,}040} - \frac{x^{14}}{9{,}676{,}800} + \frac{x^{16}}{175{,}472{,}640} - \cdots \right)$$

$$P(.1) = 0.1 \cdot 0.80 \cdot (1 - 0.0017 + 0.0000025 - \cdots)$$

Here, we could clearly stop after the term in x^2.

$$P(1) = 1 \cdot 0.80 \cdot (1 - 0.167 + 0.025 - 0.0030 + 0.00029 - 0.000024)$$

This time we could stop after the term in x^8. In other words, for all x up to 1 we could take the series to be

$$P(x) = x \left(\frac{2}{\pi}\right)^{1/2} \left(1 - \frac{x^2}{6} + \frac{x^4}{40} - \frac{x^6}{336} + \frac{x^8}{3456} \right)$$

and have the accuracy required.

$$P(2) = 2 \cdot 0.80 \cdot (1 - 0.667 + 0.400 - 0.190 + 0.0741 - 0.0243$$
$$+ 0.00685 - 0.00169 + 0.00037 - 0.000078 + 0.000013)$$

This means we would have to go out through the term in x^{18} to get the required accuracy.

$$P(3) = 3 \cdot 0.80 \cdot (1 - 1.5 + 2.02 - 2.17 + 1.90 - 1.40 + 0.887$$
$$- 0.494 + 0.0246 - 0.0110 + 0.00446 - 0.00166$$
$$+ 0.000574 - 0.0001835 + 0.0000549 - 0.0000154)$$

This time we should have to take terms through x^{28}. We shall not reproduce the arithmetic, but $P(4)$ would require terms through about x^{50}.

The decision we now face is affected by accuracy, speed, and the expected distribution of the x's. It would be prohibitive to use the series with terms through x^{50} for all x in order to get the required accuracy for $x = 4$, and even if we did the roundoff error would probably destroy the accuracy for large x. It is clearly going to be necessary to compute $P(x)$ differently for small and large x, and we may decide to break it into three or perhaps even four ranges.

Let us work first with small x. Going back to the numerical values for $P(1)$, we see that five terms, through x^8, are sufficient. Since the range $0 \leq x \leq 1$ covers 68% of the expected x values, it will be worth the trouble to speed up this part and be less concerned with speed for larger x. It looks as though it might be worth the trouble to explore telescoping the series and perhaps save a term or two.

In Appendix 1, Part B, we see that

$$x^8 = \frac{1}{128} (256x^6 - 160x^4 + 32x^2 - 1 + T_8)$$

By neglecting all terms beyond x^8 and replacing x^8 with the expression above, we get

$$P(x) = x \left(\frac{2}{\pi}\right)^{1/2} \left[\left(1 - \frac{1}{128 \cdot 3456}\right) - \left(\frac{1}{6} - \frac{32}{128 \cdot 3456}\right) x^2 \right.$$
$$\left. + \left(\frac{1}{40} - \frac{160}{128 \cdot 3456}\right) x^4 - \left(\frac{1}{336} - \frac{256}{128 \cdot 3456}\right) x^6 + \frac{1}{128 \cdot 3456} T_8 \right]$$

For $|x| < 1$, $T_8(x)$ is less than 1, and the error committed by telescoping is less than $2.2 \cdot 10^{-6}$, which is negligible compared with the accuracy required.

Could we telescope further? If we replaced x^6 by the expression from Appendix 2, we would have a telescoping error of $(1/32 \cdot 336)T_6$, which could be as large as 0.000094. This would represent an error of 1 in the last place most of the time and is therefore not acceptable.

Before going on, it might be well to write and test a program segment for this much of the job. It would be a good idea to know that this much works, for one thing, and for another it might turn out that the telescoped series is good a little beyond 1. This could happen because we are dealing with error *bounds* and by good fortune the actual errors might be smaller.

By rewriting the series as

$$P(x) = 0.79788455 \cdot x \cdot (0.99999774 - 0.16659433x^2 \\ + 0.024638310x^4 - 0.0023974867x^6)$$

we have a fairly simple formula to program. It can then be incorporated in a routine that runs through values of x and prints out the computed values of $P(x)$.

This was done with a binary computer in which floating point numbers are represented to the equivalent of eight decimal digits. The statement was incorporated in a loop to run through x values from zero to 2.00 in steps of 0.01.

The program gave results that checked with a four-place table, for $0 \le x \le 1.20$, with four exceptions. For $x = 0.96$, for instance, the table value is 0.6629, whereas the program computed 0.6630. This does *not* mean that the program was wrong, however! The correct value, to six decimals, is 0.662945. The program was actually set up to print its results to six places also; the value for $x = 0.96$ was 0.662957. Clearly, the correct value and our value will round to different fourth digits, even though the two six-place values differ by only 0.000012. It is important to remember that our basic specification was that no computed value is to differ from the true value by more than 0.00005, which is not at all the same thing as requiring the computed results to check with a published four-place table. The table would, of course, require a much "tighter" tolerance. In fact, we could not even say in advance *how* close the computed results would have to be. Suppose the correct value for some x were 0.34564999999; then, if our computed result were too large by as much as 10^{-11}, it would round to a different four-place result than the table.

The four examples in which the four-place answer printed by the program differed from the table were all of this type, in the stated range $0 \le x \le 1.2$. Above $x = 1.2$ the computed results became much less accurate, which is not surprising.

Small x values are now well taken care of; how shall we deal with large x? Use of the same series for the entire range is not very appealing. For x between 3 and 4 the series converges slowly enough that many terms are required and accuracy becomes a serious concern. For $x = 4$ one of the terms is almost 25, which raises the question whether four-decimal accuracy can be maintained, along the lines of the sine function example in Case Study 3.

An alternative approach for large x is to use an *asymptotic series*, which for the normal probability integral is found in a handbook to be

$$P(x) \simeq 1 - \left(\frac{2}{\pi}\right) \frac{e^{-x^2/2}}{x} \left(1 - \frac{1}{x^2} + \frac{1 \cdot 3}{x^4} - \frac{1 \cdot 3 \cdot 5}{x^6} \right.$$

$$\left. + \frac{1 \cdot 3 \cdot 5 \cdot 7}{x^8} - \cdots \right)$$

An asymptotic series has terms that decrease for a while, then increase, so that it does not converge at all in the sense that the truncation error may be made as small as desired by taking enough terms. The truncation error in an asymptotic series is less than the *last term retained* (rather than the first term neglected).

The question, then, is whether the smallest term would be small enough to give the required accuracy for x values of interest. Again using slide-rule accuracy, we may test a few x values to see what happens.

$$P(2) \simeq 1 - 0.80 \cdot \frac{e^{-2}}{2} (1 - 0.25 + 0.188 - 0.235 + 0.411 - \cdots)$$

This is evidently of little value to us: the smallest term, even multiplied by the terms in front, is far too large to provide the required accuracy.

$$P(3) \simeq 1 - 0.80 \cdot \frac{e^{-4.5}}{3} (1 - 0.111 + 0.037 - 0.0205 + 0.0160$$

$$- 0.016 + 0.0196 - \cdots)$$

This may be interesting. The series multiplier has the approximate value 0.0030, which multiplied by the smallest term becomes 0.000048. This is just acceptable, and it appears that the asymptotic series through the term $105/x^8$ may serve for x greater than 3.

Again, it would be a good idea to test the plan with a quick preliminary program. An arithmetic statement to compute the formula was incorporated in a loop that ran through x values from 2 to 4. The results were correct for $2.90 \le x \le 4.00$. At six points the printed four-place result was different from the table by one digit in the last place, but in each case the computed six-place result differed from the true value by less than 0.00005, as required. For $x < 2.90$, the differences were greater, as we expected: the asymptotic series becomes less accurate for small x.

We now have a plan of attack for small and large x. What can we do with the intermediate values? In one way we start with the number of terms of the original power series that would be required for the largest x and try to telescope it. Such a series, however, would have to go out through terms in about x^{26}, which would be a lot of work to telescope. In some cases it might be worth the trouble, but not for us.

Perhaps we should accept a slower speed for this range in a compromise between a fast-running program and one that can be programmed in a reasonable amount of effort. One way to do this is to take the original power series and set up a loop that continues to compute terms until it finds one smaller than the accuracy tolerance. We shall have to investigate the roundoff problem carefully, but it might work. Such an approach would also have the advantage of taking less time for the smaller x in the range than for the large, which would minimize the time penalty, since we expect to have a preponderance of small x. For $x = 1.5$, for instance, terms through x^{10} suffice, which is not too bad.

We are now talking about an economic balance between machine time, program complexity, and programming time. In this area there are no rigid guides; we must make estimates and even guesses. It does appear that a straightforward application of the series, taking as many terms as necessary, would not incur heavy time penalties for the range $1.2 < x < 2.9$.

What about roundoff? Two ways of losing significance concern us. One is the subtraction of two large numbers that are nearly equal, with the difference being of a comparable magnitude with some smaller term. The other is to add a very small number to a very large one, so that many digits at the right end of the small number are lost. A subtraction follows, which gives a difference in which the lost digits would have been significant.

It is a bit difficult to investigate these matters in complete generality. It will be adequate in the material at hand to check what happens in the worst case, near $x = 3$, knowing that if accuracy is maintained for the largest value it will be adequate for the smaller. Looking at the numbers in the expression for $P(3)$, we see that neither problem apparently will be serious for us. Subtraction of the two largest numbers, 2.02 . . . and 2.17 . . . , maintains about seven digits (assuming eight-digit floating point numbers), which is more than adequate to protect against loss of significance affecting the basic requirement for four-digit results.   The second problem is alleviated by the order of the arithmetic operations: we never add a very small number to a very large number; the small numbers are added to partial sums which, as it happens, are never much greater than 1.

It appears, then, that roundoff will not be a problem, largely because we are working with eight-digit numbers, whereas we need only four-digit accuracy.   (If we needed six or seven digits, we would not only have to take many more terms but somewhat complicated measures might be necessary to deal with the loss of significance mechanisms mentioned above.)

One final question remains: what tolerance should be used to determine when to stop computing terms?   The immediate suggestion would be 0.00005, which is the fundamental accuracy requirement. But this would not be quite right because the entire series is multiplied by $x(2/\pi)^{1/2}$, which for the largest x is about 2.4.   This would suggest that the tolerance ought to be about 0.00002.   But this, too, would not be quite right because the actual test will be on the size of a term we have just computed and added into the sum of the series so far; the truncation error is based on the size of the first term *not* used.   The tolerance can therefore be somewhat larger than 0.00002 which will save the computation of one unnecessary term.   (Saving one term in a series is, of course, not a crucial matter, but if a little extra analysis can accomplish it we may as well do it.)

What we need to know to save computing the extra term is the ratio, in the worst case, of the last term to be kept to the next term. It turns out that the worst case is for large x and that for $x = 3$ the ratio is approximately 3.3.   Thus, if a term is no more than 3.3 times the tolerance of 0.00002, we can be sure that the next term will not be significant to the accuracy required.   For a safety factor we shall use the tolerance as 0.00006 instead of pushing it to the exact 0.000066.

The computation of the terms in the series can be done by a technique similar to that used in Case Study 3, except that each term cannot be obtained *directly* from the preceding term because of the successive odd integers in the denominator.   With a separate variable for this factor, the technique is basically the same.

This segment of the program gave results that were correct, although, as usual, a number of entries did not quite check with a four-place table.   The segment was run a second time with the tolerance on terms set at 0.00007 instead of 0.00006.   All results were again correct;

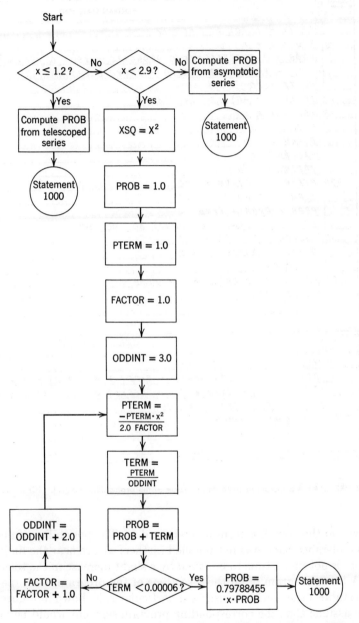

FIGURE 4.13   Block diagram of the method of computing the probability integral.   "Statement 1000" refers to whatever might follow the program segment corresponding to the block diagram. (Case Study 6.)

```
C FOR COMMENT
STATEMENT NUMBER | 6 7            FORTRAN STATEMENT
1        5 |

         IF (X - 1..20) 11, 11, 12
    11   XSQ = X * X
         PROB = 0..79788455*X*(0..99999774 - XSQ*(0..16659433
       1      - XSQ*(0..0246383.10 - XSQ*0..0023974.867))))
         GO TO 1000
    12   IF (X - 2..90) 13, 14, 14
    13   XSQ = X * X
         PROB = 1..0
         PTERM = 1..0
         FACTOR = 1..0
         ODDINT = 3..0
   970   PTERM = - PTERM * XSQ / (2..0 * FACTOR)
         TERM = PTERM / ODDINT
         PROB = PROB + TERM
         IF (ABSF(TERM) - 0..00007) 80, 90, 90
    90   FACTOR = FACTOR + 1..0
         ODDINT = ODDINT + 2..0
         GO TO 970
    80   PROB = 0..79788455 * X * PROB
         GO TO 1000
```

```
C FOR COMMENT
STATEMENT NUMBER | 6 7            FORTRAN STATEMENT
1        5 |

    14   RECXSQ = 1.. / (X * X)
         PROB = 1.. - 0..79788453 * EXPF(-X * X/2..0) / X *
       1      (1.. - RECXSQ * (1.. - RECXSQ * (3.. - RECXSQ *
       2      (15.. - RECXSQ * 105..))))
  1000   Whatever follows
```

FIGURE 4.14 .A program to compute the value of the probability integral. (Case Study 6.)

now and then one less term was required.* The possibility of pushing this tolerance back was not pursued further; we are near the limit, and there is not much time to be saved by a slight increase in the tolerance.

A block diagram of all three sections of the program, with the tests to establish the section to use for a particular x, is shown in Figure 4.13. We assume that the corresponding program segment would be part of a larger program, so that there is no input or output; we assume that

---

* The test program was arranged to print a count of the number of terms required.

a previous statement would have given a value to the variable X and that succeeding statements, beginning at statement 1000, would make use of the value of PROB.

The complete program segment is shown in Figure 4.14. In practice, a segment of this sort would ordinarily be made into a FORTRAN FUNCTION, so that by writing P(X) we could get the value of the function, just as we get the value of the sine of X simply by writing SINF(X). The techniques for setting up a program segment for this usage are discussed in Chapter 9.

—5

Roots of Equations

5.1 Introduction

Finding the roots of equations is one of the oldest problems in mathematics and one that is encountered frequently in modern computing, since it is required in a great variety of applications.

Consider the simple quadratic equation

$$ax^2 + bx + c = 0$$

We say that

$$x = \frac{-b \pm \sqrt{b^2 - 4ac}}{2a}$$

are the *roots* of this equation because, for these values of x, the quadratic equation is satisfied. More generally, we are given a function of x, $F(x)$, and we wish to find a value of x for which

$$(5.1) \qquad\qquad F(x) = 0$$

The function F may be algebraic or transcendental; we generally assume it to be differentiable.

In practice, the functions with which we deal have no simple closed formula for their roots, as the quadratic equation has. We turn instead to methods of approximating the roots, which involves two steps:

1. Finding an approximate root.
2. Refining the approximation to some prescribed degree of accuracy.

We will not concern ourselves now with step 1, which is taken up in Section 5.11. Often a first approximation is known from physical considerations.   Graphical methods can sometimes be used if this is not the case.*   Special methods exist for the important case in which $F(x)$ is a polynomial.†

We turn our attention to the second step—refining an initial approximation of or "guess" at the solution.   A numerical method in which a succession of approximations is made is called an *iterative* technique. Each step, or approximation, is called an *iteration*.   If the iterations produce approximations that approach the solution more and more closely, we say that the iteration method *converges*.

We will now discuss several iterative techniques for the solution of equations and investigate their convergence properties.

5.2   Method of successive approximations

Suppose that (5.1) is rewritten in the form

$$(5.2) \qquad\qquad x = f(x)$$

This can usually be done in many different ways.   For instance, if

$$F(x) = x^2 - c = 0$$

where $c \geq 0$, we may add x to both sides to get

$$(5.3) \qquad\qquad x = x^2 + x - c$$

or we may divide by x to get

$$(5.4) \qquad\qquad x = \frac{c}{x}$$

As a last example, we may rearrange the equation to get

$$(5.5) \qquad\qquad x = x - \frac{x^2 - c}{2x} = \frac{1}{2}\left(x + \frac{c}{x}\right)$$

It should be obvious that the values of x which are solutions to these equations are $\pm\sqrt{c}$.

Let x_0 be an initial approximation to the solution of (5.2).   Then, as the next approximation, take

$$x_1 = f(x_0)$$

As the next approximation take

$$x_2 = f(x_1)$$

---

* See, for instance, Kaiser S. Kunz, *Numerical Analysis*, McGraw-Hill, 1957.
† See, for instance, Anthony Ralston and Herbert S. Wilf, editors, *Mathematical Methods for Digital Computers*, Wiley, 1960, pp. 233–241.

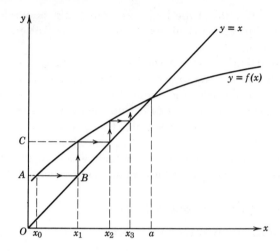

FIGURE 5.1   Diagrammatic representation of the method of successive approximations for
$0 < f'(x) < 1.$

Proceeding in this way, the nth approximation, or, as it is often called, the nth *iterate*, is

$$(5.6) \qquad\qquad x_n = f(x_{n-1})$$

The fundamental question is: do the x_n converge to a solution of (5.2) as n increases?

We will now develop *sufficient* conditions of $f(x)$ for this desired convergence. That is to say, we will develop conditions that will guarantee that x_n will get closer and closer to a solution of (5.2). These conditions are not *necessary*, however; that is, there may be functions $f(x)$ that do not satisfy these conditions but for which the iteration method (5.6) nevertheless produces a solution.

Let us first consider a geometrical representation of the process. When we wish to solve (5.2), we look for the intersection of the curve $y = f(x)$ (the right-hand side of the equation) and the line $y = x$ (the left-hand side). See Figure 5.1, in which the curve $y = f(x)$ is unspecified, except that it has the characteristic $0 < f'(x) < 1.*$ Let $x = a$ be the value of x at the point of intersection; then a is a root of (5.2), which we naturally do not know at the outset.

---

* A prime denotes a derivative with respect to x.

Now consider a guess x_0. The value of x_1 is $f(x_0)$. Since OA in Figure 5.1 is $f(x_0)$, we can find x_1 by tracing a horizontal line until we meet the 45° line $y = x$ as shown (point B). The value of $f(x_1) = x_2$ is then obtained by drawing a vertical line through x_1 (point B) to the curve $y = f(x)$. Thus x_2 is OC. We proceed in this manner, as indicated by the arrows in the figure.

We seem, in this case, to be converging toward the solution $x = a$, since each successive approximation is closer to a. It is important to remember that we took a curve $y = f(x)$ for which $0 < f'(x) < 1$.

Consider now another shape for the curve $y = f(x)$, one in which the derivative is negative but less than 1 in absolute value. (See Figure 5.2.) Again the arrows indicate the pattern of the iterations, and again the approximations seem to converge to $x = a$. Now, however, each successive approximation is on the opposite side of $x = a$ from its predecessor, whereas in the first example of Figure 5.1 all the approximations were on the same side of $x = a$.

Finally, we consider approximation formulas for which the derivatives are greater than 1 (Figure 5.3) and less than -1 (Figure 5.4). In both cases the iterations do not converge. Each succeeding guess is farther from $x = a$ than its predecessor. It seems, therefore, that

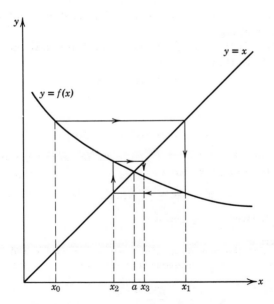

FIGURE 5.2 Diagrammatic representation of the method of successive approximations for $-1 < f'(x) < 0$.

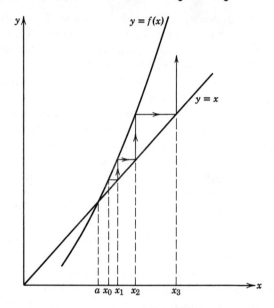

FIGURE 5.3 Diagrammatic representation of the method of successive approximations for $f'(x) > 1$.

if $f'(x)$ is less than 1 in absolute value, the iteration method described by (5.6) will converge.

This, in fact, is the case, as we can readily prove by an elementary argument. Note that

$$a = f(a)$$

$$x_n = f(x_{n-1})$$

so that

$$x_n - a = f(x_{n-1}) - f(a)$$

Multiplying on the right by $(x_{n-1} - a)/(x_{n-1} - a)$ and using the mean value theorem,* we have

$$x_n - a = f'(\xi)(x_{n-1} - a)$$

where ξ lies between x_{n-1} and a.

---

* The mean value theorem states that given two points, a and b, on a curve $y = f(x)$, where $f(x)$ has a continuous derivative, the slope of the chord between a and b

$$\frac{f(b) - f(a)}{b - a}$$

is equal to the slope of the tangent to the curve at some intermediate point.

Now let m be the maximum absolute value of $f'(x)$ over the entire interval in question (the interval including $x_0, x_1, \ldots, x_n, a$).   Then

$$|x_n - a| \leq m|x_{n-1} - a|$$

Similarly,

$$|x_{n-1} - a| \leq m|x_{n-2} - a|$$

so

$$|x_n - a| \leq m^2|x_{n-2} - a|$$

Continuing in this way,

(5.7) $$|x_n - a| \leq m^n|x_0 - a|$$

Now, if $m < 1$ over the entire interval, then, no matter what the choice of x_0, as n increases the right-hand member becomes small, and x_n comes closer to a.

On the other hand, for $|f'(x)| > 1$, $|x_n - a|$ becomes indefinitely large as n increases.   The proof is left to the reader as an exercise. *Thus if $|f'(x)| < 1$, the process (5.6) converges. If $|f'(x)| > 1$, the process (5.6) diverges.*   Observe that the inequalities are assumed to hold at *all* the approximations ($x_0, x_1, \ldots, x_n$).

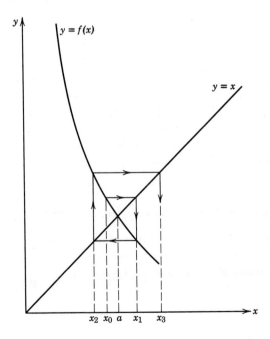

FIGURE 5.4 Diagrammatic representation of the method of successive approximations for $f'(x) < -1.$

What happens if at some points x_i the derivative $f'(x_i)$ is less than 1 in absolute value and at some other points x_j the derivative $f'(x_j)$ is greater than 1 in absolute value? The answer to this question is unresolved. The process sometimes converges and sometimes does not.

Let us return for a moment to our example of finding the square root of c. In (5.3)

$$f(x) = x^2 + x - c$$

so that

$$|f'(x)| < 1 \quad \text{if} \quad -1 < x < 0$$

If we are searching for the square root of a number c which is less than 1, the process converges to the negative square root of c.

In (5.4), however,

$$f'(x) = \frac{-c}{x^2}$$

and, if x is close to $\sqrt{c}$ (as it must eventually be in order to converge to the square root of c), $f'(x) \simeq 1$, and indeed the process diverges.

Finally, using (5.5),

$$f'(x) = \frac{1}{2}\left(1 - \frac{c}{x^2}\right)$$

and again, if $x \simeq \sqrt{c}$, $f'(x) \simeq 0$, and the process converges (rapidly, as a matter of fact). Formula 5.6 is a special case that we shall encounter again in a later section on the Newton-Raphson method.

It should be clear that, although for any equation there is in general a wide choice of functions $f(x)$ for use in the method of successive approximations, a judicious choice is necessary if convergence is to be obtained.

5.3   A modified method of successive approximations

Consider Figure 5.1 again. Notice that although each iterate is closer to the solution than its predecessor each falls short of the correct answer. It might be advantageous, therefore, to make a larger correction in each iteration. That is to say, instead of letting

$$x_{n+1} = x_n + \Delta x$$

where

$$\Delta x = f(x_n) - x_n$$

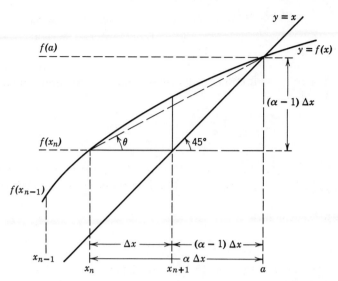

FIGURE 5.5 Diagrammatic representation of the modified method of successive approximations for $0 < f'(x) < 1$.

we might choose the next iterate after x_n to be

$$x_{n+1} = x_n + \alpha \, \Delta x$$

where $\alpha > 1$.

The situation is displayed in Figure 5.5, which is an enlargement of a small section of Figure 5.1. The best choice of α is the one shown, which would produce $x_{n+1} = a$. Let us try to determine the best value for α.

Notice that the distance between x_{n+1} and a is $(\alpha - 1) \, \Delta x$, and, since $y = x$ is a 45° line, the distance between $f(a)$ and $f(x_n)$ is also $(\alpha - 1) \, \Delta x$. Therefore, the tangent of the angle θ is

$$(5.8) \qquad \tan \theta = \frac{(\alpha - 1) \, \Delta x}{\alpha \, \Delta x} = \frac{\alpha - 1}{\alpha}$$

On the other hand,

$$\tan \theta = \frac{f(a) - f(x_n)}{a - x_n}$$

and, using the mean value theorem,

$$(5.9) \qquad \tan \theta = f'(\xi)$$

where $x_n \leq \xi \leq a$.

From (5.8) and (5.9), then,

$$(5.10) \qquad \alpha = \frac{1}{1 - f'(\xi)}$$

The value of ξ is unknown, of course, but we can approximate the value of $f'(\xi)$ by

$$(5.11) \qquad f'(\xi) \simeq \frac{f(x_n) - f(x_{n-1})}{x_n - x_{n-1}} = \frac{f(x_n) - x_n}{x_n - x_{n-1}}$$

Geometrically, this amounts to drawing the chord between the points $(x_n, f(x_n))$ and $(x_{n-1}, f(x_{n-1}))$ and finding its intersection with the line $y = x$.

The process is now

$$(5.12) \qquad x_{n+1} = x_n + \alpha(f(x_n) - x_n)$$

where α is determined as in (5.10) and (5.11).

The question arises how convergence is affected by the modified method. Notice from (5.10) that if $0 < f'(x) < 1$ then $1 < \alpha < \infty$. This is the case illustrated in Figure 5.1, in which the steps were too small; since $\alpha > 1$, the modified method will make them larger and therefore speed up convergence.

For $-1 < f'(x) < 0$, $\frac{1}{2} < \alpha < 1$ from (5.10), which is the situation in Figure 5.2. There, each step was too large; the modified method decreases each step by a factor between $\frac{1}{2}$ and 1.

More important, perhaps, are the divergent cases. If $f'(x) > 1$, then $\alpha < 0$. As shown in Figure 5.3, each step is in the wrong direction; that is, the iterates are moving away from the solution. Since α for this case is negative, the modification reverses the direction as needed.

Finally, for $f'(x) < -1$, $0 < \alpha < \frac{1}{2}$. Here, as seen in Figure 5.4, the steps were too large; the modification reduces them by a factor between zero and $\frac{1}{2}$. It is appropriate that the reduction should be greater in this case then in Figure 5.2, since it is divergent, whereas the other was convergent.

This modification is due to Wegstein.* The processes of extrapolation (overshooting) or interpolation (undershooting) is common in iterative methods. We shall encounter them again in Chapter 8 in connection with the iterative solution of simultaneous linear equations.

---

* Comm. ACM, **1**, 9–13 (1958).

A further slight modification of the method of successive approximations leads to one of the best-known numerical techniques, the Newton-Raphson method, for finding the roots of equations. Those already described, however, have a practical advantage over the Newton-Raphson in certain cases. We shall return to this question after considering the Newton-Raphson method.

5.4   The Newton-Raphson method

Recall that in (5.11) we approximated the derivative $f'(\xi)$ by a difference. Recall also that the optimum choice of ξ lay in the range $x_n \le \xi \le a$.

Suppose that for computational simplicity we chose $\xi = x_n$. Then we have

(5.13)
$$\alpha = \frac{1}{1 - f'(x_n)}$$

and

(5.14)
$$x_{n+1} = \frac{f(x_n) - x_n f'(x_n)}{1 - f'(x_n)}$$

We now note that (5.14) is equivalent to a method of successive approximations given by

$$x_{n+1} = g(x_n)$$

where

$$g(x) = \frac{f(x) - x f'(x)}{1 - f'(x)}$$

Recall also that if $|g'(x)| < 1$ then the method converges. Now

$$g'(x) = \frac{f''(x)[f(x) - x]}{(1 - f'(x))^2}$$

From (5.2), however, if x is sufficiently near a root, the term in brackets is small. Therefore, the iteration method described in (5.14) converges, provided

1. x_0 is sufficiently close to a root of $x = f(x)$
2. $f''(x)$ does not become excessively large
3. $f'(x)$ is not too close to 1.

This is the celebrated Newton-Raphson method. It is usually written in the more familiar form

(5.15)
$$x_{n+1} = x_n - \frac{F(x_n)}{F'(x_n)}$$

where

$$F(x) = f(x) - x = 0$$

That is to say, we have returned to the form given in (5.1).
The conditions for convergence now become

1. x_0 is sufficiently close to a root of $F(x) = 0$
2. $F''(x)$ does not become excessively large
3. $F'(x)$ is not too close to zero.

The last condition means that no two roots are too close together.
We shall return to a discussion of this problem in the following section.

Let us find a geometrical interpretation of the Newton-Raphson method. In (5.13) we chose the point to be at x_n. In Figure 5.5 this means that the angle θ is chosen to be the slope of the tangent to $y = f(x)$ at x_n. The process then is to draw the tangent to the curve $y = f(x)$ at $x = x_n$ and find the intersection of the tangent with the line $y = x$. Doing so produces the new value x_{n+1}. A vertical line is drawn through x_{n+1} to the curve $y = f(x)$ and a new tangent drawn. The path traced in Figure 5.6 is for the case in which $0 < f'(x) < 1$.

Notice that the convergence is much more rapid than that in Figure

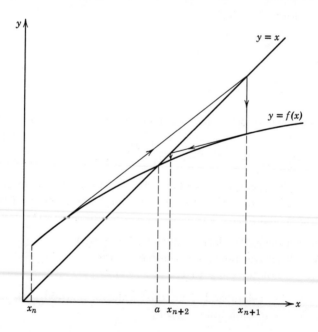

FIGURE 5.6 Diagrammatic representation of the Newton-Raphson method for $f(x) = x$.

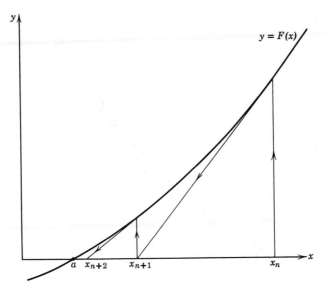

FIGURE 5.7   Diagrammatic representation of the Newton-Raphson method for $F(x) = 0$.

5.1, which is typical of the Newton-Raphson method, since $g'(x)$ is very small.

If the equation is put in the form of (5.1) and the iterative formula (5.15) is used, the geometric picture is that of Figure 5.7. We are now looking for the intersection of $y = F(x)$ and $y = 0$. Given a guess x_n, the tangent to $y = F(x)$ is drawn, and its intersection with the x-axis produces the new value of $x = x_{n+1}$. It is easily determined that this is the x_{n+1} in (5.15): find the equation of the line through the point x_n, $F(x_n)$ with slope $F'(x_n)$ and then find the intersection of this line with the x-axis.

5.5   Nearly equal roots

We have already pointed out that difficulties may arise in the Newton-Raphson method if (5.1) or (5.2) has nearly equal roots. In that case, condition 3 for convergence is violated close to the nearly equal roots. The phenomenon is illustrated in Figure 5.8. (The scale is greatly enlarged.) Notice that the derivative of $f(x)$ is near 1 at the two roots, a_1 and a_2. Moreover, from the mean value theorem the derivative is equal to 1 somewhere between a_1 and a_2.

Let us now examine what happens if we choose x_0 as an initial guess

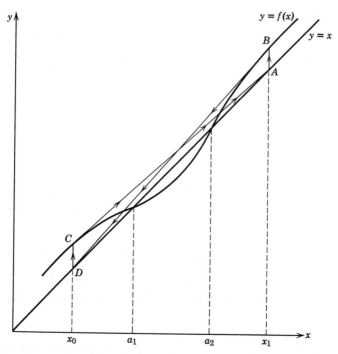

FIGURE 5.8 Diagrammatic representation of the non-convergence of the Newton-Raphson method for $|f'(x)|$ near 1.

to the root a_1.   The tangent constructed at C intersects $y = x$ at A and the new iterate is x_1.   The tangent at B intersects $y = x$ at D, yielding x_0 again.   The iteration, therefore, alternates between x_0 and x_1 indefinitely.   The process cannot *resolve* the two roots because they are too close together.   Of course, we might say that it is condition 1 that is being violated and that x_0 was not sufficiently close to a_1.

Indeed, this is true.   We should therefore explore a method ˙by which a close first approximation may be found.   Numerically, difficulties arise because the evaluation of the denominator in (5.14) requires the subtraction of two nearly equal numbers, which, as we have seen repeatedly, gives rise to inaccuracies.

Following Macon,* we will first find the value of x where $f'(x) = 1$, that is, we solve the equation

$$x = x + f'(x) - 1$$

---

* Nathaniel Macon, *Numerical Analysis*, Wiley, New York, 1963, pp. 34–36.

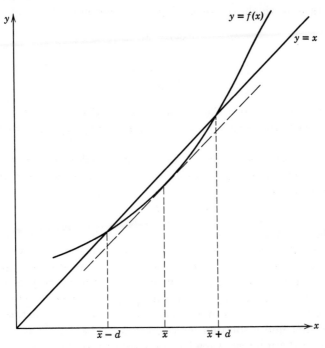

FIGURE 5.9 Diagrammatic representation of the modified Newton-Raphson method for $|f'(x)|$ near 1.

Let the solution be $x = \bar{x}$. This point lies between the two roots, a_1 and a_2. In order to obtain a first approximation, we may assume that $\bar{x}$ lies midway between a_1 and a_2. (See Figure 5.9.) That is to say, we let $\bar{x} + d$ and $\bar{x} - d$ be the two roots. Expanding $f(x)$ in a Taylor series about $\bar{x}$ and noting that $f'(\bar{x}) = 1$, we have

$$f(x) = f(\bar{x}) + (x - \bar{x}) + \tfrac{1}{2}f''(\bar{x})(x - \bar{x})^2 + \cdots$$

We now terminate the series after three terms as shown and let $x = \bar{x} + d$, so that

$$f(\bar{x} + d) = f(\bar{x}) + d + \tfrac{1}{2}f''(\bar{x})d^2$$

But

$$f(\bar{x} + d) = \bar{x} + d$$

so, solving for d,

$$d = \sqrt{\frac{2(\bar{x} - f(\bar{x}))}{f''(\bar{x})}}$$

For the case in which we are solving the equation in the form

$$F(x) = 0$$

we get

$$d = \sqrt{\frac{-2F(\bar{x})}{F''(\bar{x})}}$$

noting that $F'(\bar{x}) = 0$. The reader should satisfy himself that the quantity under the square root sign is positive by referring to Figure 5.8.

A recapitulation is in order. Given an equation with two nearly equal roots and knowing at least approximately where they are, we solve the equation

$$x = x + f'(x) - 1$$

for a value $\bar{x}$, using any convenient method, such as Newton-Raphson. Using this value of $\bar{x}$, solve for d with the expressions shown above. Finally, the values $\bar{x} - d$ and $\bar{x} + d$ are used as starting approximations for a Newton-Raphson solution for a_1 and a_2, respectively.

Of course, we may run into trouble if $f''(x)$ is near zero. This means that $f'(x) = 1$ has more than one root near x. In this event we would first find a solution for $f''(x) = 0$. The details are not discussed here; the interested reader is referred to Macon's text.

5.6   Comparison of the methods and their roundoff errors

Since the Newton-Raphson method converges much more rapidly than the method of successive approximations, we might ask why the latter is ever used. The answer lies in the requirement, in Newton-Raphson, of the evaluation of both the function and its derivative at each iteration. These evaluations may be difficult, time-consuming, or impossible. For example, the function $f(x)$ may not be given by a formula at all but by a table of values. The derivative may not even exist at all points. The method of successive approximations or its modification is often applied in such cases.

The choice of methods depends, in other words, on the particular function $f(x)$ or $F(x)$.

It is interesting and important to notice that the roundoff error does *not* build up as the iterations proceed. The total roundoff error is just the error committed in the final iteration and does not depend on the arithmetic operations in previous iterations. This property is characteristic of iterative processes and is one of their major advantages over noniterative techniques. The reason for the nonaccumu-

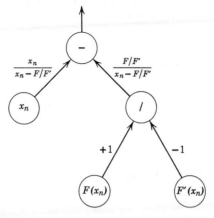

FIGURE 5.10   The process graph for the Newton-Raphson method.

lation of roundoff errors is clear: each iterate, including the next-to-last x_n, may be considered to be the *initial* approximation.   The roundoff error in the last iterate therefore depends only on the operations that produce it from the next-to-last.

The process graph for the Newton-Raphson method of (5.15) is shown in Figure 5.10.   There is no inherent error in x_n, since it may be considered to be an infinite decimal with zeros for any missing digits at the end.   There are relative roundoff errors in computing $F(x_n)$ and $F'(x_n)$; call them r and r', respectively.   Call the relative roundoff error in the division d and that in the subtraction, s.   Then the absolute roundoff error in x_{n+1} is

$$e = \frac{F(x_n)}{F'(x_n)} \left(r - r' - d + \frac{s}{x_{n+1}} \right)$$

In most cases the error is dominated by the errors r and r' in evaluating F and F'.

5.7   Roots of polynomials

We now consider the very important special case in which $F(x)$ is a polynomial of degree m:

(5.16) $F(x) = a_0 + a_1 x + a_2 x^2 + \cdots + a_m x^m$

We use the Newton-Raphson method in the form given by (5.15).

The evaluation of $F(x_n)$ by Horner's rule has already been discussed in Section 3.5. We recursively find

(5.17)
$$\begin{cases} b_m = a_m \\ b_j = a_j + x_n b_{j+1} \qquad j = m - 1, \ldots, 0 \end{cases}$$
and
$$F(x_n) = b_0$$

Now recall from Section 3.4 (3.11) that
$$F(x) = (x - x_n) G(x) + b_0$$
where
$$G(x) = b_1 + b_2 x + \cdots + b_m x^{m-1}$$
Now
$$F'(x) = (x - x_n) G'(x) + G(x)$$
so
$$F'(x_n) = G(x_n)$$

But $G(x)$ is a polynomial of degree $m - 1$, so we can use Horner's rule to evaluate $G(x_n)$ and thereby find $F'(x_n)$. Letting

(5.18)
$$\begin{cases} c_m = b_m \\ c_j = b_j + x_n c_{j+1} \qquad j = m - 1, \ldots, 1 \end{cases}$$

It follows that
$$F'(x_n) = G(x_n) = c_1$$

From (5.15), then, the Newton-Raphson method for a polynomial reduces to

$$x_{n+1} = x_n - \left(\frac{b_0}{c_1}\right)$$

where b_0 and c_1 are calculated from (5.17) and (5.18).   This procedure is often referred to as the Birge-Vieta method.

Example

Let
$$F(x) = x^3 - x - 1$$

We wish to find the root near $x_0 = 1.3$.   The sequence of calculations is shown in Table 5.1.

We see that x_2 and x_3 agree through seven digits; x_3 therefore has at least seven reliable digits and almost certainly more.

A further discussion of finding the roots of polynomials appears in Case Study 7.

Table 5.1

i	a_i	b_i	c_i
3	1	1	1
2	0	1.3	2.6
1	-1	0.69	4.07
0	-1	-0.103	

$$x_1 = x_0 - \frac{b_0}{c_1} = 1.3 - \frac{-0.103}{4.07} = 1.325$$

i	a_i	b_i	c_i
3	1	1	1
2	0	1.325	2.65
1	-1	0.755625	4.267
0	-1	0.001203	

$$x_2 = x_1 - \frac{b_0}{c_1} = 1.325 - \frac{0.001203}{4.267} = 1.3247181$$

i	a_i	b_i	c_i
3	1	1	1
2	0	1.324718	2.649436
1	-1	0.154878	4.264634
0	-1	0.0000004	

$$x_3 = x_2 - \frac{b_0}{c_1} = 1.324718 - \frac{0.0000004}{4.264634} = 1.3247179$$

5.8   Effect of uncertainty in the coefficients

Often the coefficients a_i in a polynomial (5.16) are obtained from experimental equipment or as a result of prior calculations. In either case there is some uncertainty in the values of the coefficients, that is, the a_i contain inherent errors. It is important to determine how errors in the coefficients affect the error in a computed root.

This error is independent of the method of computation used. We shall assume that there is no roundoff error in the computed root or, more precisely, that the roundoff error is negligible compared with the error due to inaccuracies in the coefficients. This is in fact often a valid assumption. For example, it is not uncommon to work with coefficients that are known to only a few percent in a computer that carries 10 digits in each number. Except in unlikely circumstances, roundoff error will not matter.

Let the error in a_i be δ_i; that is, the *true* polynomial is

$$(5.19) \quad F^*(x) = (a_0 + \delta_0) + (a_1 + \delta_1)x + (a_2 + \delta_2)x^2 \\ + \cdots + (a_m + \delta_m)x^m$$

where the $|\delta_i|$ are small compared with the $|a_i|$. We will let $\bar{x}$ be a root of the original polynomial

$$(5.20) \qquad F(x) = a_0 + a_1 x + a_2 x^2 + \cdots + a_m x^m$$

Finally we let

$$(5.21) \qquad\qquad x^* = \bar{x} + \epsilon$$

be a root of (5.19), and we proceed to estimate ϵ under the assumption that $|\epsilon|$ is much less than $|\bar{x}|$. If the estimate of ϵ does not satisfy this assumption, the analysis will not be valid. In many cases, however, the assumption is justified, and in any case its validity can easily be checked after the estimate has been obtained.

Substituting (5.21) in (5.19) and noting that

$$F^*(x^*) = 0$$

we have

$$(a_0 + \delta_0) + (a_1 + \delta_1)(\bar{x} + \epsilon) + \cdots + (a_{m-1} + \delta_{m-1})(\bar{x} + \epsilon)^{m-1} \\ + (a_m + \delta_m)(\bar{x} + \epsilon)^m = 0$$

Expanding $(x + \epsilon)^j$ and neglecting terms of second or higher powers in ϵ, we get

$$(a_0 + \delta_0) + (a_1 + \delta_1)(\bar{x} + \epsilon) + \cdots \\ + (a_{m-1} + \delta_{m-1})(\bar{x}^{m-1} + (m-1)\bar{x}^{m-2}\epsilon) \\ + (a_m + \delta_m)(\bar{x}^m + m\bar{x}^{m-1}\epsilon) = 0$$

Again neglecting terms in $\delta_i \epsilon$ and noting that $F(\bar{x}) = 0$,

$$\delta_0 + \delta_1\bar{x} + \cdots + \delta_{m-1}\bar{x}^{m-1} + \delta_m\bar{x}^m + \epsilon(a_1 + 2a_2\bar{x} + \cdots \\ + (m-1)a_{m-1}\bar{x}^{m-2} + ma_m\bar{x}^{m-1}) = 0$$

so that

$$\sum_{i=0}^{m} \delta_i \bar{x}^i + \epsilon F'(\bar{x}) = 0$$

A bound on ϵ then is

$$(5.22) \qquad\qquad |\epsilon| \leq \frac{\left| \sum_{i=0}^{m} \delta_i \bar{x}^i \right|}{|F'(\bar{x})|}$$

We now consider two special cases:

1. The coefficients are experimental data given to a fixed number of decimal places p.

2. The coefficients are the results of previous floating point calculations and have a given number of significant figures.

The difference is that between absolute and relative accuracy in the coefficients.

CASE 1.   If the a_i are each given to p decimal places,

$$|\delta_i| \leq \tfrac{1}{2} \cdot 10^{-p}$$

and from (5.22)

$$|\epsilon| \leq \frac{\tfrac{1}{2} \cdot 10^{-p}}{|F'(\bar{x})|} \left| \sum_{i=0}^{m} \bar{x}^i \right|$$

Now

$$\left| \sum_{i=0}^{m} \bar{x}^i \right| \leq \sum_{i=0}^{m} |\bar{x}|^i$$

by the triangle inequality. The right-hand member of this last inequality is a geometric series and equal to

$$\frac{1 - |\bar{x}|^{m+1}}{1 - |\bar{x}|}$$

so that

(5.23)
$$\epsilon \leq \frac{10^{-p}(1 - |\bar{x}|^{m+1})}{2|c_1|(1 - |\bar{x}|)}$$

where c_1 has replaced $F'(\bar{x})$ and was calculated by (5.17) and (5.18).

Example

$F(x) = x^3 - x - 1$. Suppose the coefficients are accurate to four decimals $(p = 4)$. One root of this equation, as shown before, is $x = 1.324718$. The bound (5.23) becomes

$$0.75 \cdot 10^{-4}$$

which indicates that

$$x = 1.324718 \pm 0.000075$$

It is not profitable, therefore, to iterate further to find the root to any greater accuracy.

CASE 2.   If the a_i are each given to t significant figures,

$$|\delta_i| \leq 5 \cdot 10^{-t}|a_i|$$

and from (5.22)

$$|\epsilon| \leq 5 \cdot 10^{-t} \frac{\sum\limits_{i=0}^{m} |a_i \bar{x}^i|}{|c_1|}$$

Example

$F(x) = x^3 - x - 1$. Suppose the coefficients are computed numbers accurate to four significant digits $(t = 4)$. Then for $x = 1.324718$

$$|\epsilon| \leq 0.00055$$

so that

$$x = 1.324718 \pm 0.00055$$

The root should therefore be stated as 1.325, with a possible error of one unit in the last place.

5.9   Simultaneous equations

Often we are faced with problems involving several unknowns and an equal number of equations. For example, we may wish to find x and y such that

$$x^2 + y = 3$$

and

$$y^2 + x = 5$$

In this case we may solve the first for y and substitute in the second to get

$$x^4 - 6x^2 + x + 4 = 0$$

Now we have a polynomial in x that can be solved by methods we know. One root is $x = 1$ and therefore $y = 2$.

Many times, however, it is difficult or impractical to reduce the problem in this way to the solution of one equation in one unknown. The most common situation occurs when the equations are linear; this special case is considered in detail in Chapter 8, since there are special methods for its solution. Here, we state results for the solution of two nonlinear equations in two unknowns, using a generalization of the Newton-Raphson method. The derivation is left to the student (see Exercise 32).

Let the equations be

$$F(x, y) = 0$$

$$G(x, y) = 0$$

and let x_n, y_n be some approximate root.

Define

$$J(x_n, y_n) = \frac{\partial F}{\partial x}(x_n, y_n)\frac{\partial G}{\partial y}(x_n, y_n) - \frac{\partial F}{\partial y}(x_n, y_n)\frac{\partial G}{\partial x}(x_n, y_n)$$

This is called the Jacobian of the system and is assumed to be non-zero. The assumption is analogous to assuming that $F'(x_n) \neq 0$ in the single variable case.

The next approximation is then given by

$$x_{n+1} = x_n - \frac{F(x_n, y_n)\dfrac{\partial G}{\partial y}(x_n, y_n) - G(x_n, y_n)\dfrac{\partial F}{\partial y}(x_n, y_n)}{J(x_n, y_n)}$$

$$y_{n+1} = y_n + \frac{F(x_n, y_n)\dfrac{\partial G}{\partial x}(x_n, y_n) - G(x_n, y_n)\dfrac{\partial F}{\partial x}(x_n, y_n)}{J(x_n, y_n)}$$

The iterations are continued until two successive approximations are found to be sufficiently close to each other. Numerical examples appear in Exercises 33 and 34.

A generalization of the method of successive approximations to two simultaneous equations is given in Exercise 35.

5.10   Complex roots

All the techniques described so far find the real roots of an equation or pair of equations. We will now discuss very briefly the solution of equations whose roots are complex numbers.

It should be clear that if the function is real-valued and if the initial guess x_0 is real, only real numbers will be produced. However, if x_0 is a complex number, then succeeding x_i may also be complex. Indeed, the methods described previously work equally well for complex numbers. Many FORTRAN systems have provisions for complex arithmetic; in these systems it is a minor problem to modify the program to make it find complex roots.

Finally, for polynomials with real coefficients we note that if $a + bi$ (where $i = \sqrt{-1}$) is a root $a - bi$ is also a root. Thus, if $p_n(x)$ is the polynomial of degree n, it can be factored into the form

$$p_n(x) = (x^2 - 2ax + (a^2 + b^2))\, p_{n-2}(x)$$

where the part in parentheses is called a *quadratic factor* and $p_{n-2}(x)$ is a polynomial of degree $n - 2$.   We may then perform the same analysis as we did in Section 5.7 to find a and b, using real arithmetic. The interested reader is referred to Chapter 10 of the text by Hildebrand* for details.

The use of the method of successive approximations in this way is usually referred to as Lin's method, and the Newton-Raphson method is known as Bairstow's method.

5.11   Finding an approximate root

An approximate root of

$$F(x) = 0$$

is sometimes known from physical considerations.   If not, a rough approximation can often be found by sketching the function.

In general, we seek two values of x for which $F(x)$ has opposite signs, that is, we seek x^* and x_* such that

$$F(x^*) > 0$$

and

$$F(x_*) < 0$$

Then there is at least one value of x between x^* and x_* for which $F(x) = 0$.   As a first approximation to a root of $F(x)$, we may take

$$x_0 = \tfrac{1}{2}(x^* + x_*)$$

One way of determining x^* and x_* is to try to find a simpler equation whose roots are near those of the original equation.   For example, let

$$F(x) = \frac{\sin x}{10} + x^3 - 1$$

Now for $0 \leq x \leq \pi/2$, the first term varies between 0 and 0.1.   Since this is small compared with the other two terms, we consider the two extreme values for $(\sin x)/10$:

$$0 + x^3 - 1 = 0$$

and

$$\tfrac{1}{10} + x^3 - 1 = 0$$

---

* F. B. Hildebrand, *Introduction to Numerical Analysis*, McGraw-Hill, New York, 1956.

A root of each of these two simple expressions is

$$x^* = +1$$

$$x_* = \sqrt[3]{0.9} = 0.965489$$

Now

$$F(x^*) = 0.084$$

and

$$F(x_*) = -0.18$$

So as a first approximation we choose

$$x_0 = \tfrac{1}{2}(1 + 0.965489) = 0.982749$$

For polynomial equations many special techniques for locating approximate roots are available. The interested reader is referred to Chapter 2 of Kaiser W. Kunz, *Numerical Analysis*, McGraw-Hill, 1957.

5.12   Case study 7: Single crystal growth from vapor

The following case study illustrates a number of features of interest to us in our study of numerical methods. It shows one way in which polynomial equations can arise from practical scientific applications; it shows how such an equation may be formulated; it shows how an equation may sometimes be simplified because of the particular data used.

When iodine vapor (I_2) and helium (He) are passed over germanium (Ge), some germanium combines with iodine to form GeI_2 and GeI_4. The resulting vapor is composed of I, I_2, GeI_2, GeI_4, and He. (See Figure 5.11.)

If this vapor is passed over a seed crystal of germanium, some of the GeI_2 disproportionates into Ge and GeI_4, and germanium is deposited epitaxially on the wafer. By appropriate incorporation of impurities

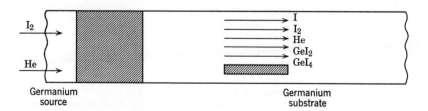

FIGURE 5.11   Vapor deposition of germanium. (Case Study 7.)

in both the substrate and the epitaxial crystal useful semiconductor devices can be fabricated.*

A brief sketch of the analysis of the problem is as follows. Assume that the total pressure is constant and equal to standard atmospheric pressure, 760 mm Hg. Assume also that the gases obey the ideal gas law. The reactions involved are

(5.24)
$$I_{2(g)} \rightleftharpoons 2I_{(g)}$$

(5.25)
$$Ge_{(s)} + I_{2(g)} \rightleftharpoons GeI_{2(g)}$$

(5.26)
$$Ge_{(s)} + GeI_{4(g)} \rightleftharpoons 2GeI_{2(g)}$$

(The subscripts s and g stand for solid and gaseous.) For a fixed temperature T the ratios of the partial pressures of the several gaseous species raised to the proper power are called the equilibrium constants. For instance, in the reaction (5.24)

$$\frac{(p_I)^2}{p_{I_2}} = K_{24}$$

where p_I = the partial pressure of monatomic iodine (I),
   p_{I_2} = the partial pressure of diatomic iodine (I_2),
$\log_{10} (K_{24}) = 8.362 - 7991/T$.

Let us now fix the temperature to be

$$T = 273.2°K = 0°C$$

Then

(5.27)
$$K_{24} = 1.30 \cdot 10^{-21} = \frac{(p_I)^2}{p_{I_2}}$$

Similarly, we can find the equilibrium constants for reactions (5.25) and (5.26):

(5.28)
$$K_{25} = 1.09 \cdot 10^4 - \frac{p_{GeI_2}}{p_{I_2}}$$

(5.29)
$$K_{26} = 3.25 \cdot 10^{-17} = \frac{(p_{GeI_2})^2}{p_{GeI_4}}$$

---

* A complete description of the thermodynamic analysis of this vapor deposition problem as well as those of many other related problems is given by A. Reisman and S. A. Alyanakyan in "Thermodynamic Analyses of Constant Pressure Germanium Disproportionation Reactions," to appear in the Journal of the Electrochemical Society, Vol. 111 (1964).

The partial pressure of the solid germanium does not enter because this partial pressure is—to a first approximation—independent of the external pressure.

Now, since the total pressure is 760,

(5.30) $P_{\text{total}} = 760 = p_{\text{I}} + p_{\text{I}_2} + p_{\text{GeI}_2} + p_{\text{GeI}_4} + p_{\text{He}}$

Furthermore, the law of the conservation of mass requires that

(5.31) $X = \dfrac{P_{\text{He}}}{P_{\text{I}_2}} = \dfrac{p_{\text{He}}}{\frac{1}{2}p_{\text{I}} + p_{\text{I}_2} + p_{\text{GeI}_2} + 2p_{\text{GeI}_4}}$

where X is the ratio of helium pressure to iodine pressure and is fixed initially and remains constant thereafter. The value of X is experimentally controlled. In the experiment described here it was equal to 49.36.

Equations 5.27 to 5.31 are five equations in five unknown partial pressures. If we let $Z^4 = p_{\text{GeI}_4}$, these five equations can be reduced to finding the value of Z for which

(5.32) $(2X + 1)Z^4 + \left[(1 + X)\sqrt{K_{26}} \left(1 + \dfrac{1}{K_{25}} \right) \right] Z^2$

$$+ \left(\dfrac{K_{24}\sqrt{K_{26}}}{K_{25}} \right)^{\!\frac{1}{2}} \left(1 + \dfrac{X}{2} \right) Z - 760 = 0$$

The other partial pressures are then obtained from

$$p_{\text{I}_2} = \dfrac{\sqrt{K_{26}}}{K_{25}} Z^2$$

$$p_{\text{I}} = \left(\dfrac{K_{24}\sqrt{K_{26}}}{K_{25}} \right)^{\!\frac{1}{2}} Z$$

$$p_{\text{GeI}_2} = \sqrt{K_{26}}\, Z^2$$

$$p_{\text{He}} = X \left[2Z^4 + \sqrt{K_{26}} \left(1 + \dfrac{1}{K_{25}} \right) Z^2 + \dfrac{1}{2} \left(\dfrac{K_{24}\sqrt{K_{26}}}{K_{25}} \right)^{\!\frac{1}{2}} Z \right]$$

With the given $T = 273.2°$ and $X = 49.32$, (5.32) becomes

(5.33) $9.972 \cdot 10^1 Z^4 + 2.870565 \cdot 10^{-7} Z^2$

$$+ 6.674356 \cdot 10^{-16} Z - 7.600 \cdot 10^2 = 0$$

Equation 5.33 is a fourth-degree polynomial in Z, which may conveniently be solved by the Newton-Raphson method. A program is shown in Figure 5.12.

```
C FOR COMMENT
STATEMENT
NUMBER
1     5 6 7                         FORTRAN STATEMENT

        Z = 5..0
        ITN = 0
  4,1   B = 99..72
        C = B
        B = 0..0 + Z * B
        C = B + Z * C
        B = 2..87.0,5.6,5.E-7 + Z * B
        C = B + Z * C
        B = 6..6,7,4,3,5,6.E-1.6 + Z * B
        C = B + Z * C
        B = -7,6,0..0 + Z * B
        ZNEW = Z - B / C
        IF (ABSF ((Z - ZNEW) / ZNEW) - 1..0,E-5) 4.2, 4.3, 4.3
  4,3   ITN = ITN + 1
        IF (ITN - 1,5) 4.4, 4.5, 4.5
  4,4   PRINT 4,6, ZNEW
        Z = ZNEW
        GO TO 4,1
  4,5   STOP 1,2,3,4
```

```
C FOR COMMENT
STATEMENT
NUMBER
1     5 6 7                         FORTRAN STATEMENT

  4,2   PRINT 4,6, ZNEW
  4,6   FORMAT (F1,5..7)
        STOP
        END
```

FIGURE 5.12   Program for solving a fourth degree polynomial equation by the Newton-Raphson method.   (Case Study 7.)

From physical considerations it is known that the partial pressure of GeI_4 is between zero and 10 mm Hg; as a first approximation Z_0 we choose 5.0.

The Newton-Raphson method was presented in terms of a succession of iterates identified by subscripts.   There is no need to retain this notation in the program: all we ever need are the previous and the present iterates.   In Figure 5.12 the variable Z designates the previous value, set equal to 5.0 initially, and ZNEW is the new value that is computed by the Newton-Raphson iteration formula.

We expect the iteration process to converge, but the experienced programmer tends to avoid situations in which errors in the data or the program could cause the machine to run indefinitely. We shall therefore establish a *counter*, here named ITN (for "iteration number"); if the process has not converged after 15 tries, it will be stopped.

The value of the function and the value of its derivative are found by the recursion process described in Section 5.7. It would, of course, be possible to write

$$\frac{F(Z)}{F'(Z)} = \frac{A_0 + Z(A_1 + Z(A_2 + Z(A_3 + ZA_4)))}{A_1 + Z(2A_2 + Z(3A_3 + 4A_4Z))}$$

The entire iteration formula could thus be written as one long statement. We prefer to do the calculation as shown in the program because it is slightly faster* and because it is more flexible and better suited to implementation with subscripted variables, as described in Chapter 7.

After the calculation of the new value of Z, ZNEW, we ask whether the two values are sufficiently close to each other to indicate convergence. As a general rule, it is better not to ask for absolute convergence. For instance, if the root were in the order of 10^{-4}, it would be meaningless to ask that two values of Z agree within 10^{-3}; the process would stop almost immediately with a "root" having little relative accuracy. On the other hand, although it cannot happen here, if the root were 10^5 and we specified a tolerance of 10^{-3}, the roundoff errors in finite floating point arithmetic might prevent the process from *ever* stopping. The obvious solution is to base the convergence test on relative accuracy. We therefore ask whether absolute value of the difference between two iterates, divided by the latest, is less than, say, 10^{-5}, which is probably adequate, considering the limited accuracy of the data.

If the process has converged, we transfer to a PRINT statement to print the final value of ZNEW and stop. If convergence has not been reached, we next check whether there have been more than 15 iterations and, if so, stop. If the limit of iterations has not been reached, we set the previous value of Z equal to the one just computed and go back to compute another.

In order to be able to observe the convergence, a PRINT statement has been inserted in the iteration loop. This would not normally be done.

---

* The reader may wish to satisfy himself that the evaluation of $F(Z)$ and $F'(Z)$ as programmed takes three fewer multiplications than the explicit form shown above.

3.7652427
2.8596258
2.2261980
1.8423436
1.6864486
1.6620756
1.6615289
1.6615286

FIGURE 5.13 Output of the program of Figure 5.12. (Case Study 7.)

The results are shown in Figure 5.13.   The rapid convergence of the Newton-Raphson method is clearly evident.

The resulting partial pressures are

$$p_{\text{GeI}_4} = 7.621 \cdot 10^0$$

$$p_{\text{I}_2} = 1.428 \cdot 10^{-12}$$

$$p_{\text{I}} = 4.3 \cdot 10^{-17}$$

$$p_{\text{GeI}_2} = 1.573 \cdot 10^{-8}$$

$$p_{\text{He}} = 7.524 \cdot 10^2$$

The reader has probably already noted that in (5.33) the coefficients of Z^2 and Z are very much smaller than the coefficients of Z^4 and Z^0. If we were to neglect the Z^2 and Z terms and solve

$$9.972 \cdot 10^1 Z^4 - 760 = 0$$

we would get identical results, $Z = 1.6615286$.   If this equation were solved by the Newton-Raphson method, the successive approximations would in fact be exactly the same as those shown in Figure 5.13.

Exercises

The "computational" exercises in the following set (and in later chapters) have been devised so that if necessary they can be done with paper and pencil or on a desk calculator.   A number of them, however, are quite suitable for solution by computer, using the routines developed in Exercises 22–27.   Applying the computer in this way will perhaps save a little time, but, more important, it will provide valuable practice in the application of the concepts.

*1. Find the negative square root of 0.5 to four decimals by writing $F(x) = x^2 - 0.5$ and solving $x = x^2 + x - 0.5$ by the method of successive approximations, with $x_0 = -0.6$.   Could the positive square root be found by this method?

2. Find the negative square root of 0.25 by the method of Exercise 1, with $x_0 = -0.6$.   Why does this converge faster?

3. Use the Newton-Raphson method to find to four decimals the square root of 4, with $x_0 = 1.5$.   Repeat with $x_0 = 2.5$, $x_0 = -1.5$, $x_0 = 10.0$.

*4. Derive a Newton-Raphson iteration formula for finding the cube root of a positive number c.

5. Derive a Newton-Raphson iteration formula for finding arcsin A, given A.

6. Using the result of Exercise 5, find arcsin 0.5 to three decimal places.

*7. Find to three decimals the root of $0.1x^2 - x \log x = 0$ between 1 and 2.

8. Find to three decimals a root of $\cosh x + \cos x - 3 = 0$.

*9. Use the Newton-Raphson method to find to three decimals all roots of
$x^3 - 1.473x^2 - 5.738x + 6.763 = 0$.

10. Use the Newton-Raphson method to find to three decimals the roots of
$x^2 - x - 6 = 0$.   Use $x_0 = 0$, then repeat with $x_0 = 4$.   The iteration
formula can be simplified considerably by algebraic manipulation.

11. The equation $4x^3 - 12.3x^2 - x + 16.2$ has two roots between 1 and 2.
Find them to four decimals.

*12. Find to three significant figures the root between 2 and 3 of $x^3 - 0.39x^2 -$
$10.5x + 11.0 = 0$.   If the coefficients contain errors of 2%, what is the
bound on the error in this root?

13. Same as Exercise 13, but the error in the coefficients is 4%.

14. Show that if the error in each of the coefficients in a polynomial equation
is $P\%$ the bound on the error in any root is a linear function of P as long
as the assumptions in the derivation of the bound are valid.

15. The equation $2.0x^2 - 5.0x + 2.0 = 0$ has roots $x_1 = 0.5$, $x_2 = 2.0$.   If
the coefficients contain errors of 20%, the error bound for x_2 is 1.33.
Yet the larger root of the equation $1.6x^2 - 6.0x + 1.6 = 0$, in which
the coefficients are 20% different from the original equation, is 3.47 for
an error of 1.47.   Why is the actual error greater than the bound?   On
the other hand, the equation $1.6x^2 - 4.0x + 1.6 = 0$, in which the
coefficients are also 20% different from the original, has a larger root
of 1.79 for an error of only 0.21.   Why is this error so much smaller than
either the error in the other root or the bound?

16. Consider the equation

$$x^4 - 26x^3 + 131x^2 - 226x + 120 = 0$$

The roots are 1, 2, 3, and 20.   Suppose first that there is a small error
in the constant term and that the other coefficients are exact.   Show that
this error has more than twice as much effect on the error bound for the
root near 3 as on the root near 1 and essentially no effect on the root
near 20.   Then suppose that there is a small error in the coefficient of x^3
and that the others are exact.   Show that the error bound on the root near
1 is much less than the error in the coefficient but that the error bound
on the root near 3 is larger than the error in the coefficient.

17. Apply the Newton-Raphson method to $x^3 - 2x^2 - 3x + 10 = 0$, with
$x_0 = 1.9$.   Can you explain the strange behavior of the successive
iterates?

18. Apply the Newton-Raphson method to $x^3 - 2x^2 - 3x + 10 = 0$, with
$x_0 = 3 + i$, using complex arithmetic throughout.

19. The equation

$$x^5 - 8x^4 + 17x^3 - 8x^2 - 14x + 20 = 0$$

has roots at -1 and $+2$.   Yet, if we apply the Newton-Raphson method
with $x_0 = -0.3$, we reach another root at $+5$.   Explain.

20. Attempt to apply the Newton-Raphson method to the equation

$$x^4 - 7x^3 + 12x^2 + 4x - 16 = 0$$

What happens?

*21. Write a FORTRAN routine to find the square root of a variable A to which a value has previously been given; call the result SQRTA.

*22. Assume an equation of the form

$$F(x) = a_6x^6 + a_5x^5 + a_4x^4 + a_3x^3 + a_2x^2 + a_1x + a_0 = 0$$

Since any of the coefficients may be zero, this represents a polynomial equation of degree six or less. Suppose now that we have a data card with the following format:

Cols.	
1–10	x_0
11–20	a_0
21–30	a_1
31–40	a_2
41–50	a_3
51–60	a_4
61–70	a_5
71–80	a_6

All numbers are punched in a form suitable for reading with an F10.0 field specification. Write a program that reads such a card, computes $F(x_0)$, and prints the coefficients, x_0 and $F(x_0)$, using F15.6 field specifications.

23. In addition to the card described in Exercise 22, there is a second card that contains in columns 1–10 a value for a variable named EPS, in F10.0 format. Write a program to apply the Newton-Raphson method to find a root of the polynomial equation defined by the coefficients, starting with x_0 and continuing the iterations until two approximations differ by less than EPS in absolute value. When the root has been found, print all data and the root. (For a first program, it would be advisable to insert a PRINT statement into the iteration loop so that the convergence may be observed.)

24. Suppose that in addition to the data described in Exercises 22 and 23, the second card also contains a value for a variable named P, which represents the maximum percentage error in the coefficients. After finding the root, compute the error bound and print it with the other information.

25. Suppose that we have two data cards. The first is the same as that described in Exercise 22, but x_0 will not be used. (With the field specifications presented, it will be necessary to read x_0 and then ignore it.) The second card contains the following information:

Cols.	
1–10	XF
11–20	XL
21–30	DELTA

Write a program to read the data cards, then carry out the following procedure:

a. Set X equal to XF.
b. Set a variable named BEFORE equal to F(X).
c. Set a variable named THIS equal to F(X + DELTA).
d. If BEFORE and THIS have different signs, print both X and X + DELTA. (The simplest way to determine whether two variables have the same sign is to inspect the sign of their product.)
e. Increment X by DELTA.
f. If X is now greater than XL, stop; otherwise go on to the next step.
g. Set BEFORE equal to THIS.
h. Go to step c.

26. Combine the techniques of the preceding exercises into a program that reads the coefficients, XF, XL, DELTA, and EPS (design your own card formats), then searches for sign changes and finds the root at each sign change. (This will be a valuable exercise and a useful program but bear in mind the lessons of Exercises 17, 19, and 20. A completely general root-finder is a complicated affair.)

27. Modify the program to Exercise 26 to incorporate a counter that stops the computation if the iteration process has not converged to a root after N iterations, where N is a fixed point number read from the second data card. (A reasonable value for N would be about 15.)

28. Given a function $F(x) = 0$ and two values of X, XL, and XH, such that XL < XH and F(XL) and F(XH) have different signs, there is at least one real root of F(x) between XL and XH. We shall assume that there is just one. Consider the following computational procedure:

a. Evaluate $F\left(\dfrac{XL + XH}{2}\right)$

b. If F(XL) and $F\left(\dfrac{XL + XH}{2}\right)$ have different signs, set

$$XH = \frac{XL + XH}{2}$$

leave XL unchanged, and go on to step c; but if F(XL) and $F\left(\dfrac{XL + XH}{2}\right)$ have the same signs, set $XL = \dfrac{XL + XH}{2}$, leave XH unchanged, and go on to step c.

c. If XH − XL is less than a preassigned tolerance EPS, stop the procedure; either XL or XH is the root of $F(x)$ within ±EPS. If XH − XL is not less than EPS, go to step a.

This procedure is called *interval halving*. It is less elegant than other methods we have considered, and it generally converges more slowly, but it is so simple that it finds occasional application. Demonstrate the process geometrically, draw a block diagram, and write a program to find the root between 2 and 3 of

$$x^4 - 0.486x^3 - 5.792x^2 + 0.486x + 4.792 = 0$$

Use a tolerance of 10^{-3}.

29. In the method of successive approximations let m^* be the minimum of $|f'(x)|$ for all x occurring in the iterations. Show that if $m^* > 1$ the process diverges.

30. Suppose that we have two values of x, x_0 and x_1, such that $F(x_0) < 0$ and $F(x_1) > 0$. Let x_2 be the point at which the x-axis intersects the straight line joining the points $(x_0, F(x_0))$ and $(x_1, F(x_1))$. Demonstrate geometrically that x_2 is a better approximation to a root of $F(x) = 0$ than either x_0 or x_1 and devise a computational procedure along the lines of that in Exercise 28—based on sign changes, that is—for finding the root.

This is called the method of *false position* or *regula falsi*.

31. Suppose we expand $F(x)$ in a Taylor series about $x = x_n$ and truncate after two terms:

$$F(x) = F(x_n) + (x - x_n) F'(x_n)$$

Show that this leads to the approximation formula

$$x = x_n - \frac{F(x_n)}{F'(x_n)}$$

What is this?

32. From the Taylor series

$$F(x, y) = F(x_n, y_n) + (x - x_n) \frac{\partial F}{\partial x}(x_n, y_n) + (y - y_n) \frac{\partial F}{\partial y}(x_n, y_n) + \cdots$$

$$G(x, y) = G(x_n, y_n) + (x - x_n) \frac{\partial G}{\partial x}(x_n, y_n) + (y - y_n) \frac{\partial G}{\partial y}(x_n, y_n) + \cdots$$

truncated as written, show that a new approximation to a root of

$$F(x, y) = 0$$

$$G(x, y) = 0$$

is given by

$$x = x_n - \left[F(x_n, y_n) \frac{\partial G}{\partial y}(x_n, y_n) - G(x_n, y_n) \frac{\partial F}{\partial y}(x_n, y_n) \right] \bigg/ J$$

$$y = y_n + \left[F(x_n, y_n) \frac{\partial G}{\partial x}(x_n, y_n) - G(x_n, y_n) \frac{\partial F}{\partial x}(x_n, y_n) \right] \bigg/ J$$

where

$$J = \frac{\partial F}{\partial x} (x_n, y_n) \frac{\partial G}{\partial y} (x_n, y_n) - \frac{\partial F}{\partial y} (x_n, y_n) \frac{\partial G}{\partial x} (x_n, y_n)$$

*33. Let

$$F(x, y) = x^2 + y^2 - 4$$

$$G(x, y) = xy - 1$$

Apply the method of Section 5.9 with $x_0 = 2$, $y_0 = 0$.   Are there other solutions?

34. Let

$$F(x, y) = x^3 - x - 2x^2 - x + 2 - y$$

$$G(x, y) = x - y$$

Apply the method of Section 5.9 with $x_0 = y_0 = 0$.   Explain the relationship between the two iteration formulas.

35. A generalization of the method of successive approximations to two equations

$$x = f(x, y)$$

$$y = g(x, y)$$

is given by

$$x_{n+1} = f(x_n, y_n)$$

$$y_{n+1} = g(x_n, y_n)$$

a. Show that sufficient conditions for convergence of this generalization are

$$\left| \frac{\partial f}{\partial x} \right| + \left| \frac{\partial g}{\partial x} \right| < 1$$

and

$$\left| \frac{\partial f}{\partial y} \right| + \left| \frac{\partial g}{\partial y} \right| < 1$$

(*Hint.*   Consider bounds on the quantity $|x - x_n| + |y - y_n|$.)
b. Are the conditions in part (a) *necessary* for convergence?
c. Consider the *linear* equations

$$a_{11}x + a_{12}y = b_1$$

$$a_{21}x + a_{22}y = b_2$$

If $a_{11} \neq 0$ and $a_{22} \neq 0$, we may rewrite these equations as

$$x = \frac{1}{a_{11}} (b_1 - a_{12}y)$$

$$y = \frac{1}{a_{22}} (b_2 - a_{21}x)$$

What do the sufficient conditions for convergence given above become in this case?   What do these conditions imply about the slopes of the lines represented by the original linear equations?

36. Consider the cubic equation

$$p_0(x) = x^3 + a_2 x^2 + a_1 x + a_0$$

a. If x_1, x_2, and x_3 are roots of $p_0(x) = 0$, show that

$$a_2 = -(x_1 + x_2 + x_3)$$

$$a_1 = x_1 x_2 + x_1 x_3 + x_2 x_3$$

$$a_0 = -x_1 x_2 x_3$$

b. Show that if x_1, x_2, and x_3 are real and

$$|x_1| \gg |x_2| \gg |x_3|$$

then

$$x_1 \simeq -a_2$$

$$x_2 \simeq -\frac{a_1}{a_2}$$

$$x_3 \simeq -\frac{a_0}{a_1}$$

c. Show that the function

$$p_1(y) = -p_0(-x)\, p_0(x)$$

$$= y^3 + (-a_2{}^2 + 2a_1)y^2 + (a_1{}^2 - 2a_0 a_2)y - a_0{}^2$$

where

$$y = x^2$$

d. Show that the roots of $p_1(y) = 0$ are

$$y_1 = x_1{}^2$$

$$y_2 = x_2{}^2$$

$$y_3 = x_3{}^2$$

e. Show that the roots of

$$p_2(z) = -p_1(-y)\, p_1(y)$$

are

$$z_1 = x_1{}^4$$

$$z_2 = x_2{}^4$$

$$z_3 = x_3{}^4$$

where

$$z = y^2 = x^4$$

f. What happens to the roots of the equations that result from iterating the process described by (c) and (e) above?

g. Describe how you would find an approximation to x_1, x_2, and x_3 after the iterations have been carried out enough times to separate the roots adequately.

This process is known as *Graeffe's root-squaring technique.* It can be generalized to higher order polynomial equations and to complex roots. See for example Section 10.11 of Hildebrand, *Introduction to Numerical Analysis*, McGraw-Hill Book Co., 1956.

37. The following familiar puzzle problem leads to the solution of a quartic equation:

Two ladders, one 20 ft long and the other 30 ft long, lean against buildings across an alley, as shown in the sketch. If the point at which the ladders cross is 8 ft above the ground, how wide is the alley?

Gruenberger and Jaffrey, in *Problems for Computer Solution* (to be published in 1964) show that this problem can be formulated to require solution of the following equation:

$$y^4 - 16y^3 + 500y^2 - 8000y + 32000 = 0$$

Then $x = \sqrt{400 - y^2}$.

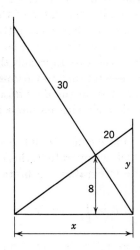

—6

Numerical Evaluation
of Integrals

6.1 Introduction

Problems requiring the evaluation of integrals arise in nearly every branch of applied mathematics. Sometimes it is possible to find a *closed* formula, that is, one that is expressible as a combination of simple algebraic and transcendental functions, which can then be evaluated between limits to give the value of the integral.

In many practical situations, however, either no suitable closed formula can be found or, even if it can, it is so complicated that it is more difficult to evaluate it than to approach the integral directly by other methods. In such cases we turn to various methods of *numerical integration,* in which we start from the definition of an integral as the limit of a sum of areas and work with methods that approximate this sum to sufficient accuracy.

To make the discussion more concrete, let us state the problem and the assumptions under which we operate in this chapter. We consider the evaluation of a definite integral over a finite interval:

$$(6.1) \qquad\qquad I = \int_a^b f(x) \, dx$$

where a and b are finite and $f(x)$ is a continuous function of x for $a \leq x \leq b$.

Cases in which either or both of the limits of integration are infinite are sometimes of interest, as is the integration of functions having singularities [points where $f(x)$ becomes infinite] within the range of integration or perhaps at the endpoints. These cases can frequently be reduced to the form (6.1), which may then be integrated by the

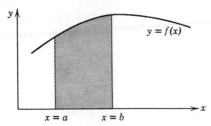

FIGURE 6.1   Geometric interpretation of the problem of numerical integration.

methods to be discussed.   We shall consider these cases only in the exercises.*

We may characterize the approach we shall take as follows.   The definite integral I represents the area under the curve $y = f(x)$ between $x = a$ and $x = b$.   We can therefore evaluate I by dividing the interval a to b into many smaller intervals, finding the approximate area of each of the strips thus formed, and summing their areas.

The techniques fall into two classes:

1. The intervals are chosen in advance; they are usually selected to be equal, and if the computation is to be done "by hand" they are usually selected so that the endpoints of each interval fall at easily computable values of x.   The methods in this category to be discussed here are the trapezoidal rule and Simpson's rule.

2. The intervals and their location are dictated by the analysis, in the sense that we first ask for the greatest accuracy possible with a given number of intervals, and let the intervals fall wherever this prior requirement dictates.   The example of this approach is Gauss's rule.

There are naturally many other integration rules of both types. The ones we shall consider adequately demonstrate the general approach to numerical evaluation of integrals and to error estimation and in fact are suitable for actual computation in a large majority of practical applications.

6.2   The trapezoidal rule

Consider the integral in (6.1), which represents the cross-hatched area in Figure 6.1.   We shall break the interval into n equal intervals,

---

* The interested reader is referred to pp. 203–205 of Franz Alt, *Electronic Digital Computers*, Academic Press, New York, 1958, and to pp. 370–386 of Z. Kopal, *Numerical Analysis*, Wiley, New York, 1961.

each of size $h = (b - a)/n$. Consider now one of those intervals, as in Figure 6.2, in which the scale along the x-axis has been greatly expanded. The area under the curve $y = f(x)$ between x_i and x_{i+1} is

$$I_i = \int_{x_i}^{x_{i+1}} f(x)\, dx$$

But if h is small enough, then I_i can be approximated fairly well by the area of the trapezoid $ABCD$. If we write $y_i = f(x_i)$, the area of the rectangle $ABED$ is $y_i h$, and the area of the triangle BEC is $\frac{1}{2}(y_{i+1} - y_i)h$, so that

$$I_i \simeq \tfrac{1}{2}h(y_i + y_{i+1})$$

Now since

(6.2) $$\int_a^b f(x)\, dx = \int_a^c f(x)\, dx + \int_c^b f(x)\, dx$$

then

(6.3) $$I = \sum_{i=0}^{n-1} I_i$$

where $x_0 = a$ and $x_n = b$. Then from (6.2) and (6.3) we have

(6.4) $$I \simeq I_h = \frac{h}{2}\,(y_0 + 2y_1 + 2y_2 + \cdots + 2y_{n-2} + 2y_{n-1} + y_n)$$

This is the well-known *trapezoidal rule*, so-called because it approximates the integral (6.1) by the sum of n trapezoids. It is one of the

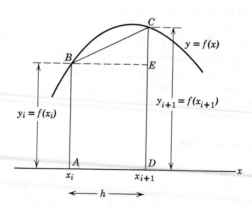

FIGURE 6.2 One interval from the cross-hatched area of Figure 6.1, with the scale along the x-axis expanded.

simplest formulas for numerical integration. The truncation error, which we investigate in the following section, is greater than for most other methods, but the very simplicity of the technique sometimes makes it attractive. The method is important to the student in any case because it demonstrates the basic idea of all integration formulas of type (6.1) (i.e., methods in which the interval size is fixed in advance). In essence, the technique is to divide the total interval into small intervals and approximate the curve $y = f(x)$ in several small intervals by some simpler curve whose integral can be calculated by using only the ordinates at the endpoints of the intervals.

6.3   Truncation error in the trapezoidal rule

The truncation error committed by using (6.4) is the sum of the areas between the curve $y = f(x)$ and the chords between y_i and y_{i+1} (BC in Figure 6.2). We approach the estimation of this error by obtaining a Taylor series expansion of the function $y = f(x)$ at the endpoints of the intervals in order to get the equation of the true curve into a form that will permit a comparison with the approximation (6.4).

Consider the Taylor series expansion of $y = f(x)$ about the point $x = x_i$. We assume that $f(x)$ has as many continuous derivatives as may be required.

$$(6.5) \qquad y = y_i + (x - x_i)y_i' + \frac{(x - x_i)^2}{2} y_i'' + \cdots$$

Similarly, the expansion about $x = x_{i+1}$ is

$$(6.6) \quad y = y_{i+1} + (x - x_i - h)y_{i+1}' + \frac{(x - x_i - h)^2}{2} y_{i+1}'' + \cdots$$

Equations 6.5 and 6.6 are, of course, both valid; neither one alone, however, leads to the result we want. Our goal can be reached by taking the average of the two, a legitimate operation:

$$y = \frac{y_{i+1} + y_i}{2} + \frac{x - x_i}{2} (y_{i+1}' + y_i') - \frac{h}{2} y_{i+1}'$$
$$+ \frac{(x - x_i)^2}{4} (y_{i+1}'' + y_i'') - \frac{(x - x_i)h}{2} y_{i+1}'' + \frac{h^2}{4} y_{i+1}'' + \cdots$$

Integrating $y \, dx$ from x_i to x_{i+1},

$$(6.7) \quad \int_{x_i}^{x_{i+1}} y \, dx = \frac{h}{2} (y_{i+1} + y_i) + \frac{h^2}{4} (y'_{i+1} + y_i') - \frac{h^2}{2} y'_{i+1}$$

$$+ \frac{h^3}{12} (y''_{i+1} + y_i'') - \frac{h^3}{4} y''_{i+1} + \frac{h^3}{4} y''_{i+1} + \cdots$$

$$= \frac{h}{2} (y_{i+1} + y_i) - \frac{h^2}{4} (y'_{i+1} - y_i') + \frac{h^3}{12} (y''_{i+1} + y_i'') + \cdots$$

This gives an estimate of the true value of the integral; we can make the estimate as accurate as we wish by taking enough terms of the Taylor series expansion. The trapezoidal rule is obtained by dropping all terms containing h^2 and higher powers of h. The truncation error in using the trapezoidal rule is therefore

$$(6.8) \quad E_{T_i} = -\frac{h^2}{4} (y'_{i+1} - y_i') + \frac{h^3}{12} (y''_{i+1} + y_i'') + \cdots$$

For small h the first term is the dominant one, so that we might be tempted to take the approximate error to be given by just the first term of (6.8). Notice, however, that if we expand $y' = df/dx$ and multiply by h^2 we have

$$y'_{i+1}h^2 = y_i'h^2 + y_i''h^3 + \cdots$$

so that terms in $y_i''h^3$ do contribute to the first term in E_{T_i} in (6.8). And, as a matter of fact, *all* higher terms in (6.8) contribute to the first term to some degree.

Let us *assume* that the error in the trapezoidal rule is of the form

$$(6.9) \quad E_{T_i} \simeq Kh^2(y'_{i+1} - y_i')$$

where K is a constant to be determined. This will, of course, be only an approximation based on the assumption that K is a constant; this is true only to the extent that y'' and higher derivatives do not vary much between x_i and x_{i+1}.

Now we have the problem of determining K. To do this, observe that (6.7) *is true for any function whatsoever.* We can, therefore, choose *any* convenient function for which there is a truncation error and the result will be valid for all functions.

One simple function would be $y = x$, but the reader can readily verify that the truncation error would turn out to be zero, which means simply that the trapezoidal rule is exact in integrating linear functions. The next most likely candidate is $y = x^2$.   In this case

$$(6.10) \qquad I_i = \int_{x_i}^{x_{i+1}} x^2 \, dx = x_i{}^2 h + x_i h^2 + \frac{h^3}{3} \quad \text{exactly}$$

But from (6.7) and (6.8), using $y_i = x_i{}^2$ and $y_{i+1} = (x_i + h)^2$, we have

$$(6.11) \qquad\qquad I_i = x_i{}^2 h + x_i h^2 + \frac{h^3}{2} + E_{T_i}$$

Equations 6.10 and 6.11 produce

$$E_{T_i} = -\frac{h^3}{6}$$

But, since $y' = 2x$, we have from (6.9)

$$E_{T_i} = 2Kh^2(x_i + h - x_i) = 2Kh^3$$

It follows, therefore, that

$$K = \frac{-1}{12}$$

and

$$(6.12) \qquad\qquad E_{T_i} \simeq -\frac{h^2}{12}(y'_{i+1} - y_i')$$

The total truncation error is estimated by

$$(6.13) \qquad\qquad e_T = \sum_{l=0}^{n-1} E_{T_i} = -\frac{h^2}{12}(y_b' - y_a')$$

where y_b' is the value of df/dx at $x = b$ and y_a' is the value of df/dx at $x = a$.

(The reader will find it instructive to carry out the evaluation of K for the function $y = x^3$ and thus perhaps satisfy himself that the result is not dependent on the particular choice of a function.   Of course, K should be determined only from the term in h^3 because of the assumption that y'' is constant.)

Another form of the error formula is perhaps more frequently encountered.   We recall from the mean value theorem that

$$y_b' - y_a' = (b - a)y''(\xi)$$

where $a < \xi < b$, so that

(6.14) $$e_T \simeq -\frac{h^2}{12}(b - a)y''(\xi)$$

Moreover, it can be shown* that if

$$M = \max y''(\xi)$$

for $a \leq \xi \leq b$, then

$$|e_T| \leq \frac{h^2}{12}(b - a)M$$

It is important to note that (6.13) provides an approximation to the truncation error, not an upper bound.

6.4   Roundoff errors in the trapezoidal rule

The process graph for the trapezoidal rule is shown in Figure 6.3, in which it is assumed that the terms to be multiplied by 2 are all added together first and their sum is multiplied by 2.   (This not only saves the time of multiplying each term separately by 2 and then adding but also reduces the roundoff error.)

Let δ_i $(i = 0, 1, \ldots, n)$ be the relative inherent error in y_i.   Let α_i $(i = 0, 1, \ldots, n)$ be the relative roundoff errors in the $n + 1$ additions.   The additions are numbered according to the small numerals adjacent to the circles with the plus signs.   For example, α_2 is the relative roundoff error in performing

Finally, let μ_1 be the relative roundoff error in performing the first multiplication, that of $(y_1 + \cdots + y_{n-1})$ by 2, and μ_2 be the rela-

---

* See for instance Macon, Chapter 9.

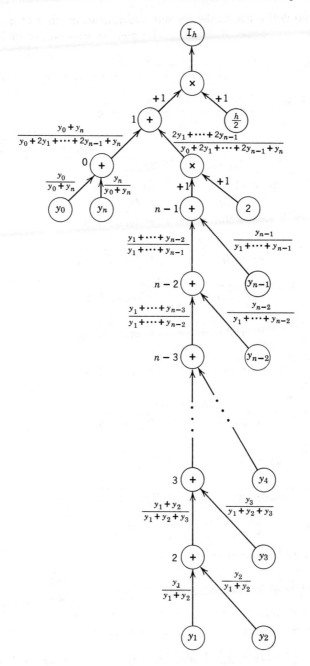

FIGURE 6.3   The process graph for the trapezoidal rule.

tive roundoff error in the second multiplication, that of $h/2$ by $(y_0 + 2y_1 + \cdots + 2y_{n-1} + y_n)$.   The relative roundoff error in I_h is

$$
\frac{e_R}{I_h} = \mu_2 + \alpha_1 + \alpha_0 \frac{y_0 + y_n}{y_0 + 2y_1 + \cdots + 2y_{n-1} + y_n}
$$

$$
+ \delta_0 \frac{y_0}{y_0 + 2y_1 + \cdots + 2y_{n-1} + y_n}
$$

$$
+ \delta_n \frac{y_n}{y_0 + 2y_1 + \cdots + 2y_{n-1} + y_n}
$$

$$
+ \mu_1 \frac{2y_1 + \cdots + 2y_{n-1}}{y_0 + 2y_1 + \cdots + 2y_{n-1} + y_n}
$$

$$
+ \alpha_{n-1} \frac{2y_1 + \cdots + 2y_{n-1}}{y_0 + 2y_1 + \cdots + 2y_{n-1} + y_n}
$$

$$
+ \alpha_{n-2} \frac{2(y_1 + \cdots + y_{n-2})}{y_0 + 2y_1 + \cdots + 2y_{n-1} + y_n}
$$

$$
+ \delta_{n-1} \frac{2y_{n-1}}{y_0 + 2y_1 + \cdots + 2y_{n-1} + y_n}
$$

$$
+ \alpha_{n-3} \frac{2(y_1 + \cdots + y_{n-3})}{y_0 + 2y_1 + \cdots + 2y_{n-1} + y_n}
$$

$$
+ \delta_{n-2} \frac{2y_{n-2}}{y_0 + 2y_1 + \cdots + 2y_{n-2} + y_n}
$$

$$
+ \cdots
$$

$$
+ \alpha_2 \frac{2(y_1 + y_2)}{y_0 + 2y_1 + \cdots + 2y_{n-1} + y_n}
$$

$$
+ \delta_3 \frac{2y_3}{y_0 + 2y_1 + \cdots + 2y_{n-1} + y_n}
$$

$$
+ \delta_2 \frac{2y_2}{y_0 + 2y_1 + \cdots + 2y_{n-1} + y_n}
$$

$$
+ \delta_1 \frac{2y_1}{y_0 + 2y_1 + \cdots + 2y_{n-1} + y_n}
$$

The absolute error is

$$
e_R = h \left(\delta_0 \frac{y_0}{2} + \delta_1 y_1 + \cdots + \delta_{n-1} y_{n-1} + \delta_n \frac{y_n}{2} \right)
$$

$$
+ h[\alpha_2(y_1 + y_2) + \alpha_3(y_1 + y_2 + y_3) + \cdots
$$
$$
+ \alpha_{n-2}(y_1 + \cdots + y_{n-2}) + \alpha_{n-1}(y_1 + \cdots + y_{n-1})]
$$

$$
+ \frac{h}{2}[\alpha_0(y_0 + y_n) + \alpha_1(y_0 + 2y_1 + \cdots + 2y_{n-1} + y_n)
$$

$$
+ \mu_1(2y_1 + \cdots + 2y_{n-1}) + \mu_2(y_0 + 2y_1 + \cdots + 2y_{n-1} + y_n)]
$$

Now suppose that $y_i = \bar{y} + \theta_i$, where $\bar{y}$ is the average of the y_i and $|\theta_i| \ll |\bar{y}|$, so that terms in $\theta_i \alpha_i$, $\theta_i \mu_i$, and $\theta_i \delta_i$ may be neglected.   Further suppose that

$$|\alpha_i| \leq \epsilon$$

$$|\mu_i| \leq \epsilon$$

$$|\delta_i| \leq \phi\epsilon$$

where ϵ is the relative roundoff error in an arithmetic operation, which we have generally written as $5 \cdot 10^{-t}$ previously, and ϕ is some fixed constant that gives the relative size of the inherent and roundoff errors. Then

$$|e_R| \leq h|\bar{y}|\epsilon\phi n + h|\bar{y}|\epsilon \sum_{j=2}^{n-1} j + h|\bar{y}|\epsilon(3n)$$

Recalling that

$$\sum_{j=1}^{m} j = \frac{m(m+1)}{2}$$

then

$$|e_R| \leq \frac{h|\bar{y}|\epsilon}{2}[n^2 + (5 + 2\phi)n - 2]$$

But

$$n = \frac{b-a}{h}$$

so

$$|e_R| \leq \frac{|\bar{y}|\epsilon}{2}\left[\frac{(b-a)^2}{h} + (5 + 2\phi)(b-a) - 2h\right]$$

Now for small h the first term in the brackets dominates the other two, and we may approximate the bound on e_R by

(6.15)
$$|e_R| \leq \frac{\bar{y}\epsilon(b-a)^2}{2}\left(\frac{1}{h}\right)$$

We thus have the interesting result that the bound on the roundoff error increases as $1/h$, which soon dominates the truncation error— which is proportional to h^2. Actually, the roundoff error itself does not grow as h^{-1} but as h^{-p}, where $0 < p < 1$, and still overtakes the truncation error if we decrease h sufficiently.

Thus we have found another discrepancy between theoretical and practical computing.   In theory we can make I_h as close to I as we

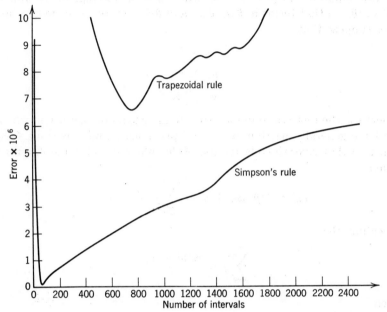

FIGURE 6.4   Plots of the total error (truncation and roundoff) in integrating $\sin x$ from 0 to π by the trapezoidal rule and by Simpson's rule.

wish by taking h sufficiently small.   In practice, however, the roundoff error prevents this arbitrarily close approach to I.

As an example consider the integral

$$I = \int_0^\pi \sin x \, dx = 1$$

A plot of the total error E_I versus n, the number of intervals, is given in Figure 6.4, which also shows the error for Simpson's rule, to be considered in Section 6.6.   Notice that as n increases the total error, which is the sum of the truncation error and the roundoff error, decreases until $n = 775$.   Thereafter the roundoff error dominates; further increases in the number of intervals *increase* the total error.

Finally, notice that the δ_i, the μ_i, and α_0 and α_1 do not contribute to the $1/h$ term in e_I.   It is the computation of

$$y_1 + \cdots + y_{n-1}$$

and the roundoff errors in these additions that affect the $1/h$ term. Thus increasing the accuracy of the computation of the y_i does not help matters.

The error may be decreased by performing the additions in double precision (see p. 90), whereas all other operations are done in single precision. This technique is referred to as *partial double precision*.

6.5 The deferred approach to the limit

A relatively simple modification of the trapezoidal rule can be used to find a better approximation to the value of an integral.

Recall from (6.14) that for an interval of size h

$$e_T = Ch^2$$

where

$$C = -\frac{b - a}{12}\, y''(\xi), \qquad a < \xi < b$$

If the second derivative of y is reasonably constant, C may also be taken to be a constant.

Suppose now that we take a different step size $k = (b - a)/m$ where $m \neq n$. Then

$$e_T = Ck^2$$

Now let I_h be the result from the trapezoidal rule using step size h in (6.4), and let I_k be the result using a step size of k. Then

(6.16)
$$I = I_h + Ch^2$$

and

$$I = I_k + Ck^2$$

If we subtract these two equations, it follows that

(6.17)
$$C = \frac{I_h - I_k}{k^2 - h^2}$$

Using (6.17) to replace C in (6.16), we have

(6.18)
$$I = I_h + \frac{I_h - I_k}{\dfrac{k^2}{h^2} - 1}$$

This produces a better approximation to I than I_h or I_k. If, in fact, the second derivative $y''(x)$ is actually a constant for $a \leq x \leq b$, the truncation error in (6.18) is zero.

The method is called Richardson's deferred approach to the limit.*

---

* L. F. Richardson and J. A. Gaunt, "The Deferred Approach to the Limit," *Trans. Roy. Soc. London*, **226A**, 300 (1927).

6.6   Simpson's rule

We now turn to one of the most widely known and used techniques in numerical integration, Simpson's rule. It is similar to the trapezoidal rule in dividing the total interval into many smaller intervals and approximating the area under them but different in that a parabola is passed through the three ordinates of two adjoining intervals. We would expect that whereas the trapezoidal rule is exact for first-degree polynomials Simpson's rule would be exact for second-degree or lower; actually, it turns out somewhat surprisingly to be exact for third-degree or lower. It is therefore a rather accurate method for the effort required, and the formula is not significantly more complex than that for the trapezoidal rule. These characteristics account for the wide usage of the method.

Recall that the number of intervals n in the trapezoidal rule was given by

$$n = \frac{b - a}{h}$$

Suppose now that n is even and let

(6.19) $$k = 2h$$

Then

(6.20) $$I_h = \frac{h}{2}(y_0 + 2y_1 + 2y_2 + \cdots + 2y_{n-2} + 2y_{n-1} + y_n)$$

(6.21) $$I_k = h(y_0 \qquad\quad + 2y_2 + \cdots + 2y_{n-2} \qquad\quad + y_n)$$

Equations 6.19, 6.20, and 6.21 can be substituted into (6.18), as follows:

$$I = I_h + \frac{I_h - I_k}{\dfrac{k^2}{h^2} - 1}$$

$$
\begin{aligned}
&= h(\quad \tfrac{1}{2}y_0 + \quad y_1 + \quad y_2 + \cdots + \quad y_{n-2} + \quad y_{n-1} + \quad y_n) \\
&+ h(\quad \tfrac{1}{6}y_0 + \tfrac{1}{3}y_1 + \tfrac{1}{3}y_2 + \cdots + \tfrac{1}{3}y_{n-2} + \tfrac{1}{3}y_{n-1} + \tfrac{1}{6}y_n) \\
&+ h(-\tfrac{1}{3}y_0 \qquad\; - \tfrac{2}{3}y_2 - \cdots - \tfrac{2}{3}y_{n-2} \qquad\qquad - \tfrac{1}{3}y_n)
\end{aligned}
$$

$$= h(\quad \tfrac{1}{3}y_0 + \tfrac{4}{3}y_1 + \tfrac{2}{3}y_2 + \cdots + \tfrac{2}{3}y_{n-2} + \tfrac{4}{3}y_{n-1} + \tfrac{1}{6}y_n)$$

So

(6.22) $$I = \frac{h}{3}(y_0 + 4y_1 + 2y_2 + 4y_3 + 2y_4 + \cdots$$

$$+ 2y_{n-4} + 4y_{n-3} + 2y_{n-2} + 4y_{n-1} + y_n)$$

The result (6.22) is called Simpson's rule.   At the expense of considerably more effort we could have arrived at this formula by finding the equation of the parabola that passes through the three ordinates of two adjacent intervals and adding all such groups.   We shall not carry out this exercise; it is mentioned to show how Simpson's rule compares geometrically with the trapezoidal rule.

Neither shall we go through the manipulations to find the truncation error, which can be done by methods similar to those in Section 6.3. The result is

$$e_T \simeq - \frac{h^4}{180} (b - a) f^{iv}(\xi) \qquad a < \xi < b$$

The important thing to notice is that the error here is proportional to h^4, whereas the error for the trapezoidal rule is proportional to h^2. This reflects the fact that Simpson's rule happens to correspond to the first *three* terms of the Taylor expansion, whereas we might expect it to agree with only the first two terms.   The method is therefore exact for a polynomial of degree no higher than third.

If we assume that the fourth derivative is reasonably constant, we can once again use the deferred approach to the limit to improve on Simpson's rule.   In fact, it is entirely possible to derive formulas akin to (6.22) of higher and higher accuracy, which amount to passing higher degree polynomials through sets of ordinates.   The results are called *Newton-Cotes* integration formulas.*

We note finally, again without displaying the derivation, that the bound on the roundoff error for Simpson's rule is proportional to $1/h$ for small h, the same as with the trapezoidal rule.

Figure 6.4 also shows the results of integrating $\sin x$ from 0 to π, using Simpson's rule.   Notice that the error diminishes much more rapidly than when the trapezoidal rule is used (h^4 versus h^2).   Since the roundoff errors are approximately equal, however, they become dominant much more rapidly and the total error increases when $n > 50$.

6.7   Gauss quadrature †

So far we have discussed integration methods in which the analyst is free to choose the interval.   We have, in fact, always chosen equal intervals.

---

* See, for instance, Chapter 3 of F. B. Hildebrand, *Introduction to Numerical Analysis*, McGraw-Hill, 1956.

† "Quadrature" is alternative terminology for "numerical integration."   The common usage "Simpson's rule" rather than "Simpson quadrature," etc., is a matter of convention.

We now ask, could we achieve a smaller truncation error for a given number of intervals if we were willing to let the endpoints of the intervals fall wherever a desire for higher accuracy might demand?   From a philosophical standpoint, we might expect improvement: since we are giving up the freedom to choose the intervals, we might expect to get something in return, namely, higher accuracy.   The answer to the question is an emphatic "yes."

Recall that with two ordinates the best we could do before was to obtain the exact value for a linear function (first degree polynomial). We shall now show that by choosing the location of the two points properly we can obtain an exact formula for the integral of a cubic (third-degree polynomial).   Although we shall not prove the fact in complete generality, it is perhaps intuitively obvious that if an integration method gives an exact result for a higher degree polynomial it is more accurate *in general.*

We first change the limits of integration from a to b to -1 to $+1$, in order to simplify the analysis.   Define a new variable

$$\mu = \frac{2x - (b + a)}{b - a}$$

so that

$$x = \tfrac{1}{2}(b - a)\mu + \tfrac{1}{2}(b + a)$$

The integral (6.1) thus becomes

(6.23) $$I = \int_{-1}^{+1} \phi(\mu)\, d\mu$$

where

$$\phi(\mu) = \tfrac{1}{2}(b - a) \cdot f[\tfrac{1}{2}(b - a)\mu + \tfrac{1}{2}(b + a)]$$

This means that the change of variable reduces all integrations to the form (6.23).   ("All" integrations within the restrictions assumed, that is: finite limits and a continuous integrand.)

We are still trying to see what we can do with only two ordinates, which means that the approximating curve will be a straight line.   In other words, we hope to find a linear function

$$y = \alpha_0 + \alpha_1\mu$$

such that

(6.24) $$\int_{-1}^{1} (\alpha_0 + \alpha_1\mu)\, d\mu = \int_{-1}^{1} \phi(\mu)\, d\mu$$

The integral on the left is the area of the trapezoid shown in Figure 6.5. This area will be identical with the area under the curve $y = \phi(\mu)$ if

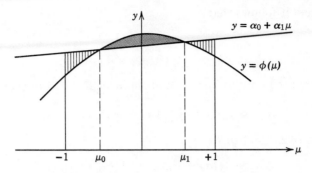

FIGURE 6.5   Geometrical interpretation of the method of Gauss quadrature with two points.

the vertically striped areas (between -1 and μ_0 and between μ_1 and $+1$) are precisely equal to the shaded area (that between μ_0 and μ_1). We evidently wish to choose the line so that this cancellation is achieved.

To this end, let

(6.25) $$I_G = A_0\,\phi(\mu_0) + A_1\,\phi(\mu_1)$$

where A_0, A_1, μ_0, and μ_1 are to be chosen.   Since there are four parameters, it is reasonable to expect that they can be chosen to give an exact formula for a cubic integrand:

$$\phi(\mu) = a_0 + a_1\mu + a_2\mu^2 + a_3\mu^3$$

We rewrite this as

$$\phi(\mu) = \alpha_0 + \alpha_1\mu + (\mu - \mu_0)(\mu - \mu_1)(\beta_0 + \beta_1\mu)$$

If α_0 and α_1 are to satisfy (6.24), then μ_0 and μ_1 must be chosen so that

$$\int_{-1}^{+1} (\mu - \mu_0)(\mu - \mu_1)(\beta_0 + \beta_1\mu)\,d\mu = 0$$

Since this must be true for *any* choice of β_0 and β_1, it follows that we must require that

$$\int_{-1}^{1} (\mu - \mu_0)(\mu - \mu_1)\,d\mu = 0$$

$$\int_{-1}^{1} \mu(\mu - \mu_0)(\mu - \mu_1)\,d\mu = 0$$

After integration these become

$$\tfrac{2}{3} + 2\mu_0\mu_1 = 0$$

$$\mu_0 + \mu_1 = 0$$

from which it follows that

(6.26)
$$\mu_1 = -\mu_0 = \frac{1}{\sqrt{3}}$$

We now need only to find A_0 and A_1 in (6.25). Note that

(6.27)
$$\int_{-1}^{1} \phi(\mu)\, d\mu = \int_{-1}^{1} (\alpha_0 + \alpha_1\mu)\, d\mu = 2\alpha_0$$

and from (6.25) and (6.26)

$$I_G = A_0(\alpha_0 + \alpha_1\mu_0) + A_1(\alpha_0 + \alpha_1\mu_1)$$

$$= \alpha_0(A_0 + A_1) - \frac{\alpha_1}{\sqrt{3}}(A_0 - A_1)$$

Since this must be equal to the integral (6.27) for all α_0 and α_1,

$$A_0 + A_1 = 2$$
$$A_0 - A_1 = 0$$

Thus

(6.28)
$$A_0 = A_1 = 1$$

Equation 6.25 becomes

$$I_G = \phi\left(-\frac{1}{\sqrt{3}}\right) + \phi\left(\frac{1}{\sqrt{3}}\right)$$

This is the Gauss quadrature formula for two points. The truncation error in integrating a polynomial of degree 3 or lower is zero. For polynomials of higher degree and for other functions the truncation error can be expected to be of the form

$$e_T = K\phi^{iv}(\xi), \qquad -1 < \xi < 1$$

where

(6.29)
$$\int_{-1}^{1} \phi(\mu)\, d\mu = I_G + e_T = \phi\left(-\frac{1}{\sqrt{3}}\right) + \phi\left(\frac{1}{\sqrt{3}}\right) + e_T$$

To find K, let

$$\phi(\mu) = \mu^4$$

then

$$\phi^{iv}(\mu) = 24$$

so

(6.30)
$$e_T = 24K$$

Now

$$\int_{-1}^{1} \phi(\mu) \, d\mu = \int_{-1}^{1} \mu^4 \, d\mu = \tfrac{2}{5}$$

But on the other hand from (6.29) and (6.30)

$$\int_{-1}^{1} \phi(\mu) \, d\mu = \left(-\frac{1}{\sqrt{3}}\right)^4 + \left(\frac{1}{\sqrt{3}}\right)^4 + 24K$$

Therefore

$$K = \tfrac{1}{135}$$

and

$$e_T = \frac{\phi^{\mathrm{iv}}(\xi)}{135}, \qquad -1 < \xi < 1$$

Higher order Gauss quadrature formulas can be found by using more points and, in general, different *weights* (the A_i):

(6.31)
$$\int_{-1}^{1} \phi(\mu) \, d\mu = \sum_{i=0}^{n-1} A_i \, \phi(\mu_i)$$

In general, with n points (as shown above), we get an exact formula for a polynomial of degree $2n - 1$.

It turns out that the μ_i in (6.31) are the roots of the Legendre polynomial of degree n.   For this reason the method described above is often referred to as *Legendre-Gauss quadrature*.   The Legendre polynomials $P_n(\mu)$ may be defined recursively by

(6.32)
$$\begin{cases} P_0(\mu) = 1 \\[4pt] P_1(\mu) = \mu \\[4pt] P_m(\mu) = \dfrac{1}{m}\left[(2m - 1)\mu \, P_{m-1}(\mu) - (m - 1) \, P_{m-2}(\mu)\right] \end{cases}$$

For example, letting $m = 2$,

$$P_2(\mu) = \tfrac{1}{2}(3\mu \cdot \mu - 1 \cdot 1) = \frac{3\mu^2}{2} - \frac{1}{2}$$

Notice that the roots of $P_2(\mu)$ are $\pm 1/\sqrt{3}$ as we found earlier.
The weights in (6.31) are given by

$$A_i = \frac{2}{(1 - \mu_i^2)[P_n{}'(\mu_i)]^2}$$

As an example consider $n = 2$, so that $\mu_0 = -1/\sqrt{3}$, $\mu_1 = 1/\sqrt{3}$, and $P_2' = 3\mu$. Then

$$A_0 = \frac{2}{(1 - \frac{1}{3}) \cdot 3} = 1$$

and likewise $A_1 = 1$ as before.

In the general case the truncation error is given by

$$e_T = \frac{\phi^{(2n)}(\xi)}{(2n)!} \left(\frac{2}{2n + 1} - \sum_{i=0}^{n} A_i \mu_i^{2n} \right)$$

A table for the μ_i and A_i for $n = 2, \ldots, 6$ is given in the appendix. Note that the μ_i are symmetric about the origin and that the coefficient A_k for μ_k is the same as that for $-\mu_k$. A more complete table for n up to 48 is given in V. I. Krylov, *Approximate Calculation of Integrals*, Appendix A, Macmillan, 1962, transl. Arthur H. Stroud.

In summary, Gauss quadrature gives more accuracy than Simpson's rule for the same number of ordinates at the expense of a complete lack of choice of locating the points. As in so many other cases, we have an economic choice, this time between the simplicity of Simpson's rule and the potential time savings of Gauss quadrature. In practice, Simpson's rule is more commonly used.

6.8   Numerical examples and comparison of methods

To illustrate the three methods we have discussed and to see how they compare in accuracy, consider the following integral

$$I = \int_{-2}^{2} e^{-x^2/2} \, dx$$

This is the probability integral of Case Study 6, without the $1/\sqrt{2\pi}$ factor in front. The exact value to four decimals is 2.3925.

Let us first apply the trapezoidal rule with the rather broad spacing of $h = 1.0$. Then

$$I_T = \frac{1.0}{2} (e^{-(-2)^2/2} + 2e^{-(-1)^2/2} + 2e^{-(0)^2/2} + 2e^{-(1)^2/2} + e^{-(2)^2})$$

$$= 0.5(0.13534 + 2 \cdot 0.60653 + 2 \cdot 1.00000 + 2 \cdot 0.60653 + 0.13534)$$

$$= 2.3484$$

$$\epsilon = 0.0441$$

Simpson's rule with $h = 1.0$ leads to

$$I_S = \frac{1.0}{3} \left(e^{-(-2)^2/2} + 4e^{-(-1)^2/2} + 2e^{-(0)^2/2} + 4e^{-(1)^2/2} + e^{-(2)^2/2} \right)$$

$$= 0.33333(0.13534 + 4 \cdot 0.60653 + 2 \cdot 1.00000 + 4 \cdot 0.60653 + 0.13534)$$

$$= 2.3743$$

$$\epsilon = 0.0182$$

Gauss integration with two points requires evaluation of

$$I_G = A_0\, \phi(\mu_0) + A_1\, \phi(\mu_1)$$

where

$$\phi(\mu) = \frac{b-a}{2} f\left(\frac{b-a}{2}\mu + \frac{b+a}{2} \right)$$

$$= 2 \cdot e^{-(2\mu)^2/2}$$

So we have

$$I_G = 2 \left\{ \exp \frac{[-(-2 \cdot 0.57735)^2]}{2} + \exp \frac{[-(2 \cdot 0.57735)^2]}{2} \right\}$$

$$= 2.0536$$

$$\epsilon = 0.3389$$

Repeating these calculations for $h = 0.5$ and $h = 0.25$, and with three, four, five, and six points in the Gauss method, we get the results shown in Table 6.1.

Valid general conclusions cannot be drawn from one small example, but it happens that the following observations about these results have fairly wide applicability.

1. Simpson's rule with n points provides the same general order of accuracy as the trapezoidal rule with $2n$ points.

2. Gauss quadrature with n points provides the same general order of accuracy as Simpson's rule with $2n$ points.

Although neither of these statements is *exactly* true, there is, in fact, some mathematical basis for them as *approximately* true.

3. For the same accuracy, Simpson's rule requires about half as much effort as the trapezoidal rule, since there are half as many ordinates to evaluate.

Table 6.1

Trapezoidal Rule	h	I_T	ϵ
	1.0	2.3484	0.0441
	0.5	2.3813	0.0112
	0.25	2.3898	0.0027

Simpson's Rule	h	I_S	ϵ
	1.0	2.3743	0.0182
	0.5	2.3923	0.0002
	0.25	2.3926	−0.0001

Gauss Quadrature	Number of Points	I_G	ϵ
	2	2.0536	0.3389
	3	2.4471	−0.0546
	4	2.3859	0.0066
	5	2.3931	−0.0006
	6	2.3925	0.0000

4. For the same accuracy, Gauss quadrature requires about half as much effort as Simpson's rule, since there are about half as many ordinates to evaluate.

For "hand" calculation (4) is somewhat offset by the fact that the abscissas are prescribed and occur—for the most part—at values that are awkward to work with. (In our example it is easier to look up $e^{-0.5}$ than $e^{-0.16667}$.) In a computer, however, this consideration is of no consequence.

The savings in Gauss quadrature are partly offset by the fact that if the integral is to be re-evaluated with more points the preceding ordinates cannot be re-used, since they are at the wrong locations (This is not so with Simpson's rule; see Exercise 14.)

For integrating experimental data Gauss quadrature can be used only if the abscissas are properly chosen in advance; this is seldom the case. Simpson's rule can be applied as long as adjacent pairs of intervals are equal. If the abscissas are randomly spaced, the only one of these methods that can be used is the trapezoidal.

In view of the quite acceptable accuracy for the number of ordinates required, the simplicity of the formula, and the ease of modifying the interval and re-evaluating, it should not be surprising that Simpson's rule is widely used in practical computations.

6.9   Case study 8: Luminous efficiency

The following case study will give us an opportunity to apply some of the ideas presented in this chapter and at the same time to illustrate interesting programming techniques.

A blackbody (perfect radiator) emits energy at a rate proportional to the fourth power of its absolute temperature, according to the Stefan-Boltzmann equation

$$E = 36.9 \cdot 10^{-12} T^4$$

where E = emissive power, watts/cm^2,
T = temperature, degrees Kelvin.

We are interested in the fraction of this total energy contained in the visible spectrum, which is taken here to be $4 \cdot 10^{-5}$ to $7 \cdot 10^{-5}$ cm. We can get the visible part by integrating Planck's equation between these limits:

$$E_{\text{visible}} = \int_{4 \cdot 10^{-5}}^{7 \cdot 10^{-5}} \frac{2.39 \cdot 10^{-11} \, dx}{x^5 (e^{\frac{1.432}{Tx}} - 1)}$$

where x = wavelength, cm,
E and T as before.

The *luminous efficiency* is defined as the ratio of the energy in the visible spectrum to the total energy. If we multiply by 100 to get the efficiency in percent and combine the constants, the problem becomes that of evaluating

$$\text{EFF} = \frac{64.77 \int_{4 \cdot 10^{-5}}^{7 \cdot 10^{-5}} \dfrac{dx}{x^5 (e^{\frac{1.432}{Tx}} - 1)}}{T^4}$$

We wish to write a program that computes EFF for a number of temperatures, ranging from an initial value of TEMP1 to a maximum value of TEMP2, in increments of TMPINC. We shall also read in values of the limits of the visible spectrum, A to B, so that these slightly indefinite numbers can be varied if desired. A fixed point number N will be read to give the number of intervals to be used in the numerical integration. We shall return to the question of what N should be to give sufficient accuracy.

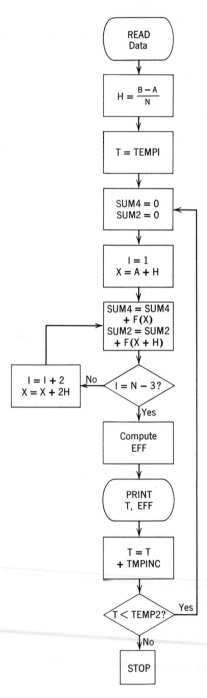

FIGURE 6.6   Block diagram of the method of computing luminous efficiency, using Simpson's rule for the integration.   (Case Study 8.)

A block diagram for the procedure to be used is shown in Figure 6.6. We begin by reading the six input values and then carry out two steps that will never be repeated: computing H, the interval size, and setting T equal to the initial temperature in the range.   Now we are ready to start into the numerical integration routine.   We establish two summing locations, SUM4 and SUM2, to hold the sum of the ordinates to be multiplied by 4 and 2, respectively, in Simpson's rule.   We shall shortly be computing a value for the integrand at the first interior point X + H (added to SUM4) and at the second interior point (added to SUM2), so we give X the suitable starting value.

Now comes a problem.   We want to set up a loop to run through the values of X at all the interior points and then stop.   If we test for the completion of this loop by comparing X with B − H, the last interior point, we are in trouble on two scores.   First, there is one more point to be multiplied by 4 than to be multiplied by 2; we must stop short in the loop and take care of the last interior point after getting out of the loop.   Second, if we start X at A + H and repeatedly add 2H to it, roundoff errors will accumulate, so that we will in general never arrive at a value of X that is *exactly* equal to B − 3H.

One solution to this impasse is to count the number of interior points computed with a fixed point variable.   We accordingly set I equal to 1 before going into the summation loop.   (A quick sketch will help to clarify the question of the proper value of I at which to stop.)

Now we compute the next two interior points, add them to the appropriate sums, and ask whether we are finished with this loop. If not, we increment I and X and go around again.   If so, we are ready to compute EFF.   SUM4 contains all the ordinates to be multiplied by 4, except the one for B − H, which must accordingly be computed.   SUM2 contains all the ordinates to be multiplied by 2.   This leaves out the ordinates for A and B.   At this point, therefore, we write a long statement to get the three ordinates not found by the loop and do the multiplications by 4 and 2.   This statement also handles the factor of H/3 from Simpson's rule, and the $64.77/T^4$ from the formula.

After printing the result, T is incremented and then tested.   If the incremented value is less than TEMP2, the input value that gives the largest temperature to be considered, we go back to do the entire integration section again.   If the luminous efficiency has been calculated for the largest temperature specified, we are finished.

The program is shown in Figure 6.7.   It contains no new FORTRAN concepts, but the reader may wish to check it carefully to determine that it actually does the processing described more graphically in the block diagram.

```
         READ 60, TEMPI, TEMP2, TMPINC, A, B, N
   60    FORMAT (5F10.0, I4)
         FN = N
         H = (B - A) / FN
         T = TEMPI
  100    SUM4 = 0.0
         SUM2 = 0.0
         I = I
         X = A + H
   12    SUM4 = SUM4+1.0/(X**5*(EXPF(1..432/(T*X))-1..0))
         SUM2 = SUM2+1.0/(((X+H)**5*(EXPF(1..432/(T*(X+H))))
     1          -1..0)))
         IF (I - N + 3) 21, 32, 32
   21    I = I + 2
         X = X + H + H
         GO TO 12
   32    EFF = 64..77*H/3..0*(4..0*SUM4 + 2..0*SUM2
     1          + 1.0/(A**5*(EXPF(1..432/(T*A))-1..0))
     2          + 4..0/((B-H)**5*(EXPF(1..432/(T*(B-H)))-1..0))
     3          + 1..0/(B**5*(EXPF(1..432/(T*B))-1..0))))/T**4
```

```
         PRINT 61, T, EFF
   61    FORMAT (2E20.8)
         T = T + TMPINC
         IF (T - TEMP2) 100, 100, 200
  200    STOP
         END
```

FIGURE 6.7 A program to compute luminous efficiency, using Simpson's rule for the integration. (Case Study 8)

Estimating the truncation error from the error bound is possible, but in practical terms it is more trouble than it is worth in this case. First we would have to find the fourth derivative of

$$\frac{1}{x^5(e^{\frac{1.432}{Tx}} - 1)}$$

which is considerable work although it can, of course, be done.   Then
we would need to have some idea of where in the interval the fourth
derivative was largest.

A much more practical approach is to let the computer help us.
A formula for the deferred approach to the limit for Simpson's rule,
similar to (6.18) for the trapezoidal rule, is easily derived:

$$I = I_h + \frac{I_h - I_k}{1 - k^4/h^4}$$

This means, for instance, that if we run the program for, say, $N = 10$
and then for $N = 20$ we have a way of estimating the true integral.
And from the size of the difference between the two computed values
we have a fairly good idea of how many intervals to use routinely.

This was done for this program, with $T = 3500°K$.   For 10 intervals
the computed value was 14.512723% and for 20 it was 14.512664%.
The difference is so much less than any practical use of the results
could possibly demand, that we immediately drop any further worry
about accuracy.

(Although it is not a question of numerical analysis, it is interesting
to plot the variation of efficiency with temperature, as shown in Figure 6.8.   We see that the visible fraction of the total energy is negligible below approximately 2000°C ($\sim$2300°K); that at the melting
point of tungsten, about 3600°K, only about 15% of the radiated
energy is visible; that the curve has a broad peak around 7000°K.
Such considerations as these set limits on the efficiency of an incan-
descent light bulb.   An interesting exercise would be to make some

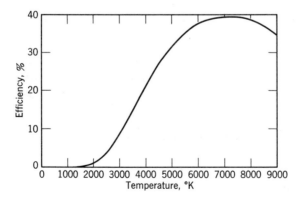

FIGURE 6.8   Luminous efficiency as a function of the temperature (°K) of the radiating black
body.   (Case Study 8.)

assumptions, such as the cost of electricity, a function giving the life of a filament in terms of temperature, and the cost of the bulb, and compute the temperature at which the "total cost" of the light—electricity and bulb—is least.)

Exercises

1. Compute the exact value of the integral $I = \int_0^2 f(x)\, dx$, the approximation from the trapezoidal rule, with $h = 1$, and the approximation from Simpson's rule, with $h = 1$, for each of the following integrands.

   a. $f(x) = 1 + x$
   b. $f(x) = 1 + x^2$
   c. $f(x) = 1 + x^3$
   d. $f(x) = 1 + x^4$

2. Demonstrate geometrically and prove analytically that if $f''(x) > 0$, $a \leq x \leq b$, the approximation to $\int_a^b f(x)\, dx$ given by the trapezoidal rule will always be greater than the true value of the integral. (Such functions are called *convex*.)

3. Consider the integral $\int_{-1}^1 (1 + x + x^2 + x^3)\, dx$. Show that Simpson's rule with $h = 1$ and Gauss's method with two points both give exact results, even though Gauss's method requires one less ordinate.

4. Consider the integral $\int_0^1 \sin x\, dx = 0.45970$. Show that the result obtained by Simpson's rule with $h = 0.5$ is surprisingly close to the exact result (within about one part in 3000). Explain "qualitatively" why the close agreement is obtained.

5. In contrast with Exercise 4, consider the simple-appearing integral $\int_{0.1}^1 dx/x = 2.30259$. The approximations given by Simpson's rule for three different interval sizes, together with the errors, are listed.

n	h	I_S	Error
2	0.45	3.3500	−1.0474
4	0.225	2.4079	−0.1053
8	0.1125	2.3206	−0.0180

Explain the difference between the results of this exercise and the preceding one.

6. Use the deferred approach to the limit with the last two lines in the list above to arrive at a better estimate for the value of the integral $\int_{0.1}^1 dx/x$. Equation 6.18 seems to imply that the result should be exact. Why is it not?

7. The complete elliptic integral of the first kind is

$$K(\theta) = \int_0^{\pi/2} \frac{d\phi}{\sqrt{1 - \sin^2 \theta \sin^2 \phi}}$$

Compute $K(30°)$, using Simpson's rule with four intervals. The exact result to four decimals is 1.6858. Evaluate $K(85°)$ with Simpson's rule and four intervals; the exact result to three decimals is 3.832. Why is this result so badly in error, whereas the other (that for $\theta = 30°$) was accurate?

8. Consider the following integral, suggested by Scarborough.*

$$\int_{-1}^{1} \frac{x^7 \sqrt{1 - x^2}\, dx}{(2 - x)^{13/2}}$$

Write a program to evaluate this integral, using Simpson's rule; arrange the program to read in a value of h, the interval size. Run with $h = 0.25$, then with $h = 0.1, 0.05, 0.02$, and 0.01. Explain the perhaps unexpected behavior of the result as h is decreased. (It might help if the program were set up to print the values of the ordinates at each point.)

*9. Consider the integral

$$I = \int_0^{10} e^{-x}\, dx = 0.999955$$

Evaluate by

a. Gauss quadrature with 6 points;
b. the trapezoidal rule with 10 intervals;
c. Simpson's rule with 10 intervals;
d. the rectangular rule of Exercise 18 with 10 intervals.

Compare the results. Is it better to integrate forward or backward? Why?

*10. Write programs to carry out the evaluations in Exercise 9.

11. Generalize your program for Simpson's rule so that it reads a data card containing values for a, b, and n, and computes the required value for h.

12. Add to your program for Exercise 11 a test to determine whether n is even and stop the program without doing the integration if it is not. (*Hint.* FORTRAN fixed point division truncates. If N is odd, $(N/2)*2$ will not be equal to N.)

*13. Modify the program in Figure 6.7 so that it computes and prints the efficiency as computed by the trapezoidal rule and by Simpson's rule, without evaluating any ordinate more than once.

14. Suppose that the computation of the program of Figure 6.7 has just been completed and that we wish to recompute the integral with twice

---

* J. B. Scarborough, *Numerical Mathematical Analysis*, The Johns Hopkins Press, 1950.

as many points. All the points previously computed and summed in SUM2 and SUM4 would be needed in the new computation; together they would be the ordinates to be multiplied by 2. In addition, we would need new ordinates at points midway between all the preceding ones. Modify the program so that after computing the integral with an interval size dictated by A, B, and N it recomputes with twice as many points but without ever recomputing any ordinates. With the two approximations to the integral, use the deferred approach to the limit to compute a more accurate value.

15. Write a program that reads values of a_0, a_1, a_2, a_3, a_4, a_5, and a_6 (one card) and also values of a, b, and n (another card), then evaluates and prints the value of

$$I = \int_a^b (a_0 + a_1x + a_2x^2 + a_3x^3 + a_4x^4 + a_5x^5 + a_6x^6)\, dx$$

Use Simpson's rule with n intervals.

16. Modify the program of Case Study 8 so that it identifies the approximate maximum efficiency, if a maximum is found in the range of temperatures called for. If three temperatures T_1, T_2, and T_3 are found such that $\text{Eff}(T_1) < \text{Eff}(T_2) > \text{Eff}(T_3)$, print the three temperatures and the three efficiencies. If three such numbers are not found in the range from TEMP1 to TEMP2, print zeros for all six numbers.

17. Given three values of $x = -h$, 0, h and three corresponding values of $y = y_0$, y_1, y_2, substitute the three pairs of values of x and y into the general equation of a parabola, $y = a + bx + cx^2$, to get three equations in the three unknowns a, b, and c. Using these values of a, b, and c, integrate the equation of the parabola between the limits $-h$ and h to get

$$\int_{-h}^{h} (a + bx + cx^2)\, dx = \frac{h}{3}(y_0 + 4y_1 + y_2)$$

which is, of course, Simpson's rule for three adjacent points. Simpson's rule is thus shown to be equivalent to approximating the given function by a series of segments of parabolas, as stated in the text.

18. Derive an integration formula for

$$I = \int_a^b f(x)\, dx$$

by dividing the interval into n equal intervals of width

$$h = \frac{b - a}{n}$$

Approximate the integral for each interval by the area of the rectangle whose height is the value of $f(x)$ at the *left* end (see sketch).

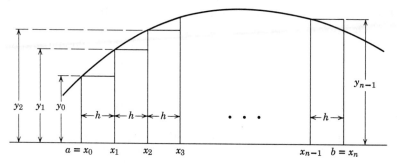

19. Show that the truncation error in the formula derived in Exercise 18 is

$$E_T = \left[\frac{b - a}{2} y'(\xi) \right] h$$

where $a < \xi < b$.

20. Use the deferred approach to the limit on the formula derived in Exercise 18, together with the truncation error in Exercise 19, assuming that $y'(x)$ is constant, to obtain a new integration formula

$$\int_a^b y(x) \, dx \simeq h(y_{\frac{1}{2}} + y_{\frac{3}{2}} + \cdots + y_{n-\frac{1}{2}})$$

where

$$y_{\frac{1}{2}} = y\left(x + \frac{h}{2} \right)$$

$$y_{\frac{3}{2}} = y\left(x + \frac{3h}{2} \right)$$

$$y_{i+\frac{1}{2}} = y(x + (i + \tfrac{1}{2})h), \qquad i = 0, \ldots, n - 1$$

Interpret the formula geometrically.

21. The truncation error in the formula of Exercise 20 is

$$E_T = \left[\frac{(b - a)y''(\xi)}{24} \right] h^2, \qquad a < \xi < b$$

Compare this with the truncation error in the trapezoidal rule. Can you explain why these truncation errors should be expected to be of the same order?

22. Show that the Gauss quadrature formula that exactly integrates a linear function and no more is

$$\int_{-1}^1 \phi(u) \, du = 2\phi(0)$$

23. Consider the trapezoidal rule with $n = 3m$; that is, the number of steps is a multiple of 3. Write down the trapezoidal rule for a step size $k = 3h$ and use the deferred approach to the limit to obtain the integration formula

$$I = \frac{3h}{8} (y_0 + 3y_1 + 3y_2 + 2y_3 + 3y_4 + 3y_5 + 2y_6 + 3y_7 + \cdots$$
$$+ 3y_{n-4} + 2y_{n-3} + 3y_{n-2} + 3y_{n-1} + y_n)$$

This is usually called the *three-eighths rule*. It is equivalent to passing a cubic equation through four successive ordinates and using the integral of the cubic to approximate the integral of the function over the three intervals.

The truncation error is

$$E_T = - \frac{(b - a)y^{iv}(\xi)}{80} h^4, \qquad a < \xi < b$$

Compare with the truncation error for Simpson's rule. What does this imply with regard to the advantage of this four-point formula over the three-point formula given by Simpson's rule?

24. Consider Simpson's rule with $n = 4m$ intervals. Write down Simpson's rule with $k = 2h$ and use the deferred approach to the limit to obtain the formula

$$I = \frac{2h}{45} (7y_0 + 32y_1 + 12y_2 + 32y_3 + 14y_4 + 32y_5 + \cdots$$
$$+ 14y_{n-4} + 32y_{n-3} + 12y_{n-2} + 32y_{n-1} + 7y_n)$$

This is the *fourth Newton-Cotes* formula (the trapezoidal, Simpson's rule, and the three-eighths rule are the first three). The truncation error is

$$E_T \simeq Kh^6$$

25. Consider the semi-infinite integral

$$I = \int_0^\infty f(x) \, dx$$

where $f(x)$ can be written as

$$f(x) = e^{-x} \phi(x)$$

Show that if $\phi(x)$ is a polynomial of degree 3 or less I can be calculated from

$$I = A_0 \phi(x_0) + A_1 \phi(x_1)$$

where $x_0 = 2 - \sqrt{2}$,
   $x_1 = 2 + \sqrt{2}$,
   $A_0 = (2 + \sqrt{2})/4$,
   $A_1 = (2 - \sqrt{2})/4$.

This is the *Laguerre-Gauss quadrature* formula of order 2. The named is derived from the fact that x_0 and x_1 are the roots of the Laguerre polynomial of second degree.

For a general development and a tabulation of the abscissas and weights for higher order Laguerre-Gauss formulas see Section 8.6 of Hildebrand, *Introduction to Numerical Analysis*, or Section 7.5 and Appendix C of Krylov, *Approximate Calculation of Integrals*.

26. Show that if $f(x)$ is a polynomial of degree 3 or less

$$\int_{-2}^{\infty} e^{-x} f(x)\, dx = \frac{e^2}{4}[(2+\sqrt{2})f(-\sqrt{2}) + (2-\sqrt{2})f(\sqrt{2})]$$

Hint. Reduce the problem by a change of variables to the form given in Exercise 25.

27. Consider the infinite integral

$$I = \int_{-\infty}^{\infty} f(x)\, dx$$

where $f(x)$ can be written

$$f(x) = e^{-x^2}\phi(x)$$

Show that if $\phi(x)$ is a polynomial of degree 3 or less

$$I = \frac{\sqrt{\pi}}{2}\left[\phi\left(-\frac{\sqrt{2}}{2}\right) + \phi\left(+\frac{\sqrt{2}}{2}\right)\right]$$

is exact.

This is the *Hermite-Gauss quadrature* formula of order 2. The name is derived from the fact that the points at which ϕ is evaluated are the roots of the Hermite polynomial of second degree.

For further information see the references listed in Exercise 25.

Hint. Recall that

$$\int_{0}^{\infty} e^{-x^2}\, dx = \frac{\sqrt{\pi}}{2}$$

28. Use the trapezoidal rule twice to obtain the formula

$$\int_{x_0}^{x_n}\int_{y_0}^{y_m} f(x,y)\, dx\, dy$$

$$= \frac{hk}{4}[f_{0,0} + f_{n,0} + f_{0,m} + f_{n,m}$$

$$+ 2(f_{1,0} + f_{2,0} + \cdots + f_{n-1,0} + f_{0,1} + \cdots + f_{0,m-1}$$

$$+ f_{n,1} + f_{n,2} + \cdots + f_{n,m-1} + f_{1,m} + f_{2,m} + \cdots + f_{n-1,m})$$

$$+ 4(f_{1,1} + f_{2,1} + \cdots + f_{n-1,1}$$

$$+ f_{1,2} + f_{2,2} + \cdots + f_{n-1,2}$$

$$\cdots$$

$$+ f_{1,m-1} + f_{2,m-2} + \cdots + f_{n-1,m-1})]$$

where $f_{i,j} = f(x_i, y_j)$
$$h = x_i - x_{i-1}$$
$$k = y_j - y_{j-1}$$

Such integration formulas over a rectangle are called *cubature formulas* for numerical integration of double integrals. Other formulas may be obtained by a double application of other quadrature formulas, such as Simpson's rule.

*29. An engineer wishes to obtain the "best" average reading of a certain meter in a plant over the span of one hour. How many minutes after the start of the hour should the readings be taken if

a. only two readings can be made,
b. three readings can be made,
c. four readings can be made.

The answers should be computed to the nearest minute.

30. Given the following experimental data, where y is assumed to be some (unknown) function of x,

x	y
1.0	1.00
1.2	1.82
1.4	2.08
1.6	3.18
1.8	3.52
2.0	4.70
3.2	5.12
3.4	6.38
2.6	6.98
2.8	8.22
3.0	9.00

find the area under the curve represented approximately by y by the following methods:

a. Using the trapezoidal rule.
b. Using Simpson's rule over the interval from 1.0 to 3.0.
c. Using the tapezoidal rule for the interval from 1.0 to 1.2 and for the interval from 2.8 to 3.0 and Simpson's rule for the interval from 1.2 to 2.8.

Without knowing more about the data, can you say which of the three answers is "best"?

31. Given the following experimental data, where y is assumed to be some (unknown) function of x,

x	y
20	0.21
25	0.30
30	0.37
40	0.45
50	0.49
60	0.50
70	0.49
80	0.47
90	0.45
100	0.43
120	0.37
140	0.33
160	0.29
180	0.25
200	0.19
250	0.13
300	0.08
400	0.04

find the area under the curve represented approximately by y, using the trapezoidal rule.

—7

Subscripted Variables and
the DO Statement

The FORTRAN techniques that have been discussed so far permit much useful computing to be done, but they do not provide us with much power in dealing with certain types of problems that occur frequently. In particular, we need better methods of handling large arrays of related data, such as those found in simultaneous equations and many other applications. In this chapter we shall investigate the use of subscripted variables, which make it possible to refer to a complete array of data by one generic name, and the use of the DO statement, which, among other things, greatly simplifies the processing of such arrays.

7.1 Definitions

Subscripted variables permit us to represent many quantities with one variable name. A particular quantity is indicated by writing a subscript (or subscripts) in parentheses after the variable name. The complete set of quantities is called an *array*, and the individual quantities are called *elements*. A subscripted variable may have one, two, or three subscripts, and it then represents a one-, two-, or three-dimensional array, respectively. (When used in this connection, one-dimensional, etc., refers to the number of *subscripts*, not to the number of *elements*: a one-dimensional array can have many elements, and a three-dimensional array could in principle have only one element.)

The first element of a one-dimensional array is element number 1, the second is element number 2, etc., up to the number of elements in the array. In mathematical notation we might write X_1, X_2, X_3,

194

. . . , X_{19}, X_{20}; in FORTRAN subscript notation we would write X(1), X(2), X(3), . . . , X(19), X(20).

A two-dimensional array may be thought of as being composed of horizontal rows and vertical columns.   The first of the two subscripts then refers to the *row number*, running from 1 up to the number of rows, and the second to the *column number*, running from 1 up to the number of columns.   For instance, an array of two rows and three columns might be shown in mathematical notation as

$$A_{1,1} \quad A_{1,2} \quad A_{1,3}$$
$$A_{2,1} \quad A_{2,2} \quad A_{2,3}$$

In FORTRAN subscript notation the elements would be written A(1,1), A(2,1), A(1,2), A(2,2), A(1,3), A(2,3).   We note that the subscripts are separated by commas, as they are in three-dimensional variables.

A three-dimensional array may be thought of, if one wishes, as being composed of planes, each plane containing rows and columns. Its interpretation, however, depends somewhat on the purpose of the computation; other interpretations are possible.

The name of a subscripted variable must not end in *F*, but the naming is otherwise the same as in nonsubscripted variables.   In particular, an array may consist of either fixed or floating point elements, and the meaning of the first character of the name is the same as in single variables.   The elements of any one array, however, must be *all* fixed point or *all* floating point.

7.2   Examples of the subscript notation

Suppose we have two points in space, represented in coordinate form by X_1, X_2, X_3 and Y_1, Y_2, Y_3.   We are required to compute the distance between them, which is given by

$$D = \sqrt{(X_1 - Y_1)^2 + (X_2 - Y_2)^2 + (X_3 - Y_3)^2}$$

Now suppose that we have set up an array called X, the three elements of which are the floating point coordinates of the point X, and another similarly for Y.   The computation of the distance between the points can be called by the statement shown in Figure 7.1.

For another example of the subscript notation consider the problem of solving two simultaneous linear algebraic equations in two unknowns.   To emphasize the similarity of subscripted variables with

```
C FOR COMMENT
STATEMENT NUMBER | Cont. | FORTRAN STATEMENT
      D = SQRTF((X(1) - Y(1))**2 + (X(2) - Y(2))**2
     1  + (X(3) - Y(3))**2)
```

FIGURE 7.1 An example of the use of subscript notation.

mathematical notation, we may write the system of equations completely in mathematical subscript form.

$$C_{1,1}X_1 + C_{1,2}X_2 = B_1$$

$$C_{2,1}X_1 + C_{2,2}X_2 = B_2$$

This problem can conveniently be set up with a one-dimensional array of two elements for the constant terms B_1 and B_2 and another for the unknowns X_1 and X_2, which we will compute. The coefficients (C's) are the four elements of a two-dimensional array of two rows and two columns.

The solution of such a small system of equations can be done conveniently by Cramer's rule, according to which

$$X_1 = \frac{B_1 \cdot C_{2,2} - B_2 \cdot C_{1,2}}{C_{1,1} \cdot C_{2,2} - C_{2,1} \cdot C_{1,2}}$$

$$X_2 = \frac{B_2 \cdot C_{1,1} - B_1 \cdot C_{1,2}}{C_{1,1} \cdot C_{2,2} - C_{2,1} \cdot C_{1,2}}$$

A program to evaluate these formulas is shown in Figure 7.2, in which we have done two things that should be explained. First,

```
C FOR COMMENT
STATEMENT NUMBER | Cont. | FORTRAN STATEMENT
      DENØM = C(1,1)*C(2,2) - C(2,1)*C(1,2)
      IF (ABSF(DENØM) - 1.E-5) 50, 51, 51
   50 STØP
   51 X(1) = (B(1)*C(2,2) - B(2)*C(1,2))/DENØM
      X(2) = (B(2)*C(1,1) - B(1)*C(2,1))/DENØM
```

FIGURE 7.2 Program segment using subscripting to solve two simultaneous equations.

since the denominator of both expressions is the same, it is computed first and used in computing both X_1 and X_2. Second, there is a possibility that this denominator will be zero, indicating either no solution or an infinite number of solutions, depending on the constant terms. Either way, Cramer's rule obviously does not apply, since a division by zero would be required. If a division by zero is attempted, some sort of error indication is usually given, the nature of which depends on the machine being used. The program should therefore include a test for this possibility.

Actually, we need to do a little more than just test the denominator for zero. Because of rounding, the denominator could be very small—indicating trouble or at least indicating inaccurate results—without actually being zero. We should therefore determine whether the absolute value of the denominator is less than some small number, say 10^{-5}.

7.3   Motivations for the use of subscripted variables

The foregoing examples show the fundamental ideas of the subscript notation, but they do not really indicate the power of the technique. After all, there is nothing in the examples that could not be done just as conveniently by giving each variable a separate name. Whey then are subscripted variables such an important feature of FORTRAN?

The reason is that the subscripts may themselves be variables or certain types of expressions. This means that we can set up a program to perform a basic computation, then make the same computation on many different values simply by changing the value of the subscript.

Suppose, for instance, that we need to compute the sum of the squares of 20 numbers, X_1 to X_{20}, stored in the computer. We could, of course, give them 20 different names and set up a long arithmetic statement to compute the sum of their squares, but this would be tedious, cumbersome, and inflexible. Instead, we set up the 20 numbers as the elements of a one-dimensional array which we call X. Now, any of the 20 can be referenced by the name X(I), and we arrange for I to take on all the values from 1 to 20.

In the usual mathematical notation

$$\text{SUMSQ} = \sum_{i=1}^{20} X_i^2$$

The computation can be done with the program shown in Figure 7.3. We first set SUMSQ equal to zero so that we may use a single expres-

```
┌─C FOR COMMENT
│STATEMENT
│NUMBER
│1    5 6 7                          FORTRAN STATEMENT

        SUMSQ = 0.0
        I = 1
   180  SUMSQ = SUMSQ + X(I)**2
        I = I + 1
        IF (I - 20) 180, 180, 181
   181
```

FIGURE 7.3   Program segment using subscripting and the IF statement to compute the sum of the squares of 20 numbers.

sion to compute each of the intermediate sums.   Then I is made 1 so that when statement 180 is first executed we get the first element from the array of values.   Then 1 is added to I and a test is made to determine whether all of the values have been used.   Note that when the IF shows that I = 20 we must still go back once more because I is modified *before the test.*

The last three statements in this program are executed exactly 20 times to give the sum of the squares of the 20 elements of the array. We shall see in Section 7.6 that this program can be made even simpler by using a DO statement.

7.4   The DIMENSION statement and other information

When subscripted variables are used in a program, certain information about them must be supplied to FORTRAN:

1. Which variables are subscripted?
2. How many subscripts are there for each subscripted variable?
3. How many elements are there in each array; that is, what is the maximum size of each subscript?

These questions are answered by the DIMENSION statement. Every subscripted variable in a program must be mentioned in a DIMENSION statement, and this statement must appear before the first occurrence of a variable in the program   A common practice is to give the dimension information for all subscripted variables in DIMENSION statements at the start of the program.   One DIMENSION statement may mention any number of variables, and there may be any number of DIMENSION statements.

The DIMENSION statement takes the form

DIMENSION V, V, V, . . .

where the V's stand for variable names followed by parentheses enclosing one, two, or three unsigned fixed point constants which give the maximum size of each subscript. When FORTRAN processes a DIMENSION statement, it sets aside enough storage locations to contain arrays of the sizes defined by the information in the statement. Thus if a program contains the statement

DIMENSION X(20), A(3,10), K(2,2,5)

FORTRAN will assign 20 locations to the one-dimensional array named X; 30 (3 x 10) to the two-dimensional array A; and 20 (2 x 2 x 5) to the three-dimensional array K.

It is the programmer's responsibility to write the program so that no subscript is ever larger than the maximum size specified in the DIMENSION statement. Furthermore, subscripts must never be smaller than 1; zero and negative subscripts are not permitted. If these restrictions are violated, the source program will be compiled, but the object program will in all probability give incorrect results.

The DIMENSION statement is said to be *nonexecutable;* that is, it provides information only to the FORTRAN processor and does not result in the creation of any instructions in the object program. It may therefore appear anywhere in the source program, even between two arithmetic statements. As previously noted, however, the dimension information for each subscripted variable must be given before the first appearance of that variable. Furthermore, a DIMENSION statement must not be the first statement in the range of a DO statement (see Section 7.6).

Subscripted variables, with a few exceptions noted later, may appear in any place in which an unsubscripted variable may be written. For a simple example consider the READ statement that might be used to read in the data for the simultaneous equations example in Section 7.2. The DIMENSION, READ, and FORMAT statements for that problem could be

DIMENSION B(2), C(2,2), X(2)
READ 16, C(1,1), C(2,1), C(1,2), C(2,2), B(1), B(2)
16 FORMAT (6F10.0)

When a READ statement is written with the elements indicated in this explicit form, the elements may be entered in any sequence desired. The programmer might choose, for instance, to write

READ 16, C(1,1), C(1,2), B(1), C(2,1), C(2,2), B(2)

The data would naturally have to be punched on the data card in the corresponding order.

We occasionally wish to deal with the elements of an array *without* explicitly naming them all. It is permissible to use an input or output statement in which the name of an array is written without any subscripting information; this will call for the reading or writing of the entire array. Thus we could follow the DIMENSION statement in the example above with

READ 16, C, B

to read all the elements of the two arrays.

It is, of course, necessary in such a case to have a convention regarding the sequence of the elements, since we are not specifying the sequence we desire. The sequence in which the elements must appear on the card in order to use an input or output statement that does not give subscripting information is as follows. For one-dimensional arrays, the elements are taken in sequence, starting with the element corresponding to the subscript 1 and proceeding to the largest subscript as defined in the DIMENSION statement. For two dimensional arrays the elements are taken in such a manner that the first subscript varies most rapidly. Thus the statements

DIMENSION R(2,3)
READ 16, R

would require that the elements be punched in the sequence R(1,1), R(2,1), R(1,2), R(2,2), R(1,3), R(2,3). This can be summarized by saying that the elements of a two-dimensional array are taken in *column-order*. For three-dimensional arrays the elements are taken in such a manner that the first subscript varies most rapidly and the last subscript varies least rapidly.

7.5   Allowable forms of subscripts

So far we have seen that subscripts may be fixed point constants or fixed point variables. Three other forms of subscripts are permitted. If I stands for a fixed point variable and if L and L' are fixed point constants, then all of the allowable forms of subscripts are

$$I$$
$$L$$
$$I \pm L$$
$$L*I$$
$$L*I \pm L'$$

The value of the subscript expression, even without the added or subtracted constant, if any, must never be less than 1 nor greater than the maximum specified in a DIMENSION statement. The variables in a subscript must not themselves be subscripted.

There are many situations in which the last three forms of subscripts find application. We may illustrate the use of one of these forms in an example that can be done in three different but equivalent ways.

Suppose that at a certain point in a program the following computation is required:

$$y = \begin{cases} a + bX + cX^2 & \text{if } K = 1 \\ d + eX + fX^2 & \text{if } K = 2 \\ g + hX + iX^2 & \text{if } K = 3 \end{cases}$$

The values of K and X have previously been established. We know how to write three statements with the different coefficients and then use an IF statement to pick the appropriate statement. The procedure, however, is much simpler with subscripting.

Suppose we make the nine coefficients the elements of a one-dimensional array which we may call C:

a	b	c	d	e	f	g	h	i
1	2	3	4	5	6	7	8	9

If K = 1, the numbers of the desired elements are

$$1 = 3K - 2$$
$$2 = 3K - 1$$
$$3 = 3K$$

If K = 2, the numbers of the desired elements are

$$4 = 3K - 2$$
$$5 = 3K - 1$$
$$6 = 3K$$

If K = 3, the numbers are

$$7 = 3K - 2$$
$$8 = 3K - 1$$
$$9 = 3K$$

Thus for any value of K the proper coefficients will be used if we write

Y = C(3*K − 2) + C(3*K − 1)*X + C(3*K)*X**2

If the coefficients had been arranged thus

$$\begin{array}{ccccccccc} a & d & g & b & e & h & c & f & i \\ 1 & 2 & 3 & 4 & 5 & 6 & 7 & 8 & 9 \end{array}$$

the statement would have been

$$Y = C(K) + C(K + 3)*X + C(K + 6)*X**2$$

Another approach, which gives the same results, is to make the coefficients the elements of a two-dimensional array:

$$\begin{array}{ccc} a & b & c \\ d & e & f \\ g & h & i \end{array}$$

In this array K can be used to select the proper row (first subscript) and 1, 2, or 3 can be used to select the proper column (second subscript).   The arithmetic statement now becomes

$$Y = C(K,1) + C(K,2)*X + C(K,3)*X**2$$

Thus we see that subscripted variables facilitate the selection of one set of data from a larger set.   We also see that the elements of an array, in contrast to ordinary mathematical usage, are not required to have any special relation to one another.

Still, the most common use of subscripted variables is in carrying out the same computation on a set of related quantities.   We shall see several more examples of this usage in connection with the DO statement.

7.6   The DO statement

A most powerful feature of the FORTRAN language is the DO statement.   This statement makes it possible to carry out a section of the program repeatedly, with changes in the value of a fixed point variable between repetitions.   Coupled with subscripted variables, the DO statement provides a simple way to make calculations that are quite complicated when done with actual machine instructions.   In view of the importance of this topic, we shall show its application in several examples.

The DO statement may be written in either of these forms:

$$\text{DO } n \ i = m_1, m_2$$

or

$$\text{DO } n \ i = m_1, m_2, m_3$$

In the statement n must be a statement number, i must be a non-subscripted fixed point variable, written without a sign, and m_1, m_2, and m_3 must each be an unsigned fixed point constant or a nonsubscripted unsigned fixed point variable. If m_3 is not stated, as in the first form of the statement, it is understood to be 1. The statements following the DO, up to and including the statement with the number n, are executed repeatedly. They are executed first with $i = m_1$; before each succeeding execution i is increased by m_3; repeated execution continues until the statements have been executed with i equal to the largest value not exceeding m_2.

To illustrate how the DO statement works and how it may be used, let us consider again the problem stated in connection with subscripting on p. 197. It will be recalled that we were required to form the sum of the squares of the 20 elements of a one-dimensional array named X. This can be done with the short program shown in Figure 7.4.

The DIMENSION statement establishes X as a variable with one subscript, the maximum value of which is 20. We first set the sum location to zero, then go into the DO statement. This says to execute repeatedly all the statements following the DO, down to and including the one numbered 180. There is, of course, only one statement in this range, and statement 180 itself is the repeated part. Statement 180 is carried out first with I = 1, so that the first time through we get X_1^2 in SUMSQ. Then I is increased by 1 and statement 180 executed again, this time adding X_2^2 to the X_1^2 which is already in SUMSQ. This process is repeated until statement 180 has been executed with I = 20, after which SUMSQ contains the sum of the squares of all 20 numbers. Control then passes on to the statement following 180.

For another example of a DO statement, suppose that we have a one-dimensional array called DATA which contains 21 elements. We

```
C FOR COMMENT
STATEMENT
NUMBER                                    FORTRAN STATEMENT
1      5 6 7
        DIMENSION X(20)
        SUMSQ = 0.0
        DO 180 I = 1, 20
  180   SUMSQ = SUMSQ + X(I)**2
```

FIGURE 7.4   A program using a DO loop to form the sum of the squares of 20 numbers.

wish to form the sum of all of the odd-numbered elements and to place this sum in a location we call SUM.   The program of Figure 7.5 will do this.

The DO statement, in this case, says to execute the statement numbered 500, with J equal to 1, 3, 5, . . . , 17, 19, 21.   The first time statement 500 is executed the value of the variable SUM is zero, so that the net effect is to move the first element of DATA to SUM. The second time it is executed the effect is to add to this the value of the third element of DATA, etc.   When it has been executed with J equal to 21, which adds in the last element, control passes on to the statement following statement 500, whatever that may be.

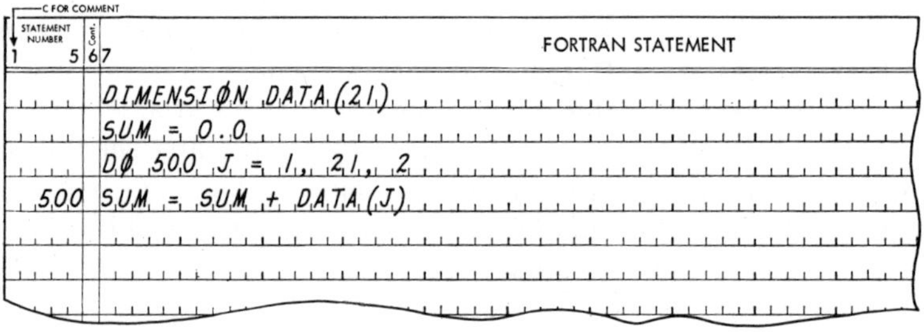

FIGURE 7.5   A program to form the sum of the odd-numbered elements of an array.

7.7   Further definitions

Before proceeding to more examples, we present a few definitions that will make it easier to talk about the DO statement.

The *range* of the DO statement is the set of repeatedly executed statements.   In short, it consists of the statements beginning with the one immediately following the DO and continuing up to and including the statement named in the DO.   The fixed point variable i in the general form of the DO statement is called its *index*.   Throughout the execution of the range i is available for any purpose permitted for a fixed point variable.   We have seen how it may be used as a subscript and shall see later how it can be applied in other ways.

There are two general methods by which control can transfer outside the range of a DO.   The *normal exit* occurs when the DO is *satisfied*, that is, at the completion of the number of executions of the range as specified by the *indexing parameters* m_1, m_2, and m_3.   When this happens, as we have seen, control passes to the statement following the one named in the DO.   The second method by which control can get outside the range of a DO is through a GO TO or IF statement. This can happen when it is desired to specify (in the DO parameters) the *maximum* number of executions of the range but to set up tests in the range to determine the *actual* number of executions.

When control is transferred outside the range of a DO *before* the DO is satisfied, the index i is available for any purpose permitted for a fixed point variable. This can be quite valuable. After the normal exit i is *not* available (at least not in most versions of FORTRAN). This is no serious inconvenience in practice. For instance, in a large majority of cases n_3 is omitted and is therefore taken to be 1; on the normal exit from such a loop the index has the value n_2.

```
C FOR COMMENT
STATEMENT NUMBER | Cont. | FORTRAN STATEMENT
1          5     | 6     | 7
      PRØD = 1.0
      DØ 6 I = 2, M
      AI = I
    6 PRØD = PRØD * AI
```

FIGURE 7.6 A program to form the product of the integers from 1 to M.

To examine another way in which the index of a DO may be used within the range, consider the following example. In a problem involving combinations we are required to form the product of all integers from 1 to M, where the value of M has been determined earlier in the program. By naming the variable M, we indicate, of course, that it is a *fixed point* variable; we wish, however, to obtain the product in a floating point form. In order to avoid the complications of possibly computing too large a fixed point number within the DO loop, we must convert each of the factors in the product from fixed point to floating point. The program of Figure 7.6 does all this and places the product in a location called PROD. We first set PROD equal to 1.0 and then go into the DO loop, asking for the range to be executed with I equal to all values from 2 to M. In order to use the index I in a floating point calculation, we execute the statement AI = I, which, as we recall from earlier rules, calls for the conversion of I to floating point form. The first time statement 6 is executed the effect is to multiply 1.0 by 2.0 (since PROD has been started at 1.0) and to store the product in PROD. The next time, this product is multiplied by 3.0 and the new product is stored back in PROD. The process continues until the two statements in the range have been executed with I equal to M.

Implicit in this program is the assumption that M is at least 2. If M could be 1, the DO statement would ask for the range to be executed with I equal to all values from 2 up to 1, which, of course, is impossible. What the DO statement would do in such a case cannot be stated in general. If M were equal to 2, the program would not get into trouble: the two statements in the range would be executed exactly once and control would then pass to the statement following 6.

This example shows that it is important to be sure that the range of a DO is executed exactly the right number of times. Experience reveals that it is all too easy to make mistakes on this point. A good way to check is to ask, "What would the parameters have to be if the range were to be executed only *once?*" Based on this, it is usually not too difficult to decide if the actual situation is properly handled.

The DO statement can often be used effectively to run through a set of values of an independent variable. In Case Study 3, for

```
C FOR COMMENT
STATEMENT
 NUMBER
1        5 6 7                      FORTRAN STATEMENT

         DO 61 I = 3,0, 29,1,0, 36,0,
         DEGREE = I
         X = DEGREE / 57..29,5,7,7,9,5,
         SUM = X
         TERM = X
         DENOM = 3..0
         XSQ = X * X
    25   TERM =-TERM * XSQ / (DENOM * (DENOM - 1..0))
         SUM = SUM + TERM
         IF (ABSF(TERM) - 1..E-8) 16, 16, 12
    12   DENOM = DENOM + 2..0
         GO 1 0 25
    16   TEST = SINF(X)
    61   PRINT 30, DEGREE, X, SUM, TEST
    30   FORMAT (F10..0, F15..8, F20..8, F15..8)
         STOP
         END
```

FIGURE 7.7   A revised version of the program of Figure 3.10, using a DO statement to run through values of the argument rather than reading them from cards.

instance, we computed the sine of a series of angles: 30°, 390°, 750°, etc., up to 2910°. It was indicated in Figure 3.10 that these angles were read from cards; the same arguments could have been generated more simply by a DO statement, as shown in Figure 7.7. The index of a DO statement must be a fixed point variable; we have used I. In the computation the angle must, of course, be a floating point variable, which was called DEGREE in Figure 3.10. Therefore, the first operation in the range of the DO is to set DEGREE equal to I; this will cause the value of the fixed point variable I to be converted to floating point. The body of the computation is as before. The end of the range is the PRINT statement that writes the results.

For a second example of this kind of use of the DO statement, consider the preliminary test programs that were described in Case Study 6. At one point we needed to run through the values 2.00 to 4.00, in steps of 0.01. This time we cannot use the value of the DO index directly, since it must be a fixed point (integer) variable and we need steps of 0.01. This problem is easily handled, however, by writing the following few steps before the body of the computation:

DO 73 I = 200, 400
X = I
X = X/100.0

The DO index will run through the values 200 to 400 in steps of 1. After conversion to floating point and division by 100.0, X will therefore run through the values 2.00 to 4.00 in steps of 0.01.

7.8   Rules governing the use of the DO statement

A great deal of flexibility is permitted in the use of the DO statement as long as certain rules are observed. We shall state all of these rules together and later illustrate the situations that some of them cover.

RULE 1.   The first statement in the range of a DO must be one that can be executed. This excludes the DIMENSION and FORMAT statements, since, rather than causing anything to happen in the object program, they simply provide information to the compiler. As we shall see later, several other statements are also nonexecutable.

RULE 2.   It is permissible for the range of one DO (which we may call the "outer" DO) to contain another DO (which we may call the "inner" DO). When this occurs, it is required that all statements in the range of the inner DO also be in the range of the outer DO. This does not prohibit the ranges of two or more DO's ending with the

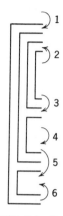

FIGURE 7.8 Examples of permissible nests of DO's and some correct and incorrect transfers of control. Transfers 2, 3, and 4 are acceptable; 1, 5, and 6 are not.

same statement, but it does prohibit a situation in which the range of an inner DO extends past the end of the range of an outer DO.

RULE 3. The last statement in the range of a DO must not be one that can cause a transfer of control. This excludes the GO TO, the IF, and the DO statements. These statements may be used freely anywhere else in the range. The CONTINUE statement described later is provided for situations that would otherwise violate this rule.

RULE 4. No statement within the range of a DO may redefine or otherwise alter any of the indexing parameters of that DO; that is, it is not permitted within the range of a DO to change the values of i, m_1, m_2, or m_3. As noted before, these numbers may still be used in any way that does not alter their values.

RULE 5. Control, with one exception, must not transfer into the range of a DO from any statement outside its range. Thus it is expressly prohibited to use a GO TO or an IF statement to transfer into the range of a DO without first executing the DO itself. This rule *does* prohibit a transfer from the range of an outer DO into the range of an inner DO, but it *does not* prohibit a transfer out of the range of an inner DO into the range of an outer DO. The latter is permissible from the standpoint of the outer DO because the transfer is executed entirely within its range. Some illustrations of this rule are provided in Figure 7.8. The brackets here represent the ranges of DO's and the arrows represent transfers of control. Transfers 2, 3, and 4 are acceptable, since 2 and 3 are transfers from the range of an inner DO to the range of an outer DO, and 4 is a transfer entirely within the range of a single DO. Transfers 1, 5, and 6 all represent transfers into the range of a DO from outside its range.

The one exception to the rule prohibiting transfers into the range of a DO from outside its range is this: it is permissible to transfer control completely outside the nest to which a DO belongs, to perform a series of calculations which make no changes in any of the indices or indexing parameters in the nest, and then transfer back to the range of the same DO from which transfer was originally made. The restriction on the exit and re-entry transfer locations may be stated another way: no DO, and no statement which is the last statement in the range of a DO, may lie between the exit and re-entry points.

CONTINUE is a dummy statement that causes no action when the object program is executed.   It merely satisfies the rule that the last statement in the range of a DO must not be one that can cause transfer of control.   It is also used to provide a statement to which an IF can transfer when the computations in the range of a DO have been completed.   This is necessary because a transfer within the range of a DO is not permitted to return to the DO itself, that is, not unless it is really intended to start the execution of the DO from the beginning again.   An example of the use of the CONTINUE statement appears in Figure 7.9.

7.9   Further examples of the use of the DO statement

Since the DO statement is so powerful and since it is so heavily used in most FORTRAN applications, we shall give some additional examples of its use.

For the use of these examples suppose that the input to a program consists of a series of experimentally measured values.   Each point in the experiment involves an X value and a Y value, corresponding to the abscissa and ordinate of a point on a graph.   The data points were gathered and entered into the computer in random order; that is, we know that the first X value goes with the first Y value and that the second X value goes with the second Y value, etc., but we cannot assume that the first X value is the smallest of all the X values.   For the purposes of calculations that are to be done later in the program, it is necessary to rearrange the data points in storage so that the first X value *is* the smallest and that the second X value is the next larger, and so on.   In other words, we must order the data points into ascending sequence on the X values.

We shall assume that the X values as they were originally read (i.e., in scrambled order) are the elements of an array named X and that there are 25 of them.   The Y values are the elements of another array called Y which also contains 25 values.

The FORTRAN program to rearrange these data points into ascending sequence on the X values involves a nest of two DO loops.   We shall show the development of the program, however, by displaying a simplified version of the inner loop before writing the entire program. This simplified loop will place the smallest X value in the first position of the X array.   This can be done by the following process.   First compare the first and second X values in the original array. If the first X is smaller than or equal to the second, leave them alone; if the first X is larger than the second, interchange these two values within the array. Having inspected the first and second elements and interchanged them if necessary, inspect the first and third elements and either leave them alone or interchange them if the first element is the larger. This "first" element now may very well be the one that was originally in second position, but this does not matter. Similarly, compare the first and fourth, first and fifth, etc., until the element in the first position has been compared with all others, interchanging at each step if necessary. This process guarantees that the smallest X will end up in the first position of the X array. Remembering that to each X there corresponds a Y, we naturally carry out the same interchange operations on the Y array as we have on the X array, but there will be no testing of the Y values.

In order to interchange two values from the array in storage, we follow a three-step process: (1) move the first value to a temporary storage location which we call TEMP; (2) move the second value to the location originally occupied by the first; (3) move the first value, which is now in TEMP, to the location originally occupied by the second.

A program to carry out all of this process is shown in Figure 7.9. We are assuming that the data values have been read in by an earlier part of the program, and we are not showing the statements that complete the rearrangement or use of the data values.

```
      DIMENSION X(25), Y(25)
      DO 12 J = 2, 25
      IF (X(1) - X(J)) 12, 12, 13
   13 TEMP = X(1)
      X(1) = X(J)
      X(J) = TEMP
      TEMP = Y(1)
      Y(1) = Y(J)
      Y(J) = TEMP
   12 CONTINUE
```

FIGURE 7.9   A program segment to place the smallest value of X in an array of X's in the first position of the array and to place the corresponding Y in the first position of an array of Y's.

This program illustrates a number of features worth noting.   We see another example of a DO loop in which the index does not start with 1.   We see an example of the use of the CONTINUE statement. This is required because if the IF statement shows that the first X value is already smaller than the other X value with which we are comparing it a transfer of control must be made to skip around the six statements that interchange the X and Y values.   What we want to do in this case is simply repeat the whole process with the index J increased by 1.   As we have already noted, however, it is not possible to transfer control back to the DO.   This would result in starting the DO loop again with J equal to 2—which is not what we want.   Therefore, we transfer control to CONTINUE, which has been identified in the DO statement as the end of the range.

In reading this program, it is well to recall the meaning of an arithmetic statement: the value of the variable on the left side of the equal sign is replaced by the value of the expression on the right.   Thus a statement such as

$$X(1) = X(J)$$

means that the number identified by the variable name $X(J)$ is to be moved to the location for the number identified by the name $X(1)$. The value in the location $X(J)$ is unchanged.

In the problem as stated there may or may not be two equal X values.   As the program has been written, however, it does not matter; if they are equal, then there is no point in exchanging them, and we simply transfer control down to CONTINUE and go around the loop again.

When this loop has been finished (when the DO has been "satisfied"), we are guaranteed that the data points have been rearranged so that the smallest X is in the first position in the X array and that the Y corresponding to the smallest X is in the first position in the Y array. What we would like to do next is to get the next larger X in the second position of the array.   This can be done by comparing the second element with the third, and all following, and interchanging whenever necessary.   After that we would like to get the next larger element in the third position.   We would similarly arrange to get the next larger X values in the fourth and then the fifth position, etc., until finally all of the X's would have been placed in the X array in order of increasing size.

It appears then that what we need to do for the complete program is to make variables of all subscripts that appear as 1's.   The subscript will then select the element to be compared with all following

```
┌─C FOR COMMENT
│STATEMENT│ │
│ NUMBER  │§│
│1      5 │6│7                        FORTRAN STATEMENT
├─────────┼─┼──────────────────────────────────────────────────────
│         │ │ DIMENSION X(25), Y(25)
│         │ │ DO 12 I = 1,24
│         │ │ IP1 = I + 1
│         │ │ DO 12 J = IP1,25
│         │ │ IF(X(I) - X(J)) 12, 12, 13
│      13 │ │ TEMP = X(I)
│         │ │ X(I) = X(J)
│         │ │ X(J) = TEMP
│         │ │ TEMP = Y(I)
│         │ │ Y(I) = Y(J)
│         │ │ Y(J) = TEMP
│      12 │ │ CONTINUE
│         │ │
```

FIGURE 7.10   A program segment to rearrange a set of X-Y data points into ascending sequence on the X values.

elements (interchanging if necessary). This subscript, which we shall call I, will start at 1 and run through 24. The subscript which appears as J in the present program will still appear as J, but it will have to start at one more than whatever the I subscript is and run to 25. All of this is easily done by another DO statement that controls the I subscript. This is the outer DO. There is one complication, however. The inner DO must specify that the J subscript will start at one more than whatever I is. Looking back at the definition of the DO statement, we see that each indexing parameter must either be a fixed point constant or a single fixed point variable. It is *not* permissible to write a statement such as

$$DO\ 12\ J = I + 1, 25$$

To avoid this restriction, we simply insert a statement that computes the value of a variable IP1, which is always one more than whatever I is. The complete program to sort the data points is shown in Figure 7.10.

This technique is often referred to as *bubble sorting*. It is by no means the most efficient sorting method known; it is presented only as an application of the DO statement.

In order to illustrate a slightly different type of DO loop, let us now make some further assumptions about the purpose of the program just written. Suppose that the data points which have been read in and by now arranged into ascending sequence lie on a curve and that we are required to find the area under this curve; that is, to find the definite integral of the curve represented approximately by these points. If we now make the further assumption that the distance between successive X points is equal to a constant value H, then the approximate integral given by the trapezoidal rule is, as we know from Chapter 6,

$$\text{AREA} = \frac{H}{2}\,(y_1 + 2y_2 + 2y_3 + \cdots + 2y_{23} + 2y_{24} + y_{25})$$

A DO loop may conveniently be used to form the sum of the Y values with subscripts of 2 through 24. Having done so, we can multiply this sum by 2, add the first and last Y values, and multiply by H/2. This program, shown in Figure 7.11, would follow the CONTINUE statement of the program shown in Figure 7.10. It includes the computation of H on the assumption that it is the interval between any two X values. If, in fact, the X values are not equally spaced, then the program naturally gives an incorrect result. If it were required that the program be able to handle unequally spaced X values, the numerical integration method would have to be modified.

Simpson's rule, with the subscripting scheme we are using, is:

$$\text{AREA} = \frac{H}{3}\,(y_1 + 4y_2 + 2y_3 + 4y_4 + 2y_5 + \cdots$$
$$+ 2y_{23} + 4y_{24} + y_{25})$$

A program to evaluate this formula will be a little more complex because of the alternating coefficients of 2 and 4. One fairly obvious way to handle the problem is to set up two DO loops and to accumulate separately the sums of the Y values corresponding to the two coefficients. See Figure 7.12.

```
┌─── C FOR COMMENT
│ STATEMENT  │
│ NUMBER   │ │
│ 1      5 │6│7                        FORTRAN STATEMENT
   SUM = 0.0
   DO 20 I = 2,24
20 SUM = SUM + Y(I)
   AREA = (X(2)-X(1))/2.*(Y(1)+2.*SUM+Y(25))
```

FIGURE 7.11   A program segment for integration by the trapezoidal rule.

```
         C FOR COMMENT
STATEMENT  |
NUMBER     |                    FORTRAN STATEMENT
1      5 6 7

        ØDD  =  0.0
        EVEN  =  0.0
        DØ  47  I  =  2,24,2
  47    EVEN  =  EVEN  +  Y(I)
        DØ  48  I  =  3,23,2
  48    ØDD  =  ØDD  +  Y(I)
        AREA  =  (X(2)  -  X(1))/3.*(Y(1)  +  4.*EVEN  +  2.*ØDD  +  Y(25))
```

FIGURE 7.12   One version of a program segment for integration by Simpson's rule.

The computation may be done with only one DO loop, which saves a little time in the running of the object program, if we proceed as follows. Suppose we set up an index that runs from 1 to 11. Two times that index will always be the subscript of a Y value that should be multiplied by 4, and two times that index plus 1 will always be the subscript of a Y value that should be multiplied by 2.   See Figure 7.13.

Flexibility in the manner of writing subscripts is very useful here. It is not possible to form the sum of the Y values with one DO loop unless some such subscripting arrangement is used.

It may be noted that we have written these integration formulas with the subscripts starting with 1, whereas it is conventional to write them with the subscripts starting at 0.   This was done to make it easier to describe the problem, since we recall that a subscript must be positive and nonzero.

It is possible to program formulas that have zero and negative subscripts, but it is somewhat more effort than it is worth to us at this

```
         C FOR COMMENT
STATEMENT  |
NUMBER     |                    FORTRAN STATEMENT
1      5 6 7

        ØDD  =  0.0
        EVEN  =  0.0
        DØ  51  I  =  1,11
        EVEN  =  EVEN  +  Y(2*I)
  51    ØDD  =  ØDD  +  Y(2*I  +  1)
        AREA  =  (X(2)  -  X(1))/3.*(Y(1)  +  4.*(EVEN  +  Y(24))
       1         +  2.*ØDD  +  Y(25))
```

FIGURE 7.13   Another version of a program segment for integration by Simpson's rule.

point.   (It may be noted that some FORTRAN systems, or languages similar to FORTRAN, do permit zero and negative subscripts.)

7.10   Case study 9: Linear interpolation

To illustrate the use of subscripted variables and the DO statement in a practical application, we shall consider linear interpolation in an array of data.   Such a computation would ordinarily be a part of a larger program; here we shall read the X and Y values, then read a series of X values for which corresponding Y values should be found by interpolation.

We assume that the X and Y values of a curve are punched in a deck of cards, each card containing one X and one Y value.   The deck is assumed to be in ascending sequence on the X values, and there may be no more than 200 of them.   We do not assume that the X values are equally spaced.   The X and Y values are taken to be punched in 10 columns each, in a form suitable for reading with F10.0 field specifications.   The last card of this part of the deck will contain a nonzero punch in column 21.

Let us look into the program statements needed to do this much of the job, as shown in Figure 7.14.   The DIMENSION statement says that 200 locations each are set aside for the subscripted variables named X and Y.   The DO statement is used this time simply to get values for the subscript I that will store the entries in the two arrays. There are to be no more than 200 entries in these tables; the DO statement is set up to run from 1 to 201, with the expectation that the DO will never be satisfied by exhaustion of the index.   If the DO *is* satisfied, it means that too many data cards were entered, and we reach a STOP.*   This form of the STOP, with a number following, will cause the number to be printed if the STOP is ever executed.   We need this identification because there will be another error stop and also a normal stop; it is necessary to know *why* the program stops, whether through error or because it is finished.

It is assumed that column 21 will be blank on all cards except the last.   A blank column in a data card is taken by FORTRAN to be

---

* As noted briefly in Section 1.11, FORTRAN for large computers is often run under the control of a *monitor system*, in which case the use of a STOP statement is at least unwise, if not actually prohibited.   Special routines are available in the monitor to provide the information the programmer needs (where his program went awry and why), yet allow the computer to continue on to another program. The proper procedure is a function of the monitor system being used; we cannot give details because monitors differ considerably.

```
C FOR COMMENT
STATEMENT NUMBER                                    FORTRAN STATEMENT
1        5 6 7
         DIMENSION X(200), Y(200)
         DO 63 I = 1, 201
         READ 57, X(I), Y(I), K
    57   FORMAT (2F10.0, I1)
         IF (K) 43, 63, 43
    63   CONTINUE
         STOP 1234
    43   READ 70, XE, L
    70   FORMAT (F10.0, I1)
         DO 110 J = 1, I
         IF (XE - X(J)) 112, 111, 110
   110   CONTINUE
         STOP 2345
   111   YE = Y(J)
         GO TO 200
   112   YE = Y(J-1) + (Y(J)-Y(J-1))/(X(J)-X(J-1))*(XE-X(J-1))
   200   PRINT 201, XE, YE
   201   FORMAT (2E15.8)
         IF(L) 202, 43, 202
   202   STOP
         END
```

FIGURE 7.14   A program for linear interpolation.   (Case Study 9.)

a zero, so that the IF statement after statement 57 will lead to the CONTINUE on all cards before the last. In other words, we keep going around the DO loop until the last card is detected, increasing the value of I by 1 each time. The X-Y pairs are thus stored in successive locations in the two arrays. When the last card is detected, with its nonzero punch in column 21, the IF statement will transfer down to statement 43, where the processing of the data begins.

Now we have in storage the pairs of X and Y values, representing a series of straight lines, as indicated in Figure 7.15. The deck of cards continues, with a series of cards containing X values only, in columns 1 to 10. We are to read a card, interpolate in the table to find the corresponding Y value, print X and Y, and go back to read another card, etc., until the last data card, which will contain a nonzero punch in column 11, is processed.

When we read an X card, we first search through the X array to find either an element that is the same or two elements that "bracket" it. This can be done by starting at the beginning of the X array and testing the experimental value, named XE in the program, to see if it is

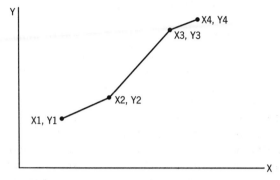

FIGURE 7.15 Schematic representation of the meaning of the X-Y pairs in linear interpolation. (Case Study 9.)

less than the succeeding elements in the X array. (Remember that we assume that the X-Y pairs are in ascending sequence on the X values.) All this is done with another DO statement, this time using the index J running from 2 up to I, the number of entries in the tables. If XE is less than or equal to the second table entry, we will immediately get out of the range of the DO, with J equal to 2. If not, J is increased to 3 and the test made again; if XE is less than or equal to the third table entry, we get out of the range of the DO with J equal to 3. This process is continued until we find that XE is less than or equal to some table entry. When this happens the value of J identifies which table entry it was. The situation is diagrammed in Figure 7.16. Only if XE, through error, should be greater than the

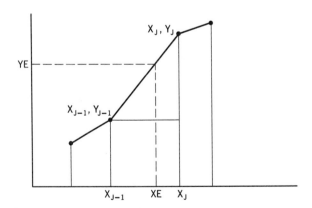

FIGURE 7.16 The geometrical basis of the method of linear interpolation, once XE has been found to exceed some entry X_J in the X table.

last table entry will the DO be satisfied, which again leads to an error STOP.

Having found that XE is greater than or equal to some table entry, we are ready to proceed with the interpolation. If XE should be equal to some entry, the problem is simple: the "interpolated" value of Y is just the corresponding value from the Y table, which we get by writing Y(J). If, as is much more common, XE is bracketed by two X table entries, we know that they are X(J − 1) and X(J) and that the corresponding values of Y are Y(J − 1) and Y(J). From simple geometry we find that the value of YE corresponding to XE is as written in statement 112. Whichever way YE was found, we now print XE and YE. An IF statement checks what was punched in column 11, returning to read another card if it was blank and stopping if it was punched with any nonzero digit.

There are, of course, interpolation schemes of higher order than the linear one described here. They amount to passing second, third, or higher degree polynomials through three, four, or more consecutive points and using the polynomial to evaluate y for any x between the points. A discussion of these techniques may be found in most texts on classical numerical analysis. Exercises 9 and 10 indicate two such methods.

Exercises

Include an appropriate DIMENSION statement in each program segment for these exercises.

*1. Suppose that the coordinates of a point in space are given by the three elements of a one-dimensional array named X. (Note the different usages of the word dimension: the elements of a one-dimensional array are being used as the coordinates of a point in three-dimensional space!) Write a statement to compute the distance of the point from the origin, which is given by the square root of the sum of the squares of the coordinates.

2. If the coordinates of a point in space are X_1, X_2, and X_3, the direction cosines of the line from the origin to the point are given by

$$CA = \frac{X_1}{\sqrt{X_1{}^2 + X_2{}^2 + X_3{}^2}}$$

$$CB = \frac{X_2}{\sqrt{X_1{}^2 + X_2{}^2 + X_3{}^2}}$$

$$CC = \frac{X_3}{\sqrt{X_1{}^2 + X_2{}^2 + X_3{}^2}}$$

Write statements to compute these three numbers, assuming that the coordinates are the elements of a one-dimensional array named X.

*3. Given two arrays named A and B, both two-dimensional, write statements to compute the elements of another two-dimensional array named C from the following equations. The maximum value of all subscripts is 2.

$$c_{11} = a_{11}b_{11} + a_{12}b_{21}$$

$$c_{12} = a_{11}b_{12} + a_{12}b_{22}$$

$$c_{21} = a_{21}b_{11} + a_{22}b_{21}$$

$$c_{22} = a_{21}b_{12} + a_{22}b_{22}$$

Readers familiar with matrix notation will recognize the multiplication of two 2×2 matrices.

4. Given a two-dimensional array named R, the elements of which are to be viewed as the elements of a 3×3 determinant, write a statement to compute the value of the determinant by any method you know. The determinant should be named DET.

*5. Two one-dimensional arrays named A and B each contain 30 elements. Compute

$$D = \left(\sum_{i=1}^{30} (A_i - B_i)^2 \right)^{\frac{1}{2}}$$

(A distance function in 30-space.)   Write a program segment with or without the DO statement.

*6. If we have a list of tabular values, represented, for instance, by a one-dimensional array, then the *first differences* of the list are formed by subtracting each element except the last from the element immediately following it. Suppose we have a one-dimensional array named X that contains 50 elements. Compute the 49 elements of another array named DX from

$$DX(I) = X(I + 1) - X(I), \qquad I = 1, 2, \ldots, 49$$

Write a program segment, with or without a DO statement.

7. Suppose we have a one-dimensional array named Y that contains 32 elements; these are to regarded as the 32 ordinates of an experimental curve at equally spaced abscissas. Assuming that a value has been given to H, compute the integral of the curve represented approximately by the Y values from

$$TRAP = \frac{H}{2} (Y_1 + 2Y_2 + \cdots + 2Y_{31} + Y_{32})$$

Write a program segment with or without a DO statement.

8. A two-dimensional array named AMATR contains 10 rows and 10 columns. A one-dimensional array named DIAG contains 10 elements. Compute the elements of DIAG from the formula

$$DIAG(I) = AMATR(I, I), \qquad I = 1, 2, \ldots, 10$$

Write a program segment with or without the DO statement.

*9. Given a one-dimensional array named Y, with 50 elements, and numbers U and I, write a statement to compute the value of S from the following equation, written in ordinary mathematical subscript notation:

$$S = y_i + u \frac{y_{i+1} - y_{i-1}}{2} + \frac{u^2}{2} (y_{i+1} - 2y_i + y_{i-1})$$

This is called *Stirling's interpolation formula* (through second differences), which may be described as follows: we have three points of a curve: (x_{i-1}, y_{i-1}), (x_i, y_i), and (x_{i+1}, y_{i+1}), such that $x_{i+1} - x_i = x_i - x_{i-1} = h$, and a value of x. We write $u = (x - x_i)/h$. Then the formula stated gives the interpolated value of y corresponding to x, found by passing a quadratic through the three ordinates.

10. Using the assumptions of Exercise 9, write a statement to compute the value of T from the following equation:

$$T = y_i + u(y_{i+1} - y_i) + \frac{u(u - 1)(y_{i+2} - y_{i+1} - y_i - y_{i-1})}{4}$$

$$+ \frac{(u - \frac{1}{2}) u(u - 1)(y_{i+2} - 3y_{i+1} + 3y_i - y_{i-1})}{6}$$

This is called *Bessel's interpolation formula* (through third differences). With the notation used in Exercise 9, this formula finds a value of y corresponding to x, by passing a cubic through the ordinates. The arrangement of the differences is somewhat different from that in Stirling's formula.

*11. Given two one-dimensional arrays named A and B of seven elements each, suppose that the seven elements of the A array are punched on one card and the seven elements of B are punched on another card. Each element is punched in 10 columns suitable for reading with an F10.0 field specification. Write a program to read the cards, then compute and print the value of ANORM from

$$ANORM = \sqrt{\sum_{i=1}^{7} a_i b_i}$$

Use an E20.8 field specification for ANORM.

A *norm* may be thought of as a generalization of the concept of distance.

12. Using the assumptions in Exercise 11, write a program to read the data cards and then carry out the following procedure. If every $a_i > b_i$,

for $i = 1, 2, \ldots, 7$, then print a fixed point 1; if this condition is not satisfied, print a zero.

Note.   Use DO statements in all following exercises.

*13. A one-dimensional fixed point array named M contains 20 elements. Write a program segment to replace each element by itself, multiplied by its element number.   In other words, replace m_i by $i \cdot m_i$, $i = 1, 2, \ldots, 20$.

*14. Two one-dimensional arrays named R and S have a *maximum* of 40 elements each.   The *actual* number of elements is given by the value of a previously computed fixed point variable M.   Compute the first M elements of an array named T, which also has a maximum of 40 elements, according to

$$T(i) = R(i) + S(i), \qquad i = 1, 2, \ldots, M$$

15. Two one-dimensional arrays, A and B, have a maximum of 18 elements each.   N is a fixed point number, the value of which does not exceed 18. Compute

$$C = \sum_{k=1}^{N} A_k B_k$$

*16. A one-dimensional array named F contains at most 50 elements.   Each of the first M elements, except the first and Mth, is to be replaced by

$$F_i = \frac{F_{i-1} + F_i + F_{i+1}}{3}$$

This is an example of techniques for *smoothing* experimental data to reduce the effect of random errors.

*17. A one-dimensional array named B contains 50 elements.   Place the largest of these elements in BIGB and place the element number of BIGB in NBIGB.

18. Two one-dimensional arrays named X and Y contain 50 elements each. A variable named XS is known to be equal to one of the elements in X. If $XS = X_i$, place Y_i in YS.

This kind of *table search* has a wide variety of applications, such as finding a value in a table of electric utility rates from a rate code or finding the numerical code corresponding to an alphabetic name.

19. Same as Exercise 18, except that it is not known whether XS is equal to any of the elements of X.   *If* XS is equal to some X_i, place Y_i in YS; if XS is not equal to any X_i, place a zero in YS.

*20. A two-dimensional array A contains 15 rows and 15 columns.   A one-dimensional array X contains 15 elements.   Compute the 15 elements of a one-dimensional array B according to

$$B_i = \sum_{j=1}^{15} A_{ij} X_j, \qquad i = 1, 2, \ldots, 15$$

This is multiplication of a matrix and a vector.

21. Three two-dimensional arrays A, B, and C have 15 rows and 15 columns each.   Given the arrays A and B, compute the elements of C from

$$C_{ij} = \sum_{k=1}^{15} A_{ik}B_{kj}, \quad i, j = 1, 2, \ldots , 15$$

This is matrix multiplication.

*22. A two-dimensional array RST has 20 rows and 20 columns.   Compute the product of the main diagonal elements of RST and store it in DPROD.   A main diagonal element is one that has the same row and column number, so that

$$\text{DPROD} = \prod_{I=1}^{20} \text{RST(I, I)}$$

*23. The formula

$$Y = 41.926 \sqrt{1 + X^2} + X^{1/3}e^X$$

is to be evaluated for

$$X = 1.00, 1.01, 1.02, \ldots , 3.00$$

Each X, Y pair is to be printed on a line, with E20.8 field specifications. Write a program using a DO loop to do this.

24. The formula

$$Z = \frac{e^{A \cdot X} - e^{-A \cdot X}}{2} \sin (X + B) + A \log \frac{B + X}{2}$$

is to be evaluated for all combinations of

$$X: 1.0(0.1)2.0$$
$$A: 0.10(0.05)0.80$$
$$B: 1.0(1.0)10.0$$

where X: 1.00(0.1)2.00 means X = 1.0, 1.1, 1.2, . . . , 2.0, etc.   For each combination of X, A, and B (there are 1650 combinations) a line giving X, A, B, and Z is to be written, with E20.8 field specifications. Write a program containing three DO loops to do this.

25. A solution to the following specialized system of equations is to be found

$$A_{11}X_1 \qquad\qquad\qquad\qquad = B_1$$

$$A_{21}X_1 + A_{22}X_2 \qquad\qquad\qquad = B_2$$

$$A_{31}X_1 + A_{32}X_2 + A_{33}X_3 \qquad\quad = B_3$$

$$\cdots\cdots\cdots\cdots\cdots\cdots\cdots\cdots\cdots$$

$$A_{n1}X_1 + A_{n2}X_2 + A_{n3}X_3 + \cdots + A_{nn}X_n = B_n$$

Such a system is easily solved, of course, by solving for X_1, substituting into equation 2, and so on.   The difficulty, from the standpoint of computer solution, is that if a two-dimensional array is set up for the coefficients, nearly half the storage locations will be empty—which uselessly restricts the size of the system that can be solved. Devise a method of storing the coefficients in a *one*-dimensional array and write a program to find the unknowns. Assume that it must be possible to handle a maximum of 30 equations in 30 unknowns and include the necessary DIMENSION statement in the program. The actual number of equations is given by the value of N.

26. Same as Exercise 25, but now the system of equations is

$$A_{1,1}X_1 + \cdots + A_{1,n-2}X_{n-2} + A_{1,n-1}X_{n-1} + A_{1n}X_n + A_{1,n+1}$$
$$\cdots\cdots\cdots\cdots\cdots\cdots\cdots\cdots\cdots\cdots\cdots\cdots\cdots\cdots\cdots\cdots$$
$$A_{n-2,n-2}X_{n-2} + A_{n-2,n-1}X_{n-1} + A_{n-2,n}X_n = A_{n-2,n+1}$$
$$A_{n-1,n-1}X_{n-1} + A_{n-1,n}X_n = A_{n-1,n+1}$$
$$A_{n,n}X_n = A_{n,n+1}$$

Note that it is *not* permissible to write a statement like DO 12 I = N, 1, -1, which would be handy here. An equivalent "IF loop" must be written to work backward through the X's. Alternatively, we may write

    DO 12 II = 1, N
    I = N − II + 1

I is then used as the subscript; it will vary from N downward to 1.

This technique is used in Chapter 8 and especially in Case Study 10.

*27. A fixed point index and a DO statement can be used quite conveniently to avoid the question whether rounding errors in adding h to x repeatedly will cause an integration routine to stop at the wrong point. Write a program segment to evaluate

$$I = \int_{1.0}^{5.0} \sqrt{1 + x^2}\, e^{-x}\, dx$$

Use the trapezoidal rule with $h = 0.2$.

28. Same as Exercise 27, but use Simpson's rule.

29. Write a program to do the calculation in Exercise 31, Chapter 6. Arrange the program to read a deck in which each card contains an x value and a y value, with a sentinel at the end in which $x = 999999$. It is necessary, of course, to use the trapezoidal rule separately for each interval, computing h for each. (Actually, the trapezoidal rule *could* be applied to groups of intervals having the same h, but it is not worth the effort.)

30. Given a two-dimensional array named C, with 10 rows and 11 columns, compare C(1, 1) with all other elements in the first column, looking for the element with the largest absolute value; make the value of L equal to the row number of the element in column 1 having the largest absolute value. If at the end of these operations, L = 1, do nothing more:

otherwise exchange the elements in row 1 with the elements in row L, whatever it is.

*31. Rewrite the program of Figure 5.12, using subscripting and a DO loop. Assume that the polynomial coefficients are contained in a one-dimensional array named A.

A(1)	A_4
A(2)	A_3
A(3)	A_2
A(4)	A_1
A(5)	A_0

32. Same as Exercise 31, except that the elements in the array are arranged as follows

A(1)	A_0
A(2)	A_1
A(3)	A_2
A(4)	A_3
A(5)	A_4

(Recall that zero subscripts are not permitted.)   See the suggestion at the end of Exercise 26.

33. Write a generalized program using the Newton-Raphson method to find a root of a polynomial equation, given only a deck of input data constructed as follows: card 1 contains in columns 1–2 a fixed point number giving N, the degree of the polynomial. Columns 3–12 of card 1 contains a value of x_0, the starting approximation for the Newton-Raphson method. All following cards contain in columns 1-10 one coefficient; card 2 contains A_0, card 3 contains A_1, etc. There are $N + 1$ coefficient cards, which must be counted in the program since there is no sentinel card. The coefficients may be placed in an array in either of the arrangements suggested in the preceding exercises by appropriate subscripting in reading the data. Do whichever you prefer.

*34. Many FORTRAN systems permit alphabetic variables, making possible a routine to plot points on an x-y graph.

Imagine the y-axis running across the page, and the x-axis up and down, as the points are printed; the completed plot can, of course, be turned for normal viewing. Let us suppose that there are 41 possible printing positions in the y-direction; these are spaced 10 to the inch on most printers. The distance along the x-direction is limited only by the amount of paper one chooses to use; the spacing is ordinarily six to the inch.

Let us set up an array of 41 elements named GRAPH. For each line of the graph we will print all 41 elements, after placing in any element the character that we wish to print. If, for instance, we want an X in the second element, we write

$$\text{GRAPH(2)} = 1\text{HX}$$

The 1H calls for one character, and X is the one we wanted in this case. The field specification for printing should be 41A1, calling for all 41 elements to be printed with one alphabetic character.

For a concrete example we may plot a sine function. Write a program to plot the value of sine x for x values from zero to 7.0 in steps of 0.2. After getting the value of the sine, you will need to compute the number of the element of GRAPH that is to receive an X, taking into account that the range from -1 to $+1$ must be transformed into the range from 1 to 41. After printing a line, the X should be cleared out by replacing it with a blank.

35. The accompanying illustration shows a plot of the type described in Exercise 34 (although the scale is slightly different), with the x- and y-axes printed as rows of periods. Write a program to produce such a plot, together with lines of dots for $y = 1$ and $y = -1$ and some kind of indication of the unit positions along the x-axis.

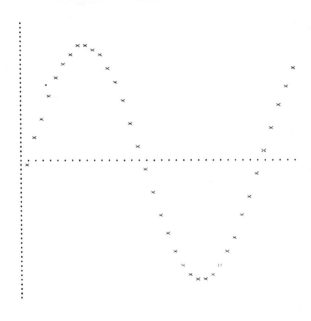

—8

Simultaneous Linear Algebraic Equations

8.1 Introduction

Simultaneous equations occur in nearly every branch of applied mathematics. In some cases they come about directly from the initial formulation of a problem; in many others the solution of a system of equations is a part of the attack on some other type of problem. We shall see in Case Study 10, for instance, that finding the curve that best approximates a set of experimental data involves solving a system of simultaneous equations, and we shall see in Chapter 11 that the solution of partial differential equations is often approached by methods that require solving simultaneous equations. There are many other applications.

Specifically, we shall consider in this chapter the solution of a set of n equations in n unknowns. Each term in each equation contains only one unknown, and each unknown appears to the first power. Such an equation is said to be *linear*. In the case of two unknowns the graph of such an equation is a straight line; for three unknowns it is a plane, and for more than three unknowns it is a hyperplane. The solution we seek is a set of values for the n unknowns, which, when substituted into the n equations, satisfy all of them simultaneously.

Given an arbitrary set of equations, we cannot say without investigation that there *is* a solution or, if there is one, that it is unique. There are three and only three possibilities.

1. The system has a unique solution. For example,

(8.1)
$$\begin{cases} 2x + y = 4 \\ x - y = -1 \end{cases}$$

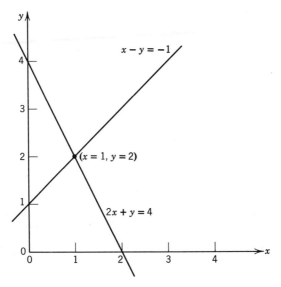

FIGURE 8.1   Geometrical representation of a system of two simultaneous equations having a unique solution; the lines are distinct and intersect.

The solution is $x = 1$ and $y = 2$; no other pair of values of x and y satisfies both equations. This type of system, which will, of course, be our primary concern, is represented geometrically in the two-dimensional case in Figure 8.1, in which we see that the two lines intersect at just one point. The coordinates of this point are the solution we seek.

2. The system has no solution. For example,

$$(8.2) \qquad \begin{cases} 4x + 6y = 10 \\ 2x + 3y = 6 \end{cases}$$

Figure 8.2 shows the graphs of these two lines. They are parallel; since they never meet, there is no solution.

3. The system has an infinite number of solutions. For example,

$$4x + 6y = 12$$

$$2x + 3y = 6$$

These are actually alternative forms of the equation of the same straight line, as we see in Figure 8.3. Any point on the line is a solution, such as $x = 0$, $y = 2$; $x = 1$, $y = \frac{4}{3}$; or $x = 3$, $y = 0$, etc.

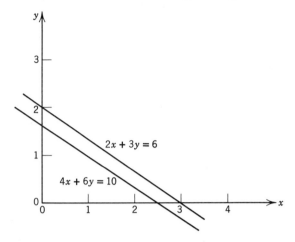

FIGURE 8.2 Geometrical representation of a system of two simultaneous equations having no solution; the lines are parallel.

A system of type 2 or 3 is said to be *singular*. Sometimes we know from the formulation of a problem that the system cannot be singular. If this information is lacking, as it usually is, we must either depend on the method of solution to signal singularity or make an explicit test for the possibility. We shall see in Section 8.2 that the Gauss elimination method does give immediate information about singularity.

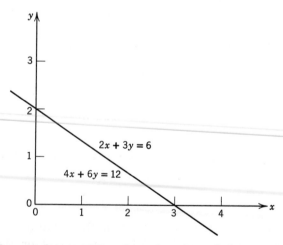

FIGURE 8.3 Geometrical representation of a system of two simultaneous equations having infinitely many solutions; the lines are identical.

A direct test is to compute the determinant of the system of coefficients; a zero value indicates singularity. Unfortunately, evaluating the determinant is almost as much work as solving the system.

From the standpoint of infinite precision arithmetic, a system is either singular or it is not. From the standpoint of practical computation, a system can be *almost* singular, leading to a "solution" that has little reliability. Consider the equations

$$(8.3) \qquad \begin{cases} 5x + 7y = 12 \\ 7x + 10y = 17 \end{cases}$$

These have the unique solution $x = 1$, $y = 1$; but consider the pair of values $x = 2.415$, $y = 0$. Then

$$(8.4) \qquad \begin{aligned} 5x + 7y &= 12.075 \\ 7x + 10y &= 16.905 \end{aligned}$$

When rounded to two digits, these right-hand sides agree with the right-hand sides of the original equations. Since the original values were given to only two figures, the solution (8.4) must be accepted as being as good as the "unique" one.

The problem is that the two lines are *nearly* parallel, as shown in Figure 8.4. The point given by (8.4), although it does not lie on either line, is very close to both.

Equations such as (8.3) are called *ill-conditioned*. Whenever two lines (or planes or hyperplanes) are almost parallel, the equations will be ill-conditioned. It is then difficult to find a numerical solution, and, as we have just seen, it will be of doubtful accuracy. Unfortunately, in three or more dimensions there are ways that a system of equations can be singular or nearly singular without any planes being parallel or nearly parallel.* Regardless of what the geometrical "mechanism" is, however, the Gauss elimination method or an explicit test will detect it.

Before delving into the details of the methods of solution, we may preview briefly the main avenues of approach.

In general, there are two types of numerical techniques for solving simultaneous equations: *direct*, which are finite (Section 8.2), and

---

* Visualize three parallel lines passing through the corners of a triangle and perpendicular to the plane of the triangle. Now pass a plane through each pair of lines: the three planes are not parallel, but they meet nowhere at one point. Now if one of the planes is tilted slightly, they will meet in a point, but the system of equations representing the planes is ill-conditioned.

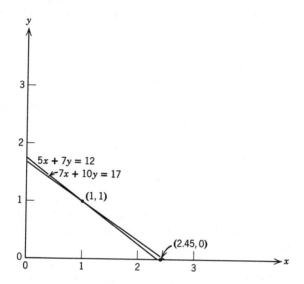

FIGURE 8.4   Geometrical representation of a system of two simultaneous equations that is almost singular; the lines are almost identical.

indirect methods, which are infinite (Section 8.6). Naturally, no practical technique can actually be infinite. What we mean is that the direct methods will in principle (neglecting roundoff errors, that is) produce an exact solution, if there is one, in a finite number of arithmetic operations. An indirect method, on the other hand, would in principle require an infinite number of arithmetic operations to produce an exact solution. Stated otherwise, an indirect method has a truncation error, whereas a direct method has not.

The "in principle" in the last paragraph is crucial, however: there *are* roundoff errors. We shall have to consider this question most carefully. In a large ill-conditioned system the roundoff errors in a direct method may make the "solution" meaningless. Despite its theoretical truncation error, an indirect method may be much more desirable because in such a method the roundoff errors do not accumulate.

After studying the most common examples of both methods and

their errors, we shall briefly compare them.   We shall see that both are useful; both have advantages and limitations.

8.2   Gauss elimination

We now turn to one of the oldest and most widely used finite techniques for the solution of simultaneous linear equations.   It is generally referred to as the method of *Gauss elimination*.

To illustrate the method, we shall first consider the case of three equations in three unknowns.

$$(8.5) \qquad a_{11}x_1 + a_{12}x_2 + a_{13}x_3 = b_1$$

$$(8.6) \qquad a_{21}x_1 + a_{22}x_2 + a_{23}x_3 = b_2$$

$$(8.7) \qquad a_{31}x_1 + a_{32}x_2 + a_{33}x_3 = b_3$$

Now at least one of a_{11}, a_{21}, and a_{31} is not zero; otherwise only two unknowns would appear in the three equations.   If a_{11} is zero, we reorder the equations so that the coefficient of x_1 in the first equation is not zero.   Interchanging two rows in the system of equations, of course, leaves the system essentially unchanged; that is, it still has the same solution.

Next define a multiplier

$$m_2 = \frac{a_{21}}{a_{11}}$$

We multiply the first equation (8.5) by m_2 and subtract from the second equation (8.6).   ("First" and "second" refer to the equations *as reordered*, if necessary.)   The result is

$$(8.8) \quad (a_{21} - m_2 a_{11})x_1 + (a_{22} - m_2 a_{12})x_2 + (a_{23} - m_2 a_{13})x_3 \\ = b_2 - m_2 b_1$$

But

$$a_{21} - m_2 a_{11} = a_{21} - \frac{a_{21}}{a_{11}} a_{11} = 0$$

so x_1 has been *eliminated* from the second equation.   (This result is, of course, the reason for the choice of m_2.)   If we now define

$$a_{22}' = a_{22} - m_2 a_{12}$$

$$a_{23}' = a_{23} - m_2 a_{13}$$

$$b_2' = b_2 - m_2 b_1$$

then (8.8) becomes

$$(8.9) \qquad a_{22}'x_2 + a_{23}'x_3 = b_2'$$

We replace the second of the original equations (8.6) by (8.9). Similarly, we define a multiplier for the third equation:

$$m_3 = \frac{a_{31}}{a_{11}}$$

We multiply the first equation by this multiplier and subtract from the third. Again the coefficient of x_1 vanishes and the result is

(8.10) $$a_{32}'x_2 + a_{33}'x_3 = b_3'$$

where

$$a_{32}' = a_{32} - m_3 a_{12}$$

$$a_{33}' = a_{33} - m_3 a_{13}$$

$$b_3' = b_3 - m_3 b_1$$

If we now use (8.10) to replace (8.7), the resulting three equations in three unknowns are

(8.5) $$a_{11}x_1 + a_{12}x_2 + a_{13}x_3 = b_1$$

(8.9) $$a_{22}'x_2 + a_{23}'x_3 = b_2'$$

(8.10) $$a_{32}'x_2 + a_{33}'x_3 = b_3'$$

These are completely equivalent to the original equations, with the added advantage that x_1 appears only in the first of them. The last two are two equations in two unknowns; if we can solve these last two for x_2 and x_3, the results can be substituted into the first to get x_1. The problem, therefore, has been reduced from that of solving three equations in three unknowns to that of solving two equations in two unknowns.

We can now proceed to eliminate x_2 from one of the last two equations. Again, if $a_{22}' = 0$, we interchange the last two equations. (If it should happen that $a_{22}' = 0$ *and* $a_{32}' = 0$, the equations are singular and have either no solutions or an infinite number of solutions.) We define a new multiplier m_3':

$$m_3' = \frac{a_{32}'}{a_{22}'}$$

We multiply (8.9) by m_3' and subtract from (8.10). The result is

$$(a_{32}' - m_3'a_{22}')x_2 + (a_{33}' - m_3'a_{23}')x_3 = b_3' - m_3'b_2'$$

Again,

$$a_{32}' - m_3'a_{22}' = 0$$

and letting

$$a_{33}'' = a_{33}' - m_3'a_{23}'$$
$$b_3'' = b_3' - m_3'b_2'$$

we get

(8.11) $$a_{33}''x_3 = b_3''$$

This replaces (8.10), so that the final set of equations is

(8.5) $$a_{11}x_1 + a_{12}x_2 + a_{13}x_3 = b_1$$

(8.9) $$a_{22}'x_2 + a_{23}'x_3 = b_2'$$

(8.11) $$a_{33}''x_3 = b_3''$$

Such a system of equations is called *triangular* from its appearance.

It is now a straightforward process to solve (8.11) for x_3, to substitute that result in (8.9) to find x_2, and finally to substitute into (8.5) to get x_1. This process, called *back substitution*, is given by

$$x_3 = \frac{b_3''}{a_{33}''}$$

$$x_2 = \frac{(b_2' - a_{23}'x_3)}{a_{22}'}$$

$$x_1 = \frac{(b_1 - a_{12}x_2 - a_{13}x_3)}{a_{11}}$$

We recall that $a_{11} \neq 0$, $a_{22}' \neq 0$. If $a_{33}'' = 0$, once again it means that the original system is singular.

Consider an example.

(8.12) $$\begin{cases} x + y + z = 4 \\ 2x + 3y + z = 9 \\ x - y - z = -2 \end{cases}$$

It is easy to verify that the multiplier for the second equation is 2 and that for the third is 1. After eliminating x from the second and third equations, the new multiplier for eliminating y from the third equation is -2. The triangular system is

$$x + y + z = 4$$
$$y - z = 1$$
$$-4z = -4$$

From the last equation, $z = 1$; from the second, $y = 2$; from the first, $x = 1$. These results may be substituted into the original equations (8.12), which are thereby exactly satisfied. We have therefore found an exact solution in a finite number of arithmetic operations. In this case there were no roundoff errors.

The reader will find it instructive to solve (8.1) by elimination and to attempt to solve the singular system (8.2).

We may now generalize the procedure to the case of n simultaneous linear equations in n unknowns. After an "algebraic" description, we shall present a block diagram which not only makes the process more graphic but also provides a direct guide to writing a program.

Let the n unknowns be $x_1, x_2, \ldots, x_n$ and let the equations be

$$(8.13) \quad \begin{cases} a_{11}x_1 + a_{12}x_2 + \cdots + a_{1j}x_j + \cdots + a_{1n}x_n = b_1 \\ a_{21}x_1 + a_{22}x_2 + \cdots + a_{2j}x_j + \cdots + a_{2n}x_n = b_2 \\ \cdots \cdots \cdots \cdots \cdots \cdots \cdots \cdots \cdots \cdots \\ a_{i1}x_1 + a_{i2}x_2 + \cdots + a_{ij}x_j + \cdots + a_{in}x_n = b_i \\ \cdots \cdots \cdots \cdots \cdots \cdots \cdots \cdots \cdots \cdots \\ a_{n1}x_1 + a_{n2}x_2 + \cdots + a_{nj}x_j + \cdots + a_{nn}x_n = b_n \end{cases}$$

We assume that the equations have been so ordered that $a_{11} \neq 0$. Define $n - 1$ multipliers:

$$m_i = \frac{a_{i1}}{a_{11}}, \quad i = 2, 3, \ldots, n$$

and subtract m_i times the first equation from the ith equation. If we define

$$a_{ij}' = a_{ij} - m_i a_{1j}, \quad i = 2, \ldots, n$$
$$b_i' = b_i - m_i b_1, \quad j = 1, \ldots, n$$

it is easy to see that

$$a_{i1}' = 0, \quad i - 2, \ldots, n$$

The transformed equations are

$$a_{11}x_1 + a_{12}x_2 + \cdots + a_{1j}x_j + \cdots + a_{1n}x_n = b_1$$
$$0 + a_{22}'x_2 + \cdots + a_{2j}'x_j + \cdots + a_{2n}'x_r = b_2'$$
$$\cdots \cdots \cdots \cdots \cdots \cdots \cdots \cdots \cdots \cdots$$
$$0 + a_{i2}'x_2 + \cdots + a_{ij}'x_j + \cdots + a_{in}'x_n = b_i'$$
$$\cdots \cdots \cdots \cdots \cdots \cdots \cdots \cdots \cdots \cdots$$
$$0 + a_{n2}'x_2 + \cdots + a_{nj}'x_j + \cdots + a_{nn}'x_n = b_n'$$

We continue in this way. At the kth stage we eliminate x_k by defining multipliers

(8.14) $$m_i^{(k-1)} = \frac{a_{ik}^{(k-1)}}{a_{kk}^{(k-1)}}, \qquad i = k+1, \ldots, n$$

where $a_{kk}^{(k-1)} \neq 0$. Then

(8.15) $$a_{ij}^{(k)} = a_{ij}^{(k-1)} - m_i^{(k-1)} a_{kj}^{(k-1)}$$

(8.16) $$b_i^{(k)} = b_i^{(k-1)} - m_i^{(k-1)} b_k^{(k-1)}$$

for $i = k+1, \ldots, n$ and for $j = k, \ldots, n$. The index k takes on consecutive integer values for 1 through and including $n-1$. At the point where $k = n-1$ we are eliminating x_{n-1} from the last equation.

The final triangular set of equations is given by

(8.17)
$$\left\{ \begin{array}{l} a_{11}x_1 + a_{12}x_2 + \cdots + a_{1j}x_j + \cdots + a_{1n}x_n = b_1 \\ \qquad a_{22}'x_2 + \cdots + a_{2j}'x_j + \cdots + a_{2n}'x_n = b_2' \\ \qquad \cdots\cdots\cdots\cdots\cdots\cdots \\ \qquad\qquad a_{jj}^{(j-1)}x_j + \cdots + a_{jn}^{(j-1)}x_n = b_j^{(j-1)} \\ \qquad\qquad\cdots\cdots\cdots\cdots \\ \qquad\qquad\qquad a_{nn}^{(n-1)}x_n = b_n^{(n-1)} \end{array} \right.$$

The block diagram for the elimination process is shown in Figure 8.5. It follows the description just given fairly closely, with two exceptions. The box marked * which contains "arrange rows so $a_{kk} \neq 0$" refers to a process that we shall consider after discussing roundoff errors in Section 8.3. We shall see that the roundoff errors in the values of the unknowns can be substantially reduced by a judicious choice of rows to interchange.

A second difference between the block diagram and the description above is that we have used one symbol, m, for all multipliers in the block diagram, for if the operations are suitably arranged we shall never need more than one multiplier at a time.

In reading this block diagram, it may help to note the meanings assigned to the subscripts i, j, and k:

k refers to the number of the equation being subtracted from other equations; it is also the number of the unknown being eliminated from the last n-k equations.

i refers to the number of the equation from which an unknown is currently being eliminated.

j refers to the number of a column.

A careful study of this block diagram is worth the effort. It will not only help to make clear the method of Gauss elimination, but it

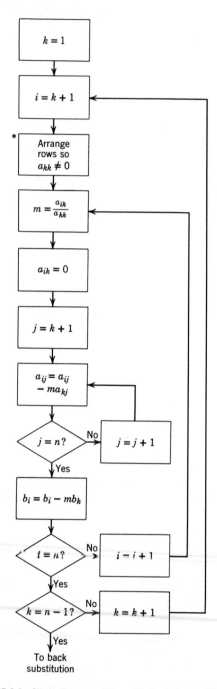

FIGURE 8.5 Block diagram of the method of Gauss elimination.

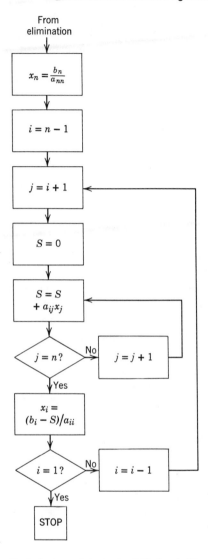

From
elimination

$$x_n = \frac{b_n}{a_{nn}}$$

$i = n - 1$

$j = i + 1$

$S = 0$

$S = S + a_{ij}x_j$

$j = n?$ No $j = j + 1$

Yes

$x_i = (b_i - S)/a_{ii}$

$i = 1?$ No $i = i - 1$

Yes

STOP

FIGURE 8.6   Block diagram of the back substitution, in Gauss elimination.

also exhibits many standard techniques in block diagramming, particularly the handling of subscript notation.

It is worth noting that the elimination process does not change the value of the determinant, although each row interchange does reverse the sign. After the elimination process is complete, the value of the determinant is just the product of the main diagonal elements, with the sign of the product reversed if there had been an odd number of row interchanges. In fact, when a determinant is to be evaluated. elimination is a good way to proceed.

The back substitution can be described as follows:

$$x_n = b_n^{(n-1)}/a_{nn}^{(n-1)}$$

(8.18)
$$x_{n-1} = \frac{(b_{n-1}^{(n-2)} - a_{n-1,n}^{(n-2)}x_n)}{a_{n-1,n-1}^{(n-2)}}$$
. . . .
$$x_j = (b_j^{(j-1)} - a_{jn}^{(j-1)}x_n - \cdots - a_{j,j+1}^{(j-1)}x_{j+1})/a_{jj}^{(j-1)}$$
$$\text{for } j = n - 2, \ldots, 1$$

The block diagram shown in Figure 8.6 is relatively straightforward. It turns out to be simpler to diagram the method if we compute the value of x_n in a separate step at the beginning. It would be possible to draw a more compact block diagram without this separate step, but it would pointlessly complicate the testing in the formation of the sum of the terms after the main diagonal term: the first "sum" would be zero, which would force us to test before accumulating. Notice that although in Figure 8.5 all subscripts *increased*, here one of them (i) *decreases*.

A program is shown in Figure 8.15, in connection with Case Study 10. The reader may wish to study the program at this time; it will be found that it follows the block diagrams closely.

8.3   Roundoff errors

We now turn to a discussion of roundoff errors when the elimination process is carried out in floating point arithmetic. Contrary to our usual approach, the goal this time will not be to obtain bounds on the errors—although this could certainly be done. Instead we shall seek a rule that will hold the roundoff error as small as possible, which is the first practical concern. The second concern—knowing the size of the errors—is discussed in Section 8.4 in connection with a method that makes it possible to use the computer itself, not only to estimate the error but to correct for the effects of roundoff.

Recall that we may have to rearrange rows at each stage of the elimination process in order to avoid division by zero. There are, in general, several such arrangements. We shall show how to choose one that reduces roundoff errors. We shall also see that rearrangement is usually desirable even if the diagonal term is *not* zero.

Let us suppose that we are about to eliminate x_k.   The appearance of the equations is

$$a_{11}x_1 + a_{12}x_2 + \cdots + a_{1k}x_k + \cdots$$
$$+ a_{1j}x_j + \cdots + a_{1n}x_n = b_1$$

$$a_{22}'x_2 + \cdots + a_{2k}'x_k + \cdots$$
$$+ a_{2j}'x_j + \cdots + a_{2n}'x_n = b_2'$$

. . . .

(8.19)

$$a_{kk}^{(k-1)}x_k + \cdots$$
$$+ a_{kj}^{(k-1)}x_j + \cdots + a_{kn}^{(k-1)}x_n = b_k^{(k-1)}$$

. . . .

$$a_{ik}^{(k-1)}x_k + \cdots$$
$$+ a_{ij}^{(k-1)}x_j + \cdots + a_{in}^{(k-1)}x_n = b_i^{(k-1)}$$

. . . .

$$a_{nk}^{(k-1)}x_k + \cdots$$
$$+ a_{nj}^{(k-1)}x_j + \cdots + a_{nn}^{(k-1)}x_n = b_n^{(k-1)}$$

Now $a_{ij}^{(k)}$ is given by (8.15) in which $m_i^{(k-1)}$ is computed from (8.14). The process graph is shown in Figure 8.7.

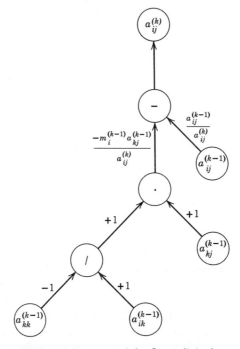

FIGURE 8.7   Process graph for Gauss elimination.

We now compute the relative roundoff error in $a_{ij}^{(k)}$. Let α_{ij} be the relative roundoff error in $a_{ij}^{(k-1)}$ and let δ, μ, and σ be the relative roundoff errors in the division, multiplication, and subtraction, respectively. Then if e_{ij} is the absolute error in $a_{ij}^{(k)}$,

$$\frac{e_{ij}}{a_{ij}^{(k)}} = - \frac{m_i^{(k-1)}a_{kj}^{(k-1)}}{a_{ij}^{(k)}} (\alpha_{ik} - \alpha_{kk} + \alpha_{kj} + \delta + \mu) + \frac{a_{ij}^{(k-1)}}{a_{ij}^{(k)}} \cdot \alpha_{ij} + \sigma$$

If δ, μ, and σ are bounded by $5 \cdot 10^{-t}$ and the α_{ij} are bounded by $K \cdot 10^{-t}$, where $K \geq 5$, we have

$$|e_{ij}| \leq \{3 \cdot (K + 5) \cdot |a_{kj}^{(k-1)}| \cdot |m_i^{(k-1)}| + (K + 5)|a_{ij}^{(k-1)}|\} \cdot 10^{-t}$$

Consider now a fixed j (a given column). The dominant term is in general the first one in the braces, which is small if $|m_i^{(k-1)}|$ is small. Thus we wish to make $|m_i^{(k-1)}|$ as small as possible. To make $|m_i^{(k-1)}|$ small requires that $|a_{kk}^{(k-1)}|$ be as large as possible. In other words, we wish to choose the row that is to become the kth row so that

$$|a_{kk}^{(k-1)}| \geq |a_{ik}^{(k-1)}|$$

because then

$$|m_i^{(k-1)}| \leq 1$$

If the kth row is not so chosen, at least one of the multipliers will be greater than 1 in absolute value.

Our rule then is rearrange the last $n - k + 1$ rows so that the largest—in absolute value—of the coefficients in the kth column is in the kth row. This is sometimes referred to as *pivotal condensation*.

A block diagram of the testing and (if necessary) the interchanging is shown in Figure 8.8. It should be thought of as replacing the box marked * in Figure 8.5. In studying Figure 8.8, recall from Figure 8.5 that as we enter this phase k has some value and i has just been set to $k + 1$. We begin by setting an auxiliary subscript l, equal to k. The first comparison is then between a_{ik}, the element just below the diagonal term a_{kk}, and a_{lk}, which is a_{kk}. If a_{ik} is found to be larger in absolute value, we set $l = i$. The subscript l therefore always represents the row number of the element in the kth column that is so far the largest one tested. The subscript i runs through all values from $k + 1$ to n, inclusive. Thus at the end of this loop l identifies the largest element, the one we want for a_{kk} after interchanging if necessary.

Of course, the original a_{kk} could already be the largest. We therefore immediately test for this possibility and omit the interchanging in that case. Before returning to the main elimination process, however, it is necessary to set i back to the value it had before we used it as a

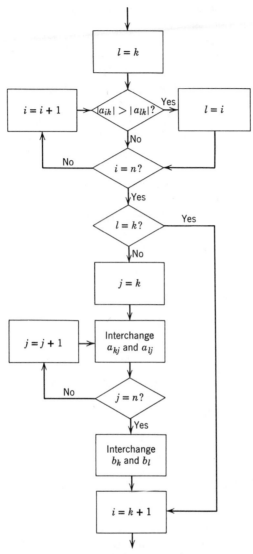

FIGURE 8.8   Block diagram of the process of choosing the kth row and performing a row interchange if necessary.   *All of this block diagram replaces the box marked * in Figure 8.5.*

subscript in the testing loop.   This is easily done: in the main block diagram the value of i had just been made $k + 1$, which we repeat here.

The actual interchanging is done on pairs of values, one from row k and one from row l, whatever l may be.   The interchange of each pair of values requires a three-step process, as described in Section 7.9.

This operation must be done on all pairs in the two rows, which is carried out by a loop using j as a subscript. Finally, the two constant terms are interchanged and the process is complete.

The roundoff error can be further reduced by testing and interchanging columns as well as rows. In other words, we search all remaining coefficients for the largest element rather than restricting the range to those in the kth column. This does in fact reduce the roundoff error even further, but at the expense of an additional complication: an interchange in columns implies renaming the variables or keeping some record of the interchanges. This can certainly be done, but it is not usually worth the programming effort or the slight extra machine time in running the program. Exercise 26 sketches the programming technique by which the renaming of the variables may be done.

To indicate the practical value of row rearrangement, consider the following simple set of equations:

$$(8.20) \quad \begin{cases} 3.241 \cdot 10^0 x_1 + 1.600 \cdot 10^2 x_2 = 1.632 \cdot 10^2 \\ 1.020 \cdot 10^4 x_1 + 1.540 \cdot 10^3 x_2 = 1.174 \cdot 10^4 \end{cases}$$

The exact solution is

$$x_1 = 1.000 \cdot 10^0$$

$$x_2 = 1.000 \cdot 10^0$$

Let us solve these equations by elimination, in the order shown, using floating point arithmetic with four-digit mantissas.

The first and only multiplier is

$$m = \frac{1.020 \cdot 10^4}{3.241 \cdot 10^0} = 3.147 \cdot 10^3$$

The new second equation is

$$5.730 \cdot 10^{-1} x_1 - 5.020 \cdot 10^5 x_2 = -5.019 \cdot 10^5$$

Naturally, the new coefficient of x_1 should be zero, but roundoff error has prevented our getting the exact result. This coefficient, however, never enters the subsequent calculations, and we proceed with the back substitution.

$$(8.21) \quad x_2 = \frac{-5.019 \cdot 10^5}{-5.020 \cdot 10^5} = 9.998 \cdot 10^{-1}$$

From the first equation, then,

$$(8.22) \quad x_1 = 9.873 \cdot 10^{-1}$$

Now let us reverse the order of the equations, which is what the row rearrangement amounts to in this case.   The multiplier now is

$$m = \frac{3.241 \cdot 10^0}{1.020 \cdot 10^4} = 3.177 \cdot 10^{-4}$$

The new second equation is

$$0.000x_1 + 1.595 \cdot 10^2 x_2 = 1.595 \cdot 10^2$$

so that

$$x_2 = 1.000 \cdot 10^0$$

and

$$x_1 = 1.000 \cdot 10^0$$

This example has coefficients that vary widely in size; often the variation is not so wide.   However, when there are many equations (a system of 10 equations is commonplace, and 100 is not unusual), the effects of roundoff errors accumulate.   What happens in the first elimination has a profound effect on later accuracy.   It is easy to construct examples of relatively small systems in which *all* accuracy is lost without rearrangement: the answers will have *no* significant figures. Any practical program for computer solution of simultaneous linear algebraic equations by Gauss elimination *must* include row interchange, except possibly in the case of very specialized systems in which a great deal is known about the coefficients.

8.4   Refinement of the solution

Whether we interchange rows or not, roundoff errors do ordinarily have some effect on the results.   We now turn to a method of refining the solution once it has been found.   This technique will ordinarily reduce the roundoff errors in the solution and may permit a reasonable solution of some ill-conditioned systems.

Let $x_1^{(0)}, x_1^{(0)}, \ldots, x_n^{(0)}$ be an approximate solution of (8.13) found by Gauss elimination or any other method.   If we substitute this solution in the left-hand sides of (8.13) we get

$$(8.23) \quad \begin{cases} a_{11}x_1^{(0)} + a_{12}x_2^{(0)} + \cdots + a_{1n}x_n^{(0)} = b_1^{(0)} \\ a_{21}x_1^{(0)} + a_{22}x_2^{(0)} + \cdots + a_{2n}x_n^{(0)} = b_2^{(0)} \\ \cdots \cdots \cdots \cdots \cdots \cdots \cdots \cdots \cdots \cdots \cdots \\ a_{n1}x_1^{(0)} + a_{n2}x_2^{(0)} + \cdots + a_{nn}x_n^{(0)} = b_n^{(0)} \end{cases}$$

If the $b_i^{(0)}$ differ from the b_i by a great deal, the $x_i^{(0)}$ are not a good approximation to the solution of (8.13).   On the other hand, even if all the $b_i^{(0)}$ and b_i are very close to one another the $x_i^{(0)}$ may still not be a good approximation to the solution.   (Recall (8.3) in Section 8.1.)

If we subtract each equation in (8.23) from the corresponding equation in (8.13) and let

(8.24) $\epsilon_i^{(0)} = x_i - x_i^{(0)}, \qquad i = 1, \ldots, n$

(8.25) $\beta_i^{(0)} = b_i - b_i^{(0)}, \qquad i = 1, \ldots, n$

then

(8.26)
$$
\begin{cases}
a_{11}\epsilon_1^{(0)} + a_{12}\epsilon_2^{(0)} + \cdots + a_{1n}\epsilon_n^{(0)} = \beta_1^{(0)} \\
a_{21}\epsilon_1^{(0)} + a_{22}\epsilon_2^{(0)} + \cdots + a_{2n}\epsilon_n^{(0)} = \beta_2^{(0)} \\
\cdots\cdots\cdots\cdots\cdots\cdots\cdots\cdots\cdots\cdots\cdots \\
a_{n1}\epsilon_1^{(0)} + a_{n2}\epsilon_2^{(0)} + \cdots + a_{nn}\epsilon_n^{(0)} = \beta_n^{(0)}
\end{cases}
$$

The $\beta_i^{(0)}$ are readily calculated and the $\epsilon_i^{(0)}$ may be calculated from (8.26) by Gauss elimination.   A new approximation to the solution of (8.13) is then

$$ x_i^{(1)} = x_i^{(0)} + \epsilon_i^{(0)}, \qquad i = 1, \ldots, n $$

Again the $x_i^{(1)}$ may be substituted into the left-hand sides of (8.13) and the resulting right-hand sides called $b_i^{(1)}$.   A new correction to the x_i is then obtained by solving

(8.27)
$$
\begin{cases}
a_{11}\epsilon_1^{(1)} + a_{12}\epsilon_2^{(1)} + \cdots + a_{1n}\epsilon_n^{(1)} = \beta_1^{(1)} \\
a_{21}\epsilon_1^{(1)} + a_{22}\epsilon_2^{(1)} + \cdots + a_{2n}\epsilon_n^{(1)} = \beta_2^{(1)} \\
\cdots\cdots\cdots\cdots\cdots\cdots\cdots\cdots\cdots\cdots\cdots \\
a_{n1}\epsilon_1^{(1)} + a_{n2}\epsilon_2^{(1)} + \cdots + a_{nn}\epsilon_n^{(1)} = \beta_n^{(1)}
\end{cases}
$$

where

$$ \beta_i^{(1)} = b_i - b_i^{(1)}, \qquad i = 1, \ldots, n $$

The new approximation is given by

$$ x_i^{(2)} = x_i^{(1)} + \epsilon_i^{(1)}, \qquad i = 1, \ldots, n $$

This process can, of course, be continued until all the ϵ_i are small. It is important that the iterations not be stopped simply because the β_i are small: we again point to the example in (8.3) to emphasize that small β_i do not necessarily imply an accurate solution.

As an example, consider the two equations (8.20) solved without interchange.   The solution obtained was

$$ x_1^{(0)} = 9.873 \cdot 10^{-1} $$
$$ x_2^{(0)} = 9.998 \cdot 10^{-1} $$

Substituting these values in (8.20) and using floating point calculations with four-digit mantissas, we get

$$b_1^{(0)} = (3.241 \cdot 10^0) \times (9.873 \cdot 10^{-1}) + (1.600 \cdot 10^2)(0.998 \cdot 10^{-1})$$
$$= 1.632 \cdot 10^2$$

$$b_2^{(0)} = (1.020 \cdot 10^4)(9.873 \cdot 10^{-1}) + (1.540 \cdot 10^3)(9.998 \cdot 10^{-1})$$
$$= 1.161 \cdot 10^4$$

So

$$\beta_1^{(0)} = b_1 - b_1^{(0)} = 0$$
$$\beta_2^{(0)} = b_2 - b_2^{(0)} = 1.300 \cdot 10^2$$

We now solve (8.20) with the right-hand sides given by $\beta_1^{(0)}$ and $\beta_2^{(0)}$, that is, we solve

$$3.241 \cdot 10^0 \epsilon_1^{(0)} + 1.600 \cdot 10^2 \epsilon_2^{(0)} = 0$$
$$1.020 \cdot 10^4 \epsilon_1^{(0)} + 1.540 \cdot 10^3 \epsilon_2^{(0)} = 1.300 \cdot 10^2$$

Again not using row interchange, the solution is

$$\epsilon_1^{(1)} = 1.284 \cdot 10^{-2}$$
$$\epsilon_2^{(1)} = -2.600 \cdot 10^{-4}$$

so the new approximation is

$$x_1^{(1)} = x_1^{(0)} + \epsilon_1^{(0)} = 1.000 \cdot 10^0$$
$$x_2^{(1)} = x_2^{(0)} + \epsilon_2^{(0)} = 9.995 \cdot 10^{-1}$$

Substituting these in (8.20), we find

$$\beta_1^{(1)} = b_1 - b_1^{(1)} = 1.000 \cdot 10^{-1}$$
$$\beta_2^{(1)} = b_2 - b_2^{(1)} = 0$$

so

$$\epsilon_1^{(1)} = -9.256 \cdot 10^{-5}$$
$$\epsilon_2^{(1)} = 6.268 \cdot 10^{-4}$$

The next approximation is

$$x_1^{(2)} = x_1^{(1)} + \epsilon_1^{(1)} = 1.000 \cdot 10^0$$
$$x_2^{(2)} = x_2^{(1)} + \epsilon_2^{(1)} = 1.000 \cdot 10^0$$

In three iterations, therefore, without row interchanges, a solution has been found that is accurate to four significant figures. (Recall that with row interchanges only one iteration was required.)

The important point, however, is that the solution was improved even though the method used produced large roundoff error. Naturally, in practice we *do* use row interchanges. The real interest in the technique of refining a solution lies in its application to a solution obtained *with* row interchanges that nevertheless contains accumulated roundoff error.

8.5   Effect of uncertainty in the coefficients: attainable accuracy

We now ask ourselves this question: if the a_{ij} and/or the b_i are the results of an experiment or are computed values, what effect will errors in these numbers have on the solution x_i?

To answer this important question, we proceed as we did in Chapter 5. Let the true coefficients be $a_{ij} + \alpha_{ij}$ and $b_i + \beta_i$, where α_{ij} and β_i are small compared with a_{ij} and b_i. That is to say, we really want the solution of

$$(8.28) \quad \begin{cases} (a_{11} + \alpha_{11})x_1 + (a_{12} + \alpha_{12})x_2 + \cdots + (a_{1n} + \alpha_{1n})x_n \\ \qquad\qquad\qquad\qquad\qquad\qquad\qquad\qquad = b_1 + \beta_1 \\ \cdots\cdots\cdots\cdots\cdots\cdots\cdots\cdots\cdots\cdots\cdots\cdots \\ (a_{i1} + \alpha_{i1})x_1 + (a_{i2} + \alpha_{i2})x_2 + \cdots + (a_{in} + \alpha_{in})x_n \\ \qquad\qquad\qquad\qquad\qquad\qquad\qquad\qquad = b_i + \beta_i \\ \cdots\cdots\cdots\cdots\cdots\cdots\cdots\cdots\cdots\cdots\cdots\cdots \\ (a_{n1} + \alpha_{n1})x_1 + (a_{n2} + \alpha_{n2})x_2 + \cdots + (a_{nn} + \alpha_{nn})x_n \\ \qquad\qquad\qquad\qquad\qquad\qquad\qquad\qquad = b_n + \beta_n \end{cases}$$

Of course, if we knew the values of the α_{ij} and β_i, we would simply solve those equations instead of the original ones. Usually, all we know is some bound on the α_{ij} and β_i. For example, if the a_{ij} and b_i are experimental results given to d decimal places, then

$$|\alpha_{ij}| \leq \tfrac{1}{2} \cdot 10^{-d}$$

$$|\beta_i| \leq \tfrac{1}{2} \cdot 10^{-d}$$

We will let $x_1, x_2, \ldots, x_n$ be the solution of the original equations (8.13) and let

$$x_i + \delta_i$$

be the solution of (8.28). We will assume that

$$|\delta_i| \ll |x_i| \qquad i = 1, \ldots, n$$

Substituting $x_i + \delta_i$ into (8.28) and using (8.13) it follows that

$$(a_{11}\delta_1 + \cdots + a_{1n}\delta_n) + (\alpha_{11}x_1 + \cdots + \alpha_{1n}x_n) = \beta_1$$
$$\cdots \cdots \cdots \cdots \cdots \cdots \cdots \cdots \cdots \cdots \cdots \cdots \cdots \cdots \cdots$$
$$(a_{i1}\delta_1 + \cdots + a_{in}\delta_n) + (\alpha_{i1}x_1 + \cdots + \alpha_{in}x_n) = \beta_i$$
$$\cdots \cdots \cdots \cdots \cdots \cdots \cdots \cdots \cdots \cdots \cdots \cdots \cdots \cdots \cdots$$
$$(a_{n1}\delta_1 + \cdots + a_{nn}\delta_n) + (\alpha_{n1}x_1 + \cdots + \alpha_{nn}x_n) = \beta_n$$

where terms involving the products of the α_{ij} and δ_i are neglected. Thus the δ_i are the solution of

$$(8.29) \quad \begin{cases} a_{11}\delta_1 + \cdots + a_{ij}\delta_j + \cdots + a_{1n}\delta_n \\ \qquad\qquad = \beta_1 - (\alpha_{11}x_1 + \cdots + \alpha_{1n}x_n) \\ \cdots \cdots \cdots \cdots \cdots \cdots \cdots \cdots \cdots \cdots \cdots \cdots \\ a_{i1}\delta_1 + \cdots + a_{ij}\delta_j + \cdots + a_{in}\delta_n \\ \qquad\qquad = \beta_i - (\alpha_{i1}x_1 + \cdots + \alpha_{in}x_n) \\ \cdots \cdots \cdots \cdots \cdots \cdots \cdots \cdots \cdots \cdots \cdots \cdots \\ a_{n1}\delta_1 + \cdots + a_{nj}\delta_j + \cdots + a_{nn}\delta_n \\ \qquad\qquad = \beta_n - (\alpha_{n1}x_1 + \cdots + \alpha_{nn}x_n) \end{cases}$$

We now consider separately four possible cases.

1. The a_{ij} are precise but the b_i are given to d decimal places; that is,

$$\alpha_{ij} = 0$$
$$|\beta_i| \leq \tfrac{1}{2} \cdot 10^{-d}$$

Then it follows from (8.29) that

$$(8.30) \quad \begin{cases} |a_{11}\delta_1 + \cdots a_{1j}\delta_j + \cdots a_{1n}\delta_n| \leq \tfrac{1}{2} \cdot 10^{-d} \\ \quad \vdots \qquad\qquad\qquad \vdots \qquad\qquad \vdots \\ |a_{i1}\delta_1 + \cdots a_{ij}\delta_j + \cdots a_{in}\delta_n| \leq \tfrac{1}{2} \cdot 10^{-d} \\ \quad \vdots \qquad\qquad\qquad \vdots \qquad\qquad \vdots \\ |a_{n1}\delta_1 + \cdots a_{nj}\delta_j + \cdots a_{nn}\delta_n| \leq \tfrac{1}{2} \cdot 10^{-d} \end{cases}$$

These inequalities can be "solved" (we shall see how to do this shortly) at the same time as the original equations (8.13) are solved, leading directly to an estimate of the effect of the uncertainty in the right-hand sides on the solution. Notice first that if Δ_i $(i = 1, \ldots, n)$ is called the solution when all of the right-hand sides of (8.30) are $+1$ then

$$\delta_i = (\tfrac{1}{2} \cdot 10^{-d})\Delta_i, \qquad i = 1, \ldots, n$$

So in solving the original system we carry along an extra column (or right-hand side, in other words). This is in addition to the b_i; it is initially set with all elements equal to $+1$. During the solution it is treated as though it were a second right-hand side, with one difference:

we never subtract when working with the extra column but always add absolute values. The reason for this is that (8.30) are inequalities, and we must never make the right-hand sides smaller.

An example is in order. Consider the equations given in (8.12) and suppose that the right-hand sides are given to two decimal places, that is, that

$$|\beta_i| \le \tfrac{1}{2} \cdot 10^{-2}$$

The second equation becomes in elimination

$$(2 - 2 \cdot 1)x + (3 - 2 \cdot 1)y + (1 - 2 \cdot 1)z = 9 - 2 \cdot 4 | 1 + 2 \cdot 1$$

or

$$y - z = 1|3$$

The number after the bar indicates the entry in the new column. Note that 2×1 was *added* to, not subtracted from, the new column. (We always add absolute values in the error column.) Similarly the third equation is

$$(1 - 1 \cdot 1)x + (-1 - 1 \cdot 1)y + (-1 - 1 \cdot 1)z = -2 - 1 \cdot 4|1 + 1 \cdot 1$$

or

$$-2y - 2z = -6|2$$

The final triangular set of equations is

$$x + y + z = 4|1$$
$$y - z = 1|3$$
$$-4z = -4|8$$

The back solution, again always adding, gives

$$\Delta_z = \tfrac{8}{4} = 2$$
$$\Delta_y = 3 + \Delta_z = 5$$
$$\Delta_x = 1 + \Delta_y + \Delta_z - 8$$

and so

(8.31)
$$\begin{cases} |\delta_x| \le 4 \cdot 10^{-2} \\ |\delta_y| \le 2.5 \cdot 10^{-2} \\ |\delta_z| \le 1 \cdot 10^{-2} \end{cases}$$

where $x = 1$
$y = 2$
$z = 1$

We turn now to a second case.

2. The b_i are precise, but the a_{ij} are given only to d decimal places, that is,

$$|\alpha_{ij}| \leq \tfrac{1}{2} \cdot 10^{-d}$$

$$\beta_i = 0$$

Then from (8.29) and the triangle inequality

$$|a_{11}\delta_1 + \cdots a_{1j}\delta_j + \cdots a_{1n}\delta_n| \leq \tfrac{1}{2} \cdot 10^{-d}(|x_1| + \cdots + |x_n|)$$

$$\vdots \qquad\qquad \vdots \qquad\qquad \vdots$$

$$|a_{i1}\delta_1 + \cdots a_{ij}\delta_j + \cdots a_{in}\delta_n| \leq \tfrac{1}{2} \cdot 10^{-d}(|x_1| + \cdots + |x_n|)$$

$$\vdots \qquad\qquad \vdots \qquad\qquad \vdots$$

$$|a_{n1}\delta_1 + \cdots a_{nj}\delta_j + \cdots a_{nn}\delta_n| \leq \tfrac{1}{2} \cdot 10^{-d}(|x_1| + \cdots + |x_n|)$$

Again, if Δ_i is the solution when the right-hand sides are $+1$, then

$$\delta_i = \tfrac{1}{2} \cdot 10^{-d}(|x_1| + \cdots + |x_n|)\Delta_i$$

As an example, consider (8.12) again and suppose that the coefficients on the left are given to two decimal places. Then, since

$$|x| + |y| + |z| = 4$$

it follows from (8.31) that

$$|\delta_x| \leq 1.6 \cdot 10^{-1}$$

$$|\delta_y| \leq 1 \cdot 10^{-1}$$

$$|\delta_z| \leq 4 \cdot 10^{-2}$$

3. Suppose now that both the a_{ij} and the b_i are given to d decimal places. Then a similar argument produces the result that

$$\delta_i = \tfrac{1}{2} \cdot 10^{-d}(1 + |x_1| + \cdots + |x_n|)\Delta_i$$

In the example of (8.12), if all coefficients and right-hand sides are given to two decimal places,

$$|\delta_x| \leq 2 \cdot 10^{-1}$$

$$|\delta_y| \leq 1.25 \cdot 10^{-1}$$

$$|\delta_z| \leq 0.5 \cdot 10^{-1}$$

4. The final case we shall consider is when the a_{ij} and the b_i are both calculated results given to t significant figures. Then

$$\left| \frac{\alpha_{ij}}{a_{ij}} \right| \leq 5 \cdot 10^{-t}$$

and

$$\left| \frac{\beta_i}{b_i} \right| \leq 5 \cdot 10^{-t}$$

The analysis then leads to

$$\delta_i = k \cdot \Delta_i \cdot 5 \cdot 10^{-t}$$

where

$$k = \max \left(|b_i| + |a_{i1}x_1| + |a_{i2}x_2| + \cdots + |a_{in}x_n| \right)$$

and the maximum is taken over all i.

Let us turn again to our example and suppose that the coefficients and right-hand sides are given to four significant digits, that is, $t = 4$. Then

$$|b_1| + |a_{11}x| + |a_{12}y| + |a_{13}z| = 4 + 1 + 2 + 1 = 8$$

$$|b_2| + |a_{21}x| + |a_{22}y| + |a_{23}z| = 9 + 2 + 6 + 1 = 18$$

$$|b_3| + |a_{31}x| + |a_{32}y| + |a_{33}z| = 2 + 1 + 2 + 1 = 6$$

Thus $k = 18$, so that

$$|\delta_x| \leq 7.2 \cdot 10^{-2}$$

$$|\delta_y| \leq 4.5 \cdot 10^{-2}$$

$$|\delta_z| \leq 1.8 \cdot 10^{-2}$$

All of these bounds are in general extremely conservative, that is, the actual δ_i are usually much smaller than predicted by these bounds. Better bounds—in the sense that they are usually smaller—can be obtained, but finding them involves matrix inversion techniques that are beyond the scope of this book.*

8.6 Iterative methods of solution

In Section 8.2 we discussed Gauss elimination, a finite method of solving a system of simultaneous linear algebraic equations. Then in Section 8.4 we saw how to improve the solution by repeatedly using Gauss elimination. This method of improvement was actually an iterative technique. We saw, in examples, the common contradiction between theory and practice: because of roundoff the "finite" and "exact" method actually produces a solution that can contain serious errors; the solution can then be significantly improved by an iterative method.

We shall now discuss another and more common iterative technique.

* See, for instance, F. B. Hildebrand, *Introduction to Numerical Analysis*, McGraw-Hill, 1956, pp. 436–437.

It is marked by its simplicity and the ease with which it may be programmed for a computer. Like the iterative techniques discussed in Chapter 5, the roundoff error is small, but the method converges (produces a solution) only under certain conditions that we shall develop.

It turns out that the conditions for convergence are often satisfied when partial differential equations are solved numerically by certain techniques. We shall return to this point in Chapter 11.

Consider now three equations in three unknowns (8.5), (8.6), and (8.7). We suppose that $a_{11} \neq 0$, $a_{22} \neq 0$, $a_{33} \neq 0$ and rewrite the equations as

(8.32) $$x_1 = \frac{1}{a_{11}} (b_1 - a_{12}x_2 - a_{13}x_3)$$

(8.33) $$x_2 = \frac{1}{a_{22}} (b_2 - a_{21}x_1 - a_{23}x_3)$$

(8.34) $$x_3 = \frac{1}{a_{33}} (b_3 - a_{31}x_1 - a_{32}x_2)$$

We now take any first approximation to the solution; call it $x_1^{(0)}$, $x_2^{(0)}$ and $x_3^{(0)}$. We solve (8.32) for a new approximation to x_1:

$$x_1^{(1)} = \frac{1}{a_{11}} (b_1 - a_{12}x_2^{(0)} - a_{13}x_3^{(0)})$$

Using the new value of x_1, together with $x_3^{(0)}$, we solve (8.33) for x_2:

$$x_2^{(1)} = \frac{1}{a_{22}} (b_2 - a_{21}x_1^{(1)} - a_{23}x_3^{(0)})$$

Finally we use the newly computed values of x_1 and x_2 in (8.34) to find a new value of x_3:

$$x_3^{(1)} = \frac{1}{a_{33}} (b_2 - a_{31}x_1^{(1)} - a_{32}x_2^{(1)})$$

This completes one iteration. We can now start all over by replacing $x_1^{(0)}$, $x_2^{(0)}$, and $x_3^{(0)}$ by $x_1^{(1)}$, $x_2^{(1)}$, and $x_3^{(1)}$ and find another approximation. In general, the kth approximation is given by

(8.35)
$$\begin{cases} x_1^{(k)} = \dfrac{1}{a_{11}} (b_1 - a_{12}x_2^{(k-1)} - a_{13}x_3^{(k-1)}) \\[2em] x_2^{(k)} = \dfrac{1}{a_{22}} (b_2 - a_{21}x_1^{(k)} - a_{23}x_3^{(k-1)}) \\[2em] x_3^{(k)} = \dfrac{1}{a_{33}} (b_3 - a_{31}x_1^{(k)} - a_{32}x_2^{(k)}) \end{cases}$$

Notice that the most recently computed values for each x are always used and that we cannot calculate $x_2^{(k)}$ until $x_1^{(k)}$ has been computed. Similarly, the calculation of $x_3^{(k)}$ requires the prior calculation of $x_1^{(k)}$ and $x_2^{(k)}$.

The technique we have illustrated here is known as the *Gauss-Seidel iteration method*. It is extremely well adapted for use on a digital computer. Before discussing the general case of n equations in n unknowns and investigating the convergence properties, we may consider a simple numerical example.

$$4x_1 - x_2 + x_3 = 4$$

$$x_1 + 6x_2 + 2x_3 = 9$$

$$-x_1 - 2x_2 + 5x_3 = 2$$

One may easily verify that $x_1 = x_2 = x_3 = 1$ is the exact solution. Let $x_1^{(0)} = x_2^{(0)} = x_3^{(0)} = 0$, which is a usual first approximation. Then, since

$$x_1 = \tfrac{1}{4}(4 + x_2 - x_3)$$

$$x_2 = \tfrac{1}{6}(9 - x_1 - 2x_3)$$

$$x_3 = \tfrac{1}{5}(2 + x_1 + 2x_2)$$

it follows that

$$x_1^{(1)} = \tfrac{1}{4}(4 + 0 + 0) = 1$$

$$x_2^{(1)} = \tfrac{1}{6}(9 - 1 - 0) = \tfrac{4}{3}$$

$$x_3^{(1)} = \tfrac{1}{5}(2 + 1 + \tfrac{8}{3}) = \tfrac{17}{15}$$

The successive solutions, using four place floating point arithmetic, are shown in Table 8.1.

Table 8.1

Iteration	x_1	x_2	x_3
0	0	0	0
1	$0.1000 \cdot 10^1$	$0.1333 \cdot 10^1$	$0.1133 \cdot 10^1$
2	$0.1050 \cdot 10^1$	$0.9473 \cdot 10^0$	$0.9889 \cdot 10^0$
3	$0.9896 \cdot 10^0$	$0.1005 \cdot 10^1$	$0.9999 \cdot 10^0$
4	$0.1001 \cdot 10^1$	$0.9999 \cdot 10^0$	$0.1000 \cdot 10^1$
5	$0.1000 \cdot 10^1$	$0.1000 \cdot 10^1$	$0.1000 \cdot 10^1$

It is interesting to note that eight-place floating point arithmetic still requires five iterations to obtain four significant figures. After another four iterations, however, the eight-place arithmetic reaches a solution accurate to eight places.

Consider now n equations in n unknowns (8.13). Again we assume that $a_{ii} \neq 0$ for all i. The kth approximation to x_i is

$$x_i^{(k)} = \frac{1}{a_{ii}} [b_i - a_{i1}x_1^{(k)} - \cdots - a_{i,i-1}x_{i-1}^{(k)} - a_{i,i+1}x_{i+1}^{(k-1)} - \cdots$$
$$- a_{in}x_n^{(k-1)}], \qquad i = 1, \ldots, n$$

The process is iterated until all $x_i^{(k)}$ are sufficiently close to $x_i^{(k-1)}$. A typical way of determining closeness is to let

$$M^{(k)} = \max \left| x_i^{(k)} - x_i^{(k-1)} \right|$$

where the maximum is taken over all i. Then if

$$M^{(k)} < \epsilon$$

where ϵ is some small positive number, the iteration process is stopped. Alternatively, the relative difference may be tested, using the test

$$M^{(k)} = \max \left| \frac{x_i^{(k)} - x_i^{(k-1)}}{x_i^{(k)}} \right|$$

A block diagram describing the Gauss-Seidel iteration method is given in Figure 8.9. It is not nearly so complicated as it might appear at first glance. It should be remembered that Gauss elimination was diagrammed in three separate places (Figures 8.5, 8.6, and 8.8).

The boxes at the left are used to read the data and initialize the starting approximations to zero and start the counter of the number of iterations, ITER, at 1. They are never repeated. At the end of this set is a *connector*, as it is called, indicating that the diagram continues at the correspondingly numbered connector at the top of the middle group. Connectors are commonly used to avoid a maze of long and crossing flow lines.

The variable BIG is used to determine the maximum value of $\left| x_i^{(k)} - x_i^{(k-1)} \right|$. It is initially set to zero; then every difference is tested against it, and any that is larger than before is placed in it. After computing all new x_i it will contain the largest difference.

Now comes the part that develops the sum of all terms in one row of the system, excluding the diagonal term. Basically, we will compute and sum all terms in the row before the diagonal and then add in all terms after the main diagonal. Separate tests are necessary to handle the fact that there is no term before the diagonal in the first equation and no term after it in the last. The logic is not complex otherwise.

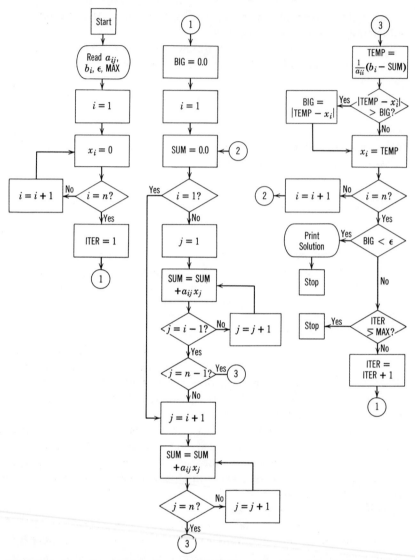

FIGURE 8.9   Block diagram of the Gauss-Seidel iteration method for solving simultaneous linear equations.

The group of boxes at the right begins by completing the computation of $x_i^{(k)}$, checks the maximum difference, and then stores the new $x_i^{(k)}$. If this was not the last equation, we increment i and return to compute the next $x_i^{(k)}$. If it was the last, we check $m_i^{(k)}$ against ϵ and print the results if the process has converged. If it has not, we do something that is not part of the numerical analysis but is rather a matter of good programming practice. It is not wise to assume that a process that *should* converge always *will*. Many strange things, from programming errors to bad data, can invalidate such an assumption. We therefore have arranged to read a fixed point number MAX that specifies the maximum number of iterations to be permitted. This number would ordinarily be chosen to be somewhat larger than the analyst expects would ever be necessary. (An indicative value would be 50 iterations for 50 equations.) Then if for any reason the process does not converge, the computer will not run indefinitely. Such a counter is a good idea in the program for any iterative method.

We have shown the data being read and the results printed; in other words, this block diagram assumes that a program to do all this would operate by itself. It should be understood that in actual practice often the data would have been generated by a preceding program and/or utilized by a following one, as in Case Study 10.

We now turn to the question of the convergence of the method. Before stating the criteria for the general case of n equations, we shall investigate a simpler case in considerable detail.

Let $n = 2$. Then

(8.36)
$$a_{11}x + a_{12}y = b_1$$

(8.37)
$$a_{21}x + a_{22}y = b_2$$

so that

(8.38)
$$x^{(k)} = \frac{1}{a_{11}} [b_1 - a_{12}y^{(k-1)}]$$

(8.39)
$$y^{(k)} = \frac{1}{a_{22}} [b_2 - a_{21}x^{(k)}]$$

If we define

$$\Delta x^{(k)} = x - x^{(k)}$$

$$\Delta y^{(k)} = y - y^{(k)}$$

then from (8.36) and (8.38)

$$\Delta x^{(k)} = -\frac{a_{12}}{a_{11}} \Delta y^{(k-1)}$$

and from (8.37) and (8.39)

$$\Delta y^{(k)} = -\frac{a_{21}}{a_{22}} \Delta x^{(k)}$$

Combining these last two equations

$$\Delta x^{(k)} = \frac{a_{12}a_{21}}{a_{11}a_{22}} \Delta x^{(k-1)}$$

Similarly,

$$\Delta x^{(k-1)} = \frac{a_{12}a_{21}}{a_{11}a_{22}} \Delta x^{(k-2)}$$

so

$$\Delta x^{(k)} = \left(\frac{a_{12}a_{21}}{a_{11}a_{22}}\right)^2 \Delta x^{(k-2)}$$

Proceeding in this way

$$\Delta x^{(k)} = \left(\frac{a_{12}a_{21}}{a_{11}a_{22}}\right)^k \Delta x^{(0)}$$

Similarly,

$$\Delta y^{(k)} = \left(\frac{a_{12}a_{21}}{a_{11}a_{22}}\right)^k \Delta y^{(0)}$$

Thus if

(8.40)
$$\left|\frac{a_{12}a_{21}}{a_{11}a_{22}}\right| < 1$$

the process converges to a solution of (8.36) and (8.37).

The observant reader will see the analogy between this argument and the one used in discussing the convergence of the method of successive approximations in Section 5.2.

We can satisfy (8.40) if

(8.41)
$$\begin{cases} |a_{11}| > |a_{12}| \\ |a_{22}| \geq |a_{21}| \end{cases}$$

or if

(8.42)
$$\begin{cases} |a_{11}| \geq |a_{12}| \\ |a_{22}| > |a_{21}| \end{cases}$$

This says that the diagonal terms a_{11} and a_{22} must be *dominant*, that is, they must be at least as large as the off-diagonal terms and actually larger in at least one case.

Consider a simple example

$$2x + y = 2$$

$$x - 2y = -2$$

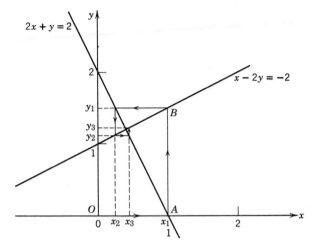

FIGURE 8.10   Geometrical representation of the method of Gauss-Seidel iteration in a convergent case.

The exact solution is $x = \frac{2}{5}$, $y = \frac{6}{5}$, as shown in Figure 8.10. The results of the iterations are

Iteration	x	y
0	0	0
1	1	$\frac{3}{2}$
2	$\frac{1}{4}$	$\frac{9}{8}$
3	$\frac{7}{16}$	$\frac{39}{32}$

A geometrical interpretation of the process will be instructive. We start at the origin $(0, 0)$. Since y is kept fixed in solving for x, we move along a horizontal line until we reach the line represented by the first equation $(2x + y = 2)$. Then, keeping x fixed, we move along a vertical line until we reach the line represented by the second equation $(x - 2y = -2)$. In Figure 8.10 we trace the path OAB. This completes one iteration.

We continue horizontally and vertically as shown by the arrows. Notice that the process is converging to a solution. Notice also the similarity between this situation and that described by Figure 5.2.

Let us now see what happens if we reverse the order of the equations, so that

$$x^{(k)} = -2 + 2y^{(k-1)}$$

$$y^{(k)} = 2 - 2x^{(k)}$$

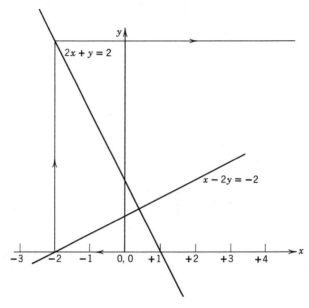

FIGURE 8.11   Geometrical representation of the method of Gauss-Seidel iteration in a divergent case.

The results are

Iteration	x	y
0	0	0
1	-2	6
2	10	-18
3	-38	78

The geometric interpretation is shown in Figure 8.11. Again, note the similarity to Figure 5.4. The difficulty is that the slope of the first equation is smaller than 1. Thus Δx tends to be large. Similarly, the large slope of the second line tends to make Δy large. In short, the process diverges.

Obviously, then, for the process to converge, the first equation should have a slope greater than 1 and the second equation should have a slope less than 1. That is precisely what (8.41) and (8.42) tell us.

Remember, however, that the actual condition we needed to satisfy was (8.40), which is not so rigid as either (8.41) or (8.42). We might ask this question: is it possible for the first equation to have a slope less than 1 and for the second equation to have such a small slope that it nevertheless forces convergence? Or, in other words, even though Δx may be large, if Δy is small enough can it overcome the effect of the large Δx?   The answer is yes.

Consider the following example:

$$x + 2y = \quad 3$$
$$x - 4y = -3$$

The slope of both equations is less than 1.   Thus

$$|a_{11}| < |a_{12}|$$

violating both (8.41) and (8.42).   Notice, however, that (8.40) is satisfied.   The geometric picture is shown in Figure 8.12.   The numerical results are

Iteration	x	y
0	0	0
1	3	$\frac{3}{2}$
2	0	$\frac{3}{4}$
3	$\frac{3}{2}$	$\frac{9}{8}$
4	$\frac{3}{4}$	$\frac{15}{16}$

The solution is $x = y = 1$.

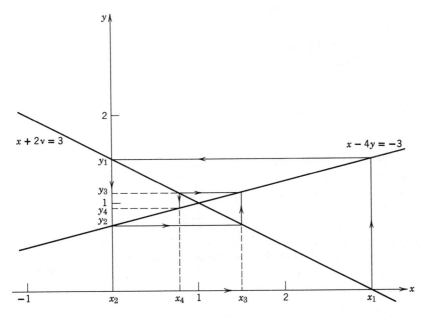

FIGURE 8.12   Geometrical representation of the method of Gauss-Seidel iteration in a case that is convergent even though it does not satisfy the sufficient conditions for convergence.

Thus the conditions (8.41) or (8.42) are *sufficient* conditions for convergence, but they are not *necessary*. That is to say, if either of them is satisfied, convergence is guaranteed, but there are systems that violate them that nevertheless converge.

We have seen an example in which the slope of the first line is less than -1 and the slope of the second line is positive but less than $+1$:

$$s_1 < -1$$

$$0 < s_2 < +1$$

This produced convergence of an oscillating nature, as we saw in Figure 8.10.

We have also seen an example in which

$$0 < s_1 < 1$$

$$s_2 < -1$$

This produced divergence of an oscillating nature, as in Figure 8.11.

It can easily be verified that if $|s_1| \geq 1$, $|s_2| \leq 1$, and at least one of the two is a strict inequality, then the following will hold:

1. If s_1 and s_2 have the same sign, the convergence is from one side.
2. If s_1 and s_2 have opposite signs, the convergence is oscillatory.

We may now proceed to a statement of sufficient conditions for the convergence of the Gauss-Seidel iteration method for n equations.

If the equations are irreducible* and

$$|a_{ii}| \geq |a_{i1}| + \cdots + |a_{i,i-1}| + |a_{i,i+1}| + \cdots + |a_{in}|$$

for all i, and if for at least one i

$$|a_{ii}| > |a_{i1}| + \cdots + |a_{i,i-1}| + |a_{i,i+1}| + \cdots + |a_{in}|$$

then the Gauss-Seidel method converges to a solution of (8.13).

These conditions guarantee convergence. We emphasize that they are by no means necessary   They are a proper generalization of (8.41) and (8.42).

It may occur to the reader to wonder whether these rather stringent conditions leave any practical applicability for the Gauss-Seidel method. As a matter of fact, they do.   Systems of equations occur in a number of different areas in which the method of generation of the coefficients automatically guarantees that these conditions will be met.   This is

---

* This means that they cannot be rearranged so that some of the variables can be solved for by solving less than n equations.   (See Exercise 24.)

particularly true with many of the equations resulting from the methods of solution of partial differential equations, as we shall see in Chapter 11.

One final note is in order to prepare for Chapter 11. From the similarity with the developments in Chapter 5 we might expect that overshooting (extrapolation) or undershooting (interpolation) might speed up convergence. This is, in fact, the case. We postpone the discussion until Chapter 11.

8.7 Comparison of the methods

We have discussed two basic methods of solving simultaneous linear algebraic equations: Gauss elimination and Gauss-Seidel iteration. The question is naturally which is preferable.

Gauss elimination has the advantage that it is finite and works— in theory—for any nonsingular set of equations. The Gauss-Seidel iteration method converges only for special systems of equations. For some systems elimination is the only course available.*

When iteration works, however, it is usually preferable.

1. The effort is proportional to n^2 per iteration, whereas in elimination it is proportional to n^3. If fewer than n iterations are required for convergence, the total effort is less.

2. In general the roundoff error is smaller, which is often important enough to justify additional computing effort.

Many systems of equations arising in practice are *sparse*, that is, they contain a high proportion of zeros. In these cases iteration— if it works—is highly preferable, since elimination usually produces a triangular system that is no longer sparse.† In computer terms a sparse system is desirable because we can test the coefficients and not multiply at all when they are zero. Equations derived from partial differential equations fall into this class.

Finally, some systems of equations are so large that they not only cannot be accurately solved by elimination but will not even fit into the high-speed storage of the computer. If the coefficients are machine-generated the latter difficulty can be overcome in iteration

---

* Actually, iteration methods exist for solving *any* nonsingular system, but they are usually impractical. See, for instance, W. E. Milne, *Numerical Solution of Differential Equations*, Wiley, 1953, Section 76.

† Some special sparse systems do remain sparse when reduced to triangular form by Gauss elimination. (See Exercise 10.)

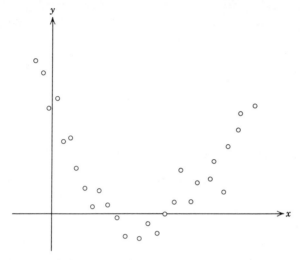

FIGURE 8.13 Illustrative experimental data for which an approximate functional relationship is sought. (Case Study 10.)

by generating each equation as it is needed (only one equation is needed at a time).   Once again, equations derived from partial differential equations fall into this class.

8.8   Case study 10: Least squares curve fitting

It is frequently necessary to represent by a functional relationship data that is given in the form of a set of x-y-points.   Suppose, for instance, that we have run some sort of experiment and have obtained the x-y-points plotted in Figure 8.13.   If these points are to be used in a computer calculation, we are now faced with several problems.

1. There are experimental errors in the y-values.*   We would like somehow to "smooth" the variations due to experimental error.
2. We may very well want to know the value of y corresponding to some x that lies between two experimental x-values.
3. It may be desirable—indeed, it may be the major purpose of the calculation—to *extrapolate*, that is, to find the y-value corresponding

---

* And perhaps in the x-values, too.   The treatment of uncertainty in the x-values is beyond the scope of this treatment, in which we shall assume that they are exact.

to an x-value outside the range of the experimental x-values.   This is particularly true of projections of economic data.

All of these considerations lead to the need for a functional relationship between x and y in the form of a formula, and hopefully a simple one.   The question then is to find a curve that *approximates* the given data with sufficient accuracy.   The first issue facing us is this: how shall we decide whether a given curve is a good "fit" to the data?

This discussion will be simpler if we now define a new term.   The *deviation* at a data point is the difference between the experimental y-value and the y-value computed from a functional relationship. The question of fitting a curve to the data can be rephrased: what condition should be placed on the deviations to lead to a suitable curve?

One possibility that might seem appealing would be to ask for the sum of the deviations to be as small as possible.   If we use a prime to denote a y-value computed from the functional relationship to be found, this means to ask that

$$\sum_{i=1}^{N} (y_i - y_i')$$

be a minimum, where N is the number of data points.   But the attractiveness disappears when we consider the simple case of fitting a line to two points, as in Figure 8.14.   We see that the dotted line

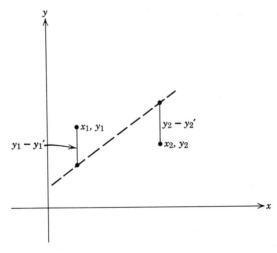

FIGURE 8.14   Example showing that minimizing the sum of the deviations is not a satisfactory criterion of goodness of fit.   (Case Study 10.)

satisfies the criterion just stated without producing a satisfactory fit. We could avoid this difficulty by specifying absolute values, asking to minimize

$$\sum_{i=1}^{N} |y_i - y_i'|$$

But now we cannot differentiate to find a minimum because the absolute-value function has no derivative at its minimum. We might think of asking that the maximum error be a minimum, which is the Chebyshev approximation, but this leads to a complex iterative procedure for finding the functional relation.

We thus reach to the *least-squares* criterion, in which we ask for a minimum of

$$\sum_{i=1}^{N} (y_i - y_i')^2$$

This can be differentiated, as we shall see in a moment, to find its minimum. It leads to equations that in many cases of practical interest are linear and, in principle at least, easy to solve. Finally, there are statistical considerations to suggest that the least-squares criterion is a good one apart from its easy computability.

Let us now see how the least-squares criterion produces a system of equations for finding a functional relationship. We shall do this first for a specific relation, a quadratic, and then sketch the situation for other relations.*

We write

$$y_i' = c_1 + c_2 x_i + c_3 x_i^2$$

The goal is to determine c_1, c_2, and c_3 in order to minimize

$$S = \sum_{i=1}^{N} (y_i - y_i')^2 = \sum_{i=1}^{N} (y_i - c_1 - c_2 x_i - c_3 x_i^2)^2$$

We know that to minimize S, considered as a function of c_1, we set

---

* We assume, however, that the *form* of the relationship is chosen in advance. The least-squares method will never tell us, for instance, that an exponential relation would have produced a good fit, *unless we try it*. In short, we will find the best relation of an assumed type; it would clearly be impossible for any method of fitting to identify the best of all possible functions.

the partial derivative of S with respect to c_1 equal to zero.* The result is

$$\frac{\partial S}{\partial c_1} = (-2) \sum (y_i - c_1 - c_2 x_i - c_3 x_i^2)$$

Setting this equal to zero and rearranging, we get

$$N c_1 + (\Sigma x_i) c_2 + (\Sigma x_i^2) c_3 = \Sigma y_i$$

Differentiating S with respect to c_2 and c_3 in turn and setting each result equal to zero, we get two more equations in the unknowns c_1, c_2, and c_3. The three simultaneous equations in these three unknowns are called *normal equations* for fitting a quadratic to a set of data:

$$N c_1 + (\Sigma x_i) c_2 + (\Sigma x_i^2) c_3 = \Sigma y_i$$

$$(\Sigma x_i) c_1 + (\Sigma x_i^2) c_2 + (\Sigma x_i^3) c_3 = \Sigma (x_i y_i)$$

$$(\Sigma x_i^2) c_1 + (\Sigma x_i^3) c_2 + (\Sigma x_i^4) c_3 = \Sigma (x_i^2 y_i)$$

To find our "best" quadratic for the given data, we need only perform the necessary summations and solve the system of three equations.

The same methods can be used to derive normal equations for fitting a polynomial of any degree to a set of data. (We shall see, however,

---

* Readers not comfortable with operations on summations may rely on the following simple identities, in which a is any nonzero constant and x_i and y_i are any variables.

1. $$\sum_{i=1}^{N} (x_i + y_i) = \sum_{i=1}^{N} x_i + \sum_{i=1}^{N} y_i$$

2. $$\sum_{i=1}^{N} (a x_i) = a \sum_{i=1}^{N} x_i$$

3. $$\frac{d}{dx} \sum_{i=1}^{N} f(x_i) = \sum_{i=1}^{N} \left[\frac{d}{dx} f(x_i) \right]$$

4. $$\sum_{i=1}^{N} a = N a$$

Henceforth we shall assume that the summations extend over all the data points, that is, that the symbol $\sum$ should be understood to mean $\sum_{i=1}^{N}$.

that roundoff errors set practical limits on the degree of polynomial that can be employed.) We may write the normal equations for fitting a polynomial of degree M as follows:

$$Nc_1 + \Sigma x_i c_2 + \cdots + \Sigma x_i^M c_{M+1} = \Sigma y_i$$

$$\Sigma x_i c_1 + \Sigma x_i^2 c_2 + \cdots + \Sigma x_i^{M+1} c_{M+1} = \Sigma(x_i y_i)$$

$$\cdots \cdots \cdots \cdots \cdots \cdots \cdots \cdots \cdots$$

$$\Sigma x_i^M c_1 + \Sigma x_i^{M+1} c_2 + \cdots + \Sigma x_i^{2M} c_{M+1} = \Sigma(x_i^M y_i)$$

For a polynomial of degree M, there are $M + 1$ equations, corresponding to the $M + 1$ free parameters. A total of $3M + 1$ summations is required.

It may be recalled that FORTRAN subscripts must be greater than zero. Since the coefficients c_i will be the elements of a one-dimensional array in the program we shall discuss shortly, the subscripts have been numbered from 1 rather than from the more conventional zero.

Before proceeding to a consideration of a program to develop the necessary sums and solve the normal equations, we may pause to observe that least-squares curve fitting can be applied to functions other than polynomials. For instance, suppose we wish to fit an exponential:

$$y = ax^b$$

A direct application of the techniques used before leads to nonlinear equations; we can avoid this difficulty by taking logarithms:

$$\log y = \log a + b \log x$$

Now we minimize the square of the differences between the logarithms of the experimental y values and the expression on the right in the foregoing equation:

$$S = \Sigma(\log y_i - \log a - b \log x_i)^2$$

Differentiating with respect to a and b, as before, we obtain the following normal equations:

$$N \log a + \Sigma(\log x_i)b = \Sigma \log y_i$$

$$\Sigma(\log x_i) \log a + \Sigma(\log x_i)^2 b = \Sigma(\log x_i \log y_i)$$

The unknowns here are $\log a$ and b; when they have been found, one final exponentiation gives a.

In principle, least-squares curve fitting can be applied to fit any function, although it will often lead to nonlinear equations. A few other types of functions are suggested in the exercises.

Let us now return to the question of writing a generalized program to perform a least-squares polynomial curve fit. The program is to be able to fit any polynomial from first to tenth degree, with the degree specified by a data card. There must be provision for reading the data pairs, forming the necessary summations, solving the normal equations, and printing the results.

A program to do all this, solving the system by Gauss elimination, is shown in Figure 8.15. It may be helpful to list the names of the principal variables and their meanings.

NUMBER   The actual number of x-y data pairs; maximum of 200

M   The degree of the polynomial; maximum of 10

N   The number of equations ($= M + 1$)

X, Y   Arrays for the data pairs

A   Array for the sums, which become the coefficients of the unknowns in the simultaneous equations

B   Array for the constant terms in the simultaneous equations

C   Array for the unknowns, which become the coefficients in the polynomial

P   Array for the powers of the x_i, from 1 to $2M$

Two DIMENSION statements are used only because of the page-size limitation in this book. The reading of the x-y pairs is set up in a

```
C FOR COMMENT
STATEMENT
NUMBER
1    5 6 7                        FORTRAN STATEMENT

        DIMENSION X(200), Y(200), A(11), B(11)
        DIMENSION C(11), P(20)
        READ 20, M
   20   FORMAT (I2)
        DO 1, I = 1, 20
        READ 10, X(I), Y(I)
   10   FORMAT (2F10.0)
        IF (X(I)) 1, 1, 2
    1   CONTINUE
        STOP
    2   NUMBER = I - 1
        MX2 = M * 2
        DO 3, I = 1, MX2
        P(I) = 0.0
        DO 3, J = 1, NUMBER
    3   P(I) = P(I) + X(J)**I
```

FIGURE 8.15   A program for least squares curve fitting.   Page 1: reading the data, forming the powers of x. (Case Study 10.)

DO loop so that the DO index will indicate the number of pairs. The end of the data is signaled by an x-value of zero. (If zero could be a legitimate data value, some other sentinel would have to be used; this could easily be done.) The normal exit from the DO can occur only when there are more than 200 pairs; if there are 200 or fewer, the IF statement takes us out of this loop to statement 12. At this point the DO index (I) will be one greater than the number of data cards, since it counted the sentinel card.

The last few statements on the first page of the program form the powers of x, placing them in the array P for use immediately following.

```
        C FOR COMMENT
┌──────────────────────┐
│ STATEMENT  │         │
│ NUMBER     │         │              FORTRAN STATEMENT
│ 1      5 │6│7
├──────────────────────┤
│          │ N = M + 1
│          │ DO 30 I = 1, N
│          │ DO 30 J = 1, M
│          │ K = I + J - 2
│          │ IF (K) 29, 29, 28
│     28   │ A (I, J) = P (K)
│          │ GO TO 30
│     29   │ A (I, 1) = NUMBER
│     30   │ CONTINUE
│          │ B (1) = 0.0
│          │ DO 21 J = 1, NUMBER
│     21   │ B (1) = B (1) + Y (J)
│          │ DO 22 I = 2, N
│          │ B (I) = 0.0
│          │ DO 22 J = 1, NUMBER
│     22   │ B (I) = B (I) + Y (J) * X (J) ** (I - 1)
│          │
└──────────────────────┘
```

FIGURE 8.15 Page 2: developing the coefficients and the constant terms of the normal equations. (Case Study 10.)

A study of the generalized system of normal equations reveals the following pattern: except for the element in the first row and first column, the power of x in each element is the sum of its row number and its column number, less 2. This fact is used in the statements in the first half of the second page of the program to set up the coefficients of the unknowns. Following this, the summations needed for the constant terms are formed. B(1) has to be formed separately because we cannot say in general what FORTRAN will do when asked to raise a number to the zero power.

Incidentally, no claim will be made that these sums are formed in the most efficient manner possible.   The job could indeed be done much more rapidly, perhaps at the expense of using more storage. This was not felt to be worth the trouble here, where we wish to concentrate on basic concepts.

The third page of the program starts the Gauss elimination, carrying the processing as far as the pivotal condensation.   The program follows the block diagram of Figure 8.8 quite closely.   The one exception is that the last box, "$i = k + 1$," is not set up explicitly, since this is done in the DO statement that follows on the last page.

On the last page statements 500 through 300 carry out the elimi-

```
         N,M,I, =, M, -, I,

         D,Ø, 3,0,0, ,K, =, I,,, N,M,I,

         K,P,I, =, K, +, I,

         L, =, K,

         D,Ø, 4,0,0, ,I, =, K,P,I,,, N,

         I,F, ,(,A,B,S,F,(,A,(,I,,, ,K,),), -, ,A,B,S,F,(,A,(,L,,, ,K,),),), ,4,0,0,,, 4,0,0,,, 4,0,I,

   4,0,I   L, =, I,

   4,0,0   C,Ø,N,T,I,N,U,E,

         I,F, ,(,L, -, K,), ,5,0,0,,, 5,0,0,,, 4,0,5,

   4,0,5   D,Ø, 4,1,0, ,J, =, K,,, N,

         T,E,M,P, =, A,(,K,,, J,),

         A,(,K,,, J,), =, A,(,L,,, J,),

   4,1,0   A,(,L,,, J,), =, T,E,M,P,

         T,E,M,P, =, B,(,K,),

         B,(,K,), =, B,(,L,),

         B,(,L,), =, T,E,M,P,
```

FIGURE 8.15   Page 3: pivotal condensation.   (Case Study 10.)

nation process.   It should be borne in mind that statement 300 is the end of the range of *two* DO loops: the one at the top of the third page that controls K and statement 500 controlling I.   The first of these uses all equations from the first to the N − 1(st) to eliminate variables; the second eliminates variable K from all equations from the K + 1(st) to the Nth.

The back substituation begins after statement 300.   The processing follows the block diagram of Figure 8.6 fairly closely, with some obvious changes to make the program more compact.

For a first trial of the program let us generate some data from a

```
STATEMENT
NUMBER                          FORTRAN STATEMENT
1      5  6 7

 500    DØ 300 I = KP1, N
        FACTØR = A(I, K) / A(K, K)
        A(I, K) = 0.0
        DØ 301 J = KP1, N
 301    A(I, J) = A(I, J) - FACTØR * A(K, J)
 300    B(I) = B(I) - FACTØR * B(K)
        C(N) = B(N) / A(N, N)
        I = NM1
 710    IP1 = I + 1
        SUM = 0.0
        DØ 700 J = IP1, N
 700    SUM = SUM + A(I, J) * C(J)
        C(I) = (B(I) - SUM) / A(I, I)
        I = I - 1
        IF (I) 800, 800, 710
 800    DØ 900 I = 1, N
 900    PRINT 901, I, C(I)
 901    FØRMAT (I5, F15.7)
        STØP
        END
```

FIGURE 8.15   Page 4: elimination, back solution, and printing results.   (Case Study 10.)

known equation, and see whether the program will give us the equation back.   Take

$$y = 2 + 4x + x^2$$

and from it generate the following data points:

x	y
1	7
2	14
3	23
4	34
5	47

Setting M = 2 and providing the five x-y pairs shown, the program clearly ought to give us back $c_1 = 2$, $c_2 = 4$, and $c_3 = 1$.   The computed results are fairly close:

$$c_1 = 1.9999947$$

$$c_2 = 4.0000044$$

$$c_3 = 0.9999993$$

It might be interesting to see what would happen if we tried to fit a cubic to the same data; the first three coefficients *ought* to be the same, and c_4 ought to be zero.   The actual results:

$$c_1 = \quad 2.0001345$$

$$c_2 = \quad 3.9998111$$

$$c_3 = \quad 1.0000721$$

$$c_4 = \quad -0.0000080$$

The variation in the results is perhaps a little more than one might expect.   Does disaster lie ahead?   How about a fourth degree?

$$c_1 = \quad 1.9959750$$

$$c_2 = \quad 4.0075371$$

$$c_3 = \quad 0.9954456$$

$$c_4 = \quad 0.0010951$$

$$c_5 = \quad -0.0000907$$

This is really not very good.   All we are asking, in this case, is that a fourth-degree polynomial be passed through five points, and five points ought to determine a fourth-degree polynomial exactly.

We would expect some trouble if we tried to fit a fifth-degree polynomial to five points: there are infinitely many fifth-degree curves that pass through five specified points.   We would expect, therefore, that an attempt to do such a fit would lead to a system of equations having infinitely many solutions.

In terms of the Gauss elimination process, this should lead to a row consisting of all zeros, and if the back solution is attempted a division by zero should stop the process.   (Exercise 36 asks you to demonstrate this for the case of attempting to pass a quadratic through two arbitrary points.)   Let us try it anyway:

$$c_1 = \quad 2.0754113$$

$$c_2 = \quad 3.8280203$$

$$c_3 = \quad 1.1410277$$

$$c_4 = \quad -0.0532048$$

$$c_5 = \quad 0.0093776$$

$$c_6 = \quad -0.0006245$$

Thus we see the full perversity of roundoff errors: things will not even *fail* when they should!

We are being led to serious doubts about the accuracy of some step in this process. Let us try another example to see just how bad things can get. From the equation

$$y = 40 + 10x + 5x^2 + 3x^3 + 2x^4 + x^5 + x^6$$

we generate y-values for $x = 1, 2, 3, \ldots, 50$, then try to fit a sixth-degree polynomial. The first coefficient was printed as 1018375.2890625; it may, in fact, have been larger, with the additional digits dropped because of the way the FORMAT statement was written. This is clearly meaningless, as were the other values printed.

Something has obviously broken down completely. Was it the formation of the summations? The solution of the normal equations? Or perhaps the least-squares procedure has failed? Let us see if we can devise tests to establish the source of the trouble.

Let us try this same function, but with a smaller range of x-values: $x = 1.0, 1.1, 1.2, \ldots, 5.0$. There will be 50 x-y pairs, as before, and still a sixth-degree polynomial. The results this time are

$$c_1 = 41.3747716$$

$$c_2 = 1.4650151$$

$$c_3 = 19.4771159$$

$$c_4 = -7.3396831$$

$$c_5 = 5.5579804$$

$$c_6 = 0.4154199$$

$$c_7 = 1.0368103$$

Compared with the true values, these are surely not very confidence-inspiring, but they are at least somewhere in the right range. This suggests that part of the difficulty with the preceding system was the range of sizes of the different summations. This stands to reason. The value of a_{11} in the normal equations is just 50, whereas a_{77} is in the neighborhood of 10^{21}. With computer numbers that are the equivalent of eight decimal digits, we are clearly going to have trouble working with this range of sizes, along the lines of the computation of the sines of large angles in Case Study 3.

The difficulty is with both the formation of the summations and in the Gauss elimination. When 49, for instance, is raised to the twelfth power, some digits at the right-hand end are lost; these cannot be recovered when the elimination process should have reduced these quantities to smaller values.   And even if the sums were exact, round-off errors in the elimination process itself would preclude accurate results.

We can satisfy ourselves that the trouble is roundoff error and not the least-squares method by using double precision.   In the computer employed here this means that all arithmetic is done with the equivalent of 16 decimal digits.   The results for the original values $x = 1, 2, 3, \ldots , 50$

$$c_1 = 39.9945393$$

$$c_2 = 10.0036631$$

$$c_3 = 4.9993401$$

$$c_4 = 3.0000494$$

$$c_5 = 1.9999982$$

$$c_6 = 1.0000000$$

$$c_7 = 1.0000000$$

These are quite respectable, all things considered.

The reader might nevertheless pause to ponder the state of affairs brought on by a particularly severe case of roundoff trouble: in an application in which simple theory predicts certain exact results, we had to use 16-digit arithmetic to get four reliable digits in the answers.

The reader interested in a more complete exposition of the source of the trouble here is referred to Arden's excellent treatment.*

The way out of the problem is to use *orthogonal polynomials*.   For example, in Exercise 3 of Chapter 3 we found that the Chebyshev polynomials are orthogonal over the interval $-1 \leq x \leq 1$ with the proper weighting function.   If we use $T_n(x)$ in our approximating polynomial, the off-diagonal terms in general will be small compared with the diagonal terms.   This permits more accurate solutions and sometimes even allows for solution by the Gauss-Seidel method.

Ideally, of course, we would like the off-diagonal terms to vanish because then the solution is trivial.   The interested reader is referred to the paper by Forsythe.†

We have chosen to present these illustrations to impress on the

---

* Bruce W. Arden, *An Introduction to Digital Computing*, Addison-Wesley, 1963. The general treatment of approximation methods (least squares, Chebyshev, polynomial, etc.) is also good.

† G. E. Forsythe, "Generation and Use of Orthogonal Polynomials for Data Fitting with a Digital Computer," *SIAM J.*, **5**, 74–88 (June 1957).

reader the seriousness of roundoff error in extreme cases. We do not wish to leave the impression, however, that least squares is always rendered useless by such problems. To dispel such an impression, let us close this case study with a simple example of a perfectly straightforward application of the technique.

Following Worthing and Geffner,[*] we list the values of the specific heat of water as a function of temperature, in terms of the 15° calorie.

T, °C	c_p	T, °C	c_p
0	1.00762	55	0.99919
5	1.00392	60	0.99967
10	1.00153	65	1.00024
15	1.00000	70	1.00091
20	0.99907	75	1.00167
25	0.99852	80	1.00253
30	0.99826	85	1.00351
35	0.99818	90	1.00461
40	0.99828	95	1.00586
45	0.99849	100	1.00721
50	0.99878		

A quick plot of the data suggests that a quadratic would be fairly close and that a cubic ought to be quite good. Using the program to fit a cubic, we get

$$c_p = 1.006447 - 0.0004987884T + 0.000008459123T^2$$
$$- 0.00000003453391T^3$$

Roundoff leads to no difficulties this time, as we can see by rerunning in double precision. The coefficients thus computed differ only slightly from the single-precision results, and the sum of the squares of the deviations is the same.

Figure 8.16 shows a plot of the fitted curve with experimental values (small circles). We see that the positive and negative deviations are more or less balanced, as we would expect. A comparison of the computed values and the experimental values shows a maximum deviation of 0.0012 at 0°C, with most deviations being considerably less.

If errors of this size are acceptable, we can now use the fitted cubic in any calculation that requires the specific heat of water as a function of temperature.

---

[*] Archie G. Worthing and Joseph Geffner, *Treatment of Experimental Data*, Wiley, 1943, p. 268.

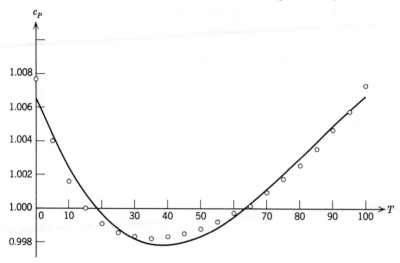

FIGURE 8.16   Experimental values of the specific heat of water (circles) and a fitted cubic.   (Case Study 10.)

Exercises

*1. Solve the following system of simultaneous equations by the method of Gauss elimination.   No row interchanges will be necessary.

$$x - y + z = -4$$
$$5x - 4y + 3z = -12$$
$$2x + y + z = 11$$

2. Solve the following system of simultaneous equations by the method of Gauss elimination.   No row interchanges will be necessary.

$$w + x + y + z = 10$$
$$2w + 3x + y + 5z = 31$$
$$-w + x - 5y + 3z = -2$$
$$3w + x + 7y - 2z = 18$$

*3. Solve the following system by Gauss elimination, using four-digit floating point arithmetic and row interchanges.

$$2x + 6y - z = -12$$
$$5x - y + 2z = 29$$
$$-3x - 4y + z = 5$$

4. Attempt to solve the following system by Gauss elimination. What happens and what causes the trouble?

$$x + y + z = 2$$
$$2x - 3y + z = 11$$
$$4x - y + 3z = 10$$

5. Attempt to solve the following system by Gauss elimination. What happens and what causes the trouble?

$$2x - 3y + 4z = 8$$
$$4x + 2y - 3z = -1$$
$$6x + 7y - 10z = -10$$

*6. Solve the following system by Gauss elimination, using complex arithmetic throughout.

$$(2 + 3i)x + (2 - i)y = 2 + i$$
$$(4 + 6i)x + (3 - 6i)y = -2 - 5i$$

7. In the system of Exercise 6 write $x = x_r + x_i i$, $y = y_r + y_i i$. Multiply out and equate the real and imaginary parts of each equation separately. Show that the result is a system of four equations in four unknowns, the solution of which gives the real and imaginary parts of the solution of Exercise 6.

*8. Solve the following system by Gauss elimination, first without row interchanges and then with row interchanges, using four-digit floating point arithmetic.

$$x + 592y = 437$$
$$592x + 4308y = 2251$$

9. Recall that in solving (8.5), (8.6), and (8.7) by Gauss elimination we first eliminated x_1 and obtained

(8.5) $$a_{11}x_1 + a_{12}x_2 + a_{13}x_3 = b_1$$
(8.9) $$a_{22}'x_2 + a_{23}'x_3 = b_2'$$
(8.10) $$a_{32}'x_2 + a_{33}'x_3 = b_3'$$

We then defined a multiplier

$$m_3' = \frac{a_{32}'}{a_{22}'}$$

and subtracted m_3' times (8.9) from (8.10) to obtain

(8.11) $$a_{33}''x_3 = b_3''$$

Show that if we define

$$m_1' = \frac{a_{12}}{a_{22}},$$

and subtract m_1' times (8.9) from (8.5) we obtain

(*) $$a_{11}'x_1 + a_{13}'x_3 = b_1'$$

Find expressions for a_{11}', a_{13}', and b_1'.
Now define multipliers

$$m_1'' = \frac{a_{13}'}{a_{33}'}$$

$$m_2'' = \frac{a_{23}'}{a_{33}'}$$

Show that if we subtract m_1'' times (8.10) from the equation marked (*) and m_2'' times (8.10) from (8.9) the resulting three equations are of the form

$$a_{11}''x_1 = b_1''$$

$$a_{22}''x_2 = b_2''$$

$$a_{33}''x_3 = b_3''$$

Find expressions for a_{11}'', a_{22}'', and a_{33}''.
Notice that these three equations may be solved *without* back substitution. This method of elimination is called the *Gauss-Jordan method*.

10. Consider the following "sparse" set of equations.

$$2x_1 - x_2 = 1$$

$$-x_1 + 2x_2 - x_3 = 1$$

$$- x_2 + 2x_3 - x_4 = 1$$

$$- x_3 + 2x_4 - x_5 = 1$$

$$- x_4 + 2x_5 - x_6 = 1$$

$$- x_5 + 2x_6 = 1$$

Show that the system remains sparse when reduced to triangular form by Gauss elimination. A system like the original set is called *tridiagonal* because of the arrangement of the coefficients. Such systems appear frequently in the solution of partial differential equations. (See Chapter 11.)

11. Suppose you wish to solve two sets of simultaneous linear equations that are identical except for their right-hand sides. If Gauss elimination is used, would the triangular sets of equations for the two sets differ on the left-hand sides? On the right-hand sides?

Describe an addition to the Gauss elimination method as stated in the text that will find the solutions to both sets of equations with only one elimination process.

12. The method suggested in Exercise 11 applies as well to three different right-hand sides. Using the technique, solve the following three sets of equations.

$$x - y \quad\ = 1$$
$$x + y + z = 0$$
$$y - z = 0$$

$$x - y \quad\ = 0$$
$$x + y + z = 1$$
$$y - z = 0$$

$$x - y \quad\ = 0$$
$$x + y + z = 0$$
$$y - z = 1$$

Now let x_1, y_1, z_1 be the solution to the first set, x_2, y_2, z_2 the solution to the second set, and x_3, y_3, z_3 the solution to the third set. Show that the solution to the system

$$x - y \quad\ = b_1$$
$$x + y + z = b_2$$
$$y - z = b_3$$

is given by

$$x = b_1 x_1 + b_2 x_2 + b_3 x_3$$
$$y = b_1 y_1 + b_2 y_2 + b_3 y_3$$
$$z = b_1 z_1 + b_2 z_2 + b_3 z_3$$

What conclusion can you draw from this example regarding the number of sets of equations that must be solved in order to be able to obtain the solution for *any* right-hand side in a straightforward manner?

13. Using the method of Section 8.4, refine the solution to the system in Exercise 8 that you found *without* row interchanges.

*14. The following system has the approximate solution $x_1 = 2$, $x_2 = 3$, $x_3 = 4$. Refine it by using the method in Section 8.4.

$$1.781x_1 + 3.008x_2 - 4.880x_3 = -7.704$$
$$4.632x_1 - 1.064x_2 - 2.274x_3 = -6.359$$
$$-3.387x_1 + 9.814x_2 - 4.779x_3 = \quad 3.946$$

15. The following system has the approximate solution $x = 10$, $y = -3.99$. Refine it, first using four-digit floating point arithmetic, then six-digit floating point arithmetic.

$$234x + 546y = 156$$

$$158x + 371y = 103$$

16. In the system of Exercise 15 change the 371 to 371.2 and resolve. Compare the percentage change in the coefficient with the resulting percentage change in y.

*17. In the following system assume that the a_{ij} are precise but that the b_i are given to two decimal places. Find the bounds on the errors in the solution. Do this first with the equations as written, then repeat with the equations reversed.

$$x + y = 2$$

$$x + 2y = 3$$

*18. Consider the following system.

$$x - y + 4z = 6$$

$$2x + 3y - z = 18$$

$$3x + y + z = 19$$

Solve the system without row interchanges (which, as we have seen in Exercise 17, would change the error bounds) and find the bounds on the errors in the solution under the following assumptions:

a. The a_{ij} are precise; the b_i are given to two decimals.
b. The b_i are precise; the a_{ij} are given to two decimals.
c. The a_{ij} and b_i are both given to two decimals.
d. The a_{ij} and b_i both have two significant figures.

19. Same as Exercise 18, with the following system:

$$2x + y + z = 7$$

$$2x + 2y + 3z = 10$$

$$-4x + 4y + 5z = 14$$

*20. Solve the following system by the method of Gauss-Seidel iteration, continuing the iteration process until the maximum difference between successive values of x, y, or z is less than 0.02. Does this mean that the approximate solution is within 0.02 of the exact solution?

$$10x + 2y + 6z = 28$$

$$x + 10y + 9z = 7$$

$$2x - 7y - 10z = -17$$

21. Solve the following system by the method of Gauss-Seidel iteration, continuing the iteration process until the maximum difference between successive values of x, y, or z is less than 0.02. Compare the convergence rate with that in Exercise 20. Why the difference?

$$20x + 2y + 6z = 38$$
$$x + 20y + 9z = -23$$
$$2x - 7y - 20z = -57$$

22. Consider two simultaneous equations

$$a_1x + b_1y = c_1$$
$$a_2x + b_2y = c_2$$

Let s_1 be the slope of the first equation and let s_2 be the slope of the second. Show the following:

a. If $s_1 > 1$ and $-1 < s_2 < 0$, the convergence by Gauss-Seidel iteration is oscillatory.
b. If $s_1 > 1$ and $0 < s_2 < 1$, the convergence by Gauss-Seidel iteration is from one side.
c. If $s_1 < -1$ and $-1 < s_2 < 0$, the convergence by Gauss-Seidel iteration is from one side.

23. Consider the two linear equations

$$a_{11}x_1 + a_2x_{12} = b_1$$
$$a_{21}x_1 + a_{22}x_2 = b_2$$

Suppose we use the following iteration procedure to solve these two equations:

$$x_1^{(k)} = \frac{1}{a_{11}} (b_1 - a_{12}x_2^{(k-1)})$$

$$x_2^{(k)} = \frac{1}{a_{22}} (b_2 - a_{21}x_1^{(k-1)})$$

a. Show that a necessary and sufficient condition for convergence of the iteration procedure is

$$\left| \frac{a_{12}a_{21}}{a_{11}a_{22}} \right| < 1$$

Compare this with the condition for the Gauss-Seidel method.
b. Show that the Gauss-Seidel method converges twice as fast as this method.
c. Verify the relative rates of convergence stated in (b) by carrying out four iterations on

$$2x + y = 2$$
$$x - 2y = -2$$

and comparing with the results for the Gauss-Seidel method shown on p. 257.

d. Give a geometric interpretation of this iterative method.

24. Which of the following systems of equations are *reducible?*   (See footnote on p. 260.)

a.

$$-x_1 \qquad + 3x_3 + x_4 = 3$$
$$3x_1 + 2x_2 + x_3 - 2x_4 = 4$$
$$2x_1 \qquad\qquad + 4x_4 = 6$$
$$x_3 - x_4 = 0$$

b.

$$-x_1 \qquad + 3x_3 + x_4 = 3$$
$$3x_1 + 2x_2 + x_3 - 2x_4 = 4$$
$$2x_2 \qquad + 4x_4 = 6$$
$$x_3 - x_4 = 0$$

c.

$$x_2 + x_3 = 2$$
$$x_1 \qquad - x_3 = 0$$
$$2x_1 + x_2 \qquad = 3$$

d.

$$x_1 + 2x_2 \qquad = 3$$
$$x_1 + x_2 + x_3 = 3$$
$$2x_1 + x_2 \qquad = 3$$

25. Solve the following four equations by the Gauss-Seidel method:

$$x_1 \qquad\qquad + x_4 = 2$$
$$x_1 + 4x_2 \qquad - x_4 = 4$$
$$x_1 \qquad + x_3 \qquad = 2$$
$$x_3 + x_4 = 2$$

Do the coefficients in these equations satisfy the inequalities required for convergence? Why does the process diverge? What is the solution of these equations?

26. Referring to the program of Figure 8.15 in Case Study 10, suppose we had an array named NROW. It is one-dimensional with 11 elements; at the beginning of the program each element is loaded with its element number, so that NROW(I) = I. Let us pretend that a variable in a FORTRAN subscript expression can itself be subscripted, and consider a modification of the program as follows.

a. When the pivotal condensation search has established that rows L and K should be interchanged, interchange NROW(L) and NROW(K) but leave the actual coefficients unchanged.

b. On the third and fourth pages of Figure 8.15, whenever a subscript, say I, refers to a row number, write NROW(I) in place of I. For instance, statement 301 would become

301 A(NROW(I), J) = A(NROW(I), J) − FACTOR*A(NROW(K), J)

Devise a small example to show that if FORTRAN permitted such subscripts the Gauss elimination process would be carried out properly without ever actually performing any row interchanges.

Some algebraic compilers do permit such subscripts, sometimes with time penalties. Many computers have a feature called *indirect addressing* that reduces the time penalty considerably.

*27. FORTRAN of course does not permit variables in subscript expressions to be subscripted. However, we can program the same thing by preceding each statement in which a row number appears as a subscript, with one or more statements that accomplish the same result. Indicate with an example how this can be done.

28. Write a program to do row *and column* pivotal condensation without any actual interchanges, following the ideas in Exercises 26 and 27. Demonstrate with an example that the problem of variable identification in column interchanges is properly handled.

29. Write a program to solve a system of six simultaneous equations by Gauss-Jordan elimination (see Exercise 9), assuming that the coefficients and constant terms are given.

30. Modify the program in Figure 8.15 so that if D is a one-dimensional array containing a second right-hand side both systems will be solved in one elimination process.

31. Modify the program in Exercise 30 so that the elements of D are initially set to +1 and all operations on D involve addition of absolute values. The back solution, again adding absolute values and ignoring any minus signs in division, will produce the Δ_i of Section 8.5.

32. Write a program to solve a system of N equations by Gauss-Seidel iteration, following the block diagram in Figure 8.9.

33. Write a program to evaluate an Nth order determinant. Use Gauss elimination to form a triangular system, then form the product of the main diagonal elements; this product is the determinant. If row interchanges are used, and they should be, set up a variable to count the number of row interchanges; if this count is odd, the sign of the product of the main diagonal elements must be reversed.

34. Show that the method of least squares applied to the relation

$$y = a$$

yields an expression for the arithmetic mean of the y-values.

35. Show that the method of least squares applied to the relation

$$y = a + bx$$

using just two points x_1, y_1 and x_2, y_2 yields the equation of a straight line in two-point form.

36. Show that if we try to fit a quadratic to two points the normal equations will have an infinite number of solutions, corresponding to the fact that an infinite number of quadratics can be passed through two points.

*37. Suppose that the x-values in a data set are just the integers from 1 to N. Devise simplified normal equations for fitting a straight line to the points, in which the left-hand sides require no summations.

*38. Find normal equations for fitting a curve of the form

$$y = ae^{bx}$$

Use logarithms.

39. Find normal equations for fitting a curve of the form

$$y = y_0 e^{-h^2 x^2}$$

40. Find normal equations for fitting a curve of the form

$$y = a + \frac{b}{x} + \frac{c}{x^2}$$

It is possible to choose the quantities to be summed so that the normal equations are linear.

41. Find normal equations for fitting a curve of the form

$$y = a\sqrt{1 + bx^2}$$

Can you solve them?

42. Define

$$\Omega = \frac{\Sigma(y_i - y_i')^2}{n - m}$$

where y_i = an experimental value,

$\quad y_i'$ = a value computed from a least-squares fit,

$\quad n$ = the number of x-y pairs,

$\quad m$ = the number of parameters in the relation.

Then the *Gauss criterion of goodness of fit* states that the best fit is the one that minimizes Ω.

Given the following data:

x	y
0	0
1	20
2	40
3	50
4	70

By the Gauss criterion, does a linear or a quadratic relation give a better fit?

—9

Functions and Specification Statements

9.1 Introduction

One of the major reasons for using electronic computers is that they reduce the human effort required to carry out calculations. Our attitude is, roughly speaking, "Why do anything the computer can do for us?" This approach applies as well to writing programs. In this chapter we explore the question: "Why do anything twice if once will do?"

This, among other things, is what the various types of *functions* in the FORTRAN system do. We write a statement or a group of statements once and then refer to the statement or to the group whenever we want to carry out the operations described in the one place.

There are several different types of functions; they serve different purposes and follow different rules of formation and use. We shall explore each of them in turn, starting with a type that we have already discussed briefly, the functions supplied with the system. We shall then investigate two additional statements that are related to two of the types of functions.

9.2 Supplied functions

Most FORTRAN systems provide several dozen functions to compute such things as trigonometric functions, logarithms, and absolute values. The exact list depends not only on the computer and the version of FORTRAN used but on the particular installation. Most installations provide special-purpose functions to meet their individual needs. Some provide a common logarithm *and* a natural logarithm, even though one can easily be obtained from the other, because both are frequently needed. An installation doing orbit calculations may have a special function to compute air density as a function of altitude. Each programmer must have an up-to-date list of the functions available at his installation, along with a precise write-up that gives such information as accuracy, speed, the form of the data (whether angles are in degrees or radians, for instance), and so on.

In order to use these functions, it is necessary only to write their names where they are needed, entering the desired expression(s) for the argument(s). (Many permit several arguments, such as the function that finds the smallest of the values of the arguments listed.) The names of these functions are established in advance, and the programmer must write them exactly as specified. Although the programmer has no control over their naming, we may note that the names are always four to seven characters in length, always end in F, and always begin with a letter, which is X if and only if the value of the function is fixed point.

The functions available as a part of the system are actually of two different types, depending on the mechanics of their insertion in the object program. The *open* functions require only a few machine instructions; these instructions are inserted into the object program every time the function is used. The *closed* functions are in general considerably longer; they are inserted into the object program in one place only, and the object program transfers to that one place whenever it is needed. The closed functions are more common.

9.3   Arithmetic statement functions

It often happens that a programmer will find some relatively simple computation recurring through his program, making it desirable to be able to set up a function to carry out the computation. This function would be needed only in the one program, so that there would be no point in setting up a new supplied function for the purpose—which is a bit of work. Instead, a function can be defined for the purpose of the one program and then used whenever desired in that program. It has no effect on any other program.

An arithmetic statement function is *defined* by writing a single statement of the form $a = b$, where a is the name of the function and b is an expression. The name, which is invented by the programmer, must conform to the same rules as the functions supplied with the system: it must be four to seven characters in length, the last letter must be F, and the first must be a letter, which is X if and only if the value of the function is fixed point. It must not, of course, be the same as the name of any supplied function. The name of the function is followed by parentheses enclosing the argument(s), which are separated by commas if there is more than one. The arguments *in the definition* may not be subscripted.

The right-hand side of the definition statement may be any expression not involving subscripted variables. It may use variables not specified as arguments and it may use other functions (except itself). All function definitions must appear before the first executable statement of the program.

As an illustration, suppose that in a certain program it is frequently necessary to compute one of the roots of the quadratic equation $aX^2 + bX + c = 0$, given values of a, b, and c. A function can be defined to carry out this computation, by writing

ROOTF(A, B, C) = $(-B + $ SQRTF(B**2 $-$ 4.*A*C))/(2.*A)

The compiler will produce a sequence of instructions in the object program to compute the value of the function, given three values to use in the computation.

This is *only* the definition of the function; it does not cause computation to take place. The variable names used as arguments are only dummies; they may be the same as variable names appearing elsewhere in the program. The argument names are unimportant, except as they specify fixed or floating point.

An arithmetic statement function is *used* by writing its name wherever the function value is desired and substituting appropriate expressions for the arguments. "Appropriate" here means, in particular, that if a variable in the definition is floating point the expression substituted for that variable must be floating point and similarly for fixed point. The values of these expressions will be substituted into the program segment established by the definition and the value of the function computed. The actual arguments may be subscripted if desired.

Suppose, now, that it is desired to use this function with 16 9 for a, R $-$ S for b, and T $+$ 6.9 for c; the value of the function (root) is to be added to the cosine of X and the sum stored as the new value of ANS. All this can be done with the statement

ANS = ROOTF(16.9, R $-$ S, T $+$ 6.9) $+$ COSF(X)

Suppose that later in the program it is necessary to compute the function with DATA(I) for a, DATA (I $+$ 1) for b, and 0.087 for c; the function value is to be cubed and stored as the value of TEMP:

$$TEMP = ROOTF(DATA(I), DATA(I + 1), 0.087)**3$$

It must be emphasized that the variables A, B, and C in the function definition have no relation to any variables of the same name that may appear elsewhere in the program. To illustrate, suppose that the value of the root is needed for an equation

$$22.97X^2 + AX + B = 0$$

where A and B are simply variables in the program. The root may be found by writing

$$VAL = ROOTF(22.97, A, B)$$

The A and B that appear here in the *use* of the function are completely unrelated to the A and B in the *definition* of the function. In summary, the variables in the definition are simply dummies that establish how the expression values in the use should be substituted into the object program segment set up from the definition.

A good example of the usefulness of arithmetic statement functions is provided by Case Study 8 in Chapter 6. We recall that it was necessary to compute the value of the integrand at five different places in the program, using a different value for the argument in each case. We can now write a single arithmetic statement function at the beginning of the program and refer to it whenever needed.

The expression for the integrand was

$$E = \frac{1}{x^5 (e^{\frac{1.432}{Tx}} - 1)}$$

This is easily set up as a function:

$$EFFF(X) = 1.0/(X**5*(EXPF(1.432/(T*X)) - 1.0))$$

The name was chosen to satisfy the rule that it be four to seven characters in length and end in F. The X here, as always in a function definition, is only a dummy variable that defines a computational procedure; when an expression is written in using the function, the same actions are carried out on the actual value as are shown being done with X in the definition.

We see here an example of something that was mentioned earlier in passing: the use of a variable in the function definition that is not an argument. The only argument is X; this is a dummy. T, however, since it is not an argument, is *not* a dummy: it is the same T that appears elsewhere in the program. This use of variables that are not

```
C FOR COMMENT
STATEMENT
NUMBER   C
1      5 6 7                          FORTRAN STATEMENT

        EFFF(X) = 1..0 / (X**5 * (EXPF(1..432/((T*X))) - 1..0))
        READ 60, TEMP1, TEMP2, TMPINC, A, B, N
  60    FORMAT (5F10.0, I4)
        FN = N
        H = (B - A) / FN
        T = TEMP1
 100    SUM4 = 0..0
        SUM2 = 0..0
        I = 1
  12    FI = I
        X = A + FI * H
        SUM4 = SUM4 + EFFF(X)
        SUM2 = SUM2 + EFFF(X + H)
        IF (I - N + 3) 21, 32, 32
  21    I = I + 2
        GO TO 12
  32    EFFIC = 64..77 * H / 3..0 * (4..0*SUM4 + 2..0*SUM2
   1        + EFFF(A) + 4..0*EFFF(B - H) + EFFF(B)) / T**4
        PRINT 61, T, EFFIC
  61    FORMAT (2E20..8)
```

```
C FOR COMMENT
STATEMENT
NUMBER   C
1      5 6 7                          FORTRAN STATEMENT

        T = T + TMPINC
        IF (T - TEMP2) 100, 100, 200
 200    STOP
        END
```

FIGURE 9.1   A revised version of the program of Figure 6.7, using an arithmetic statement function and with other minor changes.

arguments is perfectly legal; as we see, it saves the effort of making arguments out of variables that do not change as the function is called into action from different places in the program.

The complete program is shown in Figure 9.1. We may note a few changes from the program of Figure 6.7.

We recall from a brief mention in Chapter 1 that a variable name may not be the same as the name of any function or the same as any function without its final F. This applies to arithmetic statement functions as well as to supplied functions. Therefore, the variable name EFF in Figure 6.7 is not permissible if we are to use EFFF for the function name. It is quite immaterial which of the two is changed, so long as the rule is satisfied; Figure 9.1 shows EFFIC for the final efficiency and EFFF for the function.

The program contains a slight modification of the method of getting the successive values of X. Rather than adding 2H repeatedly, which accumulates roundoff errors, we convert I to floating point and multiply the floating point value by H.

There are no other changes.

9.4   FUNCTION and SUBROUTINE subprograms

Useful as an arithmetic statement function often is, it does have two rather serious restrictions: the definition is limited to one statement and it can compute only one value. The FUNCTION and SUB-ROUTINE subprograms remove these restrictions.

This is only half the story, however. The outstanding feature of these two types of functions is that they are *subprograms;* they can be compiled independently of the main program of which they are a part. Their variable names are completely independent of the variable names in the main program and in other subprograms. They may have their own DIMENSION statements (and the other specification statements described below). In short, FUNCTION and SUBROUTINE sub-programs can be completely independent of the main program—yet it is quite easy to set up "communication" between the main program and the subprograms. This means that a large program can be divided into parts that can be compiled independently, making possible two important kinds of flexibility in writing and using programs.

The ability to compile a subprogram independently of the main pro-gram of which it is a part means that one subprogram can be used with different main programs. For instance, many different programmers in an installation may need a subprogram to solve a system of simulta-neous equations by Gauss elimination. Since arrays are involved and since many statements are required, arithmetic statement functions are out of the question. However, a SUBROUTINE subprogram can be written to do the job. It can be compiled by itself, and it can be combined with *any* main program. All that is necessary is for the main program to have been written with the conventions of the sub-program in mind.

The other flexibility provided by separate compilation is the freedom to compile and run segments of one program independently of each other. This means that parts of a program can be checked out as they are written, which can be an important advantage.   It can sometimes be quite difficult to determine whether the main program is working properly unless there is the assurance that the subprograms are correct. With separate compilation it is possible to compile each subprogram by itself and check it out before placing any dependence on it.

Subprograms thus have three major advantages.   One is the primary motivation for any function, as stated in the introduction to the chapter: a group of statements written in one place in a program can be called into action from anywhere else in the program, thus avoiding wasteful duplication of effort in writing the source program and the waste of storage space that would be caused by duplication of segments of the object program.   A second advantage is that of avoiding duplication of programmer effort by making it possible for a subprogram to be used with many different main programs.   The third advantage is that of separate checkout.

Whatever the motivation for their use, subprograms are a powerful feature of the FORTRAN language.

As with the arithmetic statement function, we must distinguish carefully between the definition and the use.   The computation desired in a FUNCTION subprogram is *defined* by writing the necessary statements in a segment, writing the word FUNCTION and the name of the function before the segment, and writing the word END after it. The name may have one to six characters, the first of which must be alphabetic; the first character must be I, J, K, L, M, or N if and only if the value of the function is fixed point; the last character must *not* be F if the name is more than three characters long.   (Note the difference in naming.)   The name must appear at least once in the subprogram as a variable on the left-hand side of an arithmetic statement or in the list of an input statement.   The name of the subprogram is followed by parentheses enclosing the argument(s), which are separated by commas if there is more than one.

As before, the arguments in the subprogram definition are only dummy variables.   The arguments in the function name must be distinct nonsubscripted variables or array names.   Within the subprogram itself, however, subscripted variables may be used freely. The subprogram must contain at least one RETURN statement for reasons that we shall see immediately below.

To *use* the FUNCTION subprogram, it is necessary only to write the name of the function where its value is desired, with suitable expressions for arguments.   The mechanics of the operation of the object program are as follows.   The FUNCTION subprogram is compiled as a set of machine instructions in one place in storage.   Wherever the name of the subprogram appears in the source program, a transfer to the subprogram is set up in the object program. When the computations of the subprogram have been completed, a transfer is made back to the section of the program that brought the subprogram into action. The RETURN statement(s) in the subprogram results in object program instructions to transfer back to wherever in the main program the subprogram was called from. (This is actually quite similar to the way an arithmetic statement function is set up, except that in that case there can be only one statement in the definition and there is no question when the function's operations are complete.)

As a simple example of the use of a FUNCTION subprogram, suppose that in a certain program it is frequently necessary to compute the function shown on p. 29. The function can be defined with the statements in Figure 9.2, in which the name Y has been given to the function.

If we now want to compute this function for an argument equal to GRS − 6.8 and divide the result by 12.99 to get the value of EWR, we can write

$$EWR = Y(GRS - 6.8)/12.99$$

To get this function of the square root of one plus RHO, with PDX being set equal to the square root of the result, we can write

$$PDX = SQRTF(Y(SQRTF(1.0 + RHO)))$$

A FUNCTION subprogram may have many arguments, including arrays. For example, suppose that it is necessary to find the product of the main diagonal elements (those having the same row and column numbers) of square arrays. The arrays from which this product is computed must have been mentioned in a DIMENSION statement in the program that uses the subprogram, as always, and all the arrays

STATEMENT NUMBER 1 5	6	7 FORTRAN STATEMENT
		FUNCTION Y(X)
		IF (X − 2./1.) 40, 40, 30
40		Y = 0.5*X + 0.95
		RETURN
30		Y = 0.7*X + 0.53
		RETURN
		END

FIGURE 9.2   An example of a FUNCTION subprogram.

```
C FOR COMMENT
STATEMENT
NUMBER
1       5 6 7                           FORTRAN STATEMENT

        FUNCTION DIAGPR (A, N)
        DIMENSION A (10, 10)
        DIAGPR = A (1, 1)
        DO 69 I = 2, N
   69   DIAGPR = DIAGPR * A (I, I)
        RETURN
        END
```

FIGURE 9.3   Another example of a FUNCTION subprogram.

must have the same dimensions.   The array names in the FUNCTION argument list and subprogram will be dummies, but the dummy array names must still be mentioned in a DIMENSION statement in the subprogram.   Suppose that the arrays in question are all 10 x 10 but that they are not necessarily full; the value of a fixed point variable gives the number of rows and columns.   The subprogram could be as shown in Figure 9.3.

Now, if we wanted the product of the main diagonal elements of an array named DATA, in which the actual size is given by the value of LAST, we could write

$$DET = DIAGPR(DATA, LAST)$$

To find the square of the product of the main diagonal elements of an array named X, in which the actual number of rows and columns is given by the value of JACK, we could write

$$EIG = DIAGPR(X, JACK)**2$$

A FUNCTION subprogram is seen to be quite similar to an arithmetic statement function, except that it can use many statements instead of just one and it can use any of the FORTRAN statements instead of just an arithmetic statement.   A subprogram can call upon other subprograms as long as it does not call itself and as long as two subprograms do not call each other.*

---

* A subprogram that calls itself is said to be *recursive*.   This *is* permitted in the ALGOL language, where it finds greatest utility in non-numerical applications, such as writing compiler programs, processing natural languages (e.g., English), and operations on the *symbols* of mathematics as distinguished from their values. Recursiveness can be accomplished in some cases in FORTRAN by "stacking" arguments in arrays.

A FUNCTION subprogram has been described as computing just one value, the one associated with the name of the FUNCTION. Actually, there can be any number of output values: any of the arguments may refer to output. For an example of how this might be useful, consider the following extension of the requirements of the preceding illustration. Suppose that if the product of the main diagonal elements is less than or equal to 100, we wish to go to statement 12; if it is between 100 and 1000, we wish to go to statement 123; if it is greater than or equal 1000, we wish to go to statement 1234. All of these statement numbers refer to statements in the *main* program. This could, of course, be done with IF statements in the main program, but if it has to be done frequently we would prefer some simpler way.

To accomplish the simplification, let us first change the name of the FUNCTION to NDIAGP, so that its value is fixed point. We write the modified subprogram so that the value of NDIAGP is negative, zero, or positive, depending on whether the product is less than 100, between 100 and 1000, or greater than 1000, respectively. We also add DIAGPR as an argument and within the subprogram give it the value of the product of the diagonal elements. The program as modified is shown in Figure 9.4.

Now suppose that we want the product of the main diagonal elements of an 8 x 8 array named BETA, with the product to be called PRODCT. We are to transfer to one of the three statements numbered 12, 123, or 1234, as described above.

```
STATEMENT                    FORTRAN STATEMENT
NUMBER
1      5 6 7

        FUNCTION NDIAGP (A, N, DIAGPR),
        DIMENSION A(10, 10),
        DIAGPR = A(1, 1),
        DO 69 I = 2, N
69      DIAGPR = DIAGPR * A(I, I),
        IF (DIAGPR - 100.0) 68, 68, 67
68      NDIAGP = -1
        RETURN
67      IF (DIAGPR - 1000.0) 66, 65, 65
66      NDIAGP = 0
        RETURN
65      NDIAGP = 1
        RETURN
        END
```

FIGURE 9.4 An example of a SUBROUTINE subprogram.

IF (NDIAGP(BETA, 8, PRODCT)) 12, 123, 1234

The appearance of the name of the FUNCTION, written with appropriate arguments, causes the FUNCTION to be called into operation, in the course of which a value is given to its name and a value is also given to the other output parameter, which is PRODCT in this case. Control returns from the subprogram to the IF statement in the main program, where the proper transfer is made.   At any of these locations the newly computed value of PRODCT may be used.

The basics of a SUBROUTINE subprogram are quite similar to those of a FUNCTION subprogram, with three differences.

1. A SUBROUTINE has no value associated with its name.   All outputs are defined in terms of arguments; there may be any number of outputs.

2. A SUBROUTINE is not called into action simply by writing its name, since no value is associated with the name.   Instead, we write a CALL statement to bring it into operation; this specifies the arguments and results in storing all the output values.

3. Since the output of a SUBROUTINE may be a combination of fixed and floating point numbers, the first letter of the name is not used to designate fixed or floating point.   The naming of a SUBROUTINE is otherwise the same as the naming of a FUNCTION.

In all other respects the two types of subprograms are entirely analogous.

The essential features of the SUBROUTINE subprogram are illustrated in the following example.   Suppose that in a certain program it is frequently necessary to find the largest element (in absolute value) in a specified row of a 10 x 10 array.   The input to the SUBROUTINE is therefore the array name and the row number.   The output will be the absolute value of the largest element in that row and its column number.   The SUBROUTINE could be as shown in Figure 9.5.

Now suppose that the largest element in the third row of a 10 x 10 array named ZETA is needed.   The absolute value of the element is to be called DIVIS and the column number is to be called NCOL.   We write the statement

CALL LARGE (ZETA, 3, DIVIS, NCOL)

This brings the subprogram into operation, stores the values of DIVIS and NCOL found by the subprogram, and returns control to the state-

```
----C FOR COMMENT
STATEMENT
NUMBER        FORTRAN STATEMENT
1      5 6 7
       SUBRØUTINE LARGE (ARRAY, I, BIG, J)
       DIMENSIØN ARRAY(10, 10)
       BIG = ABSF(ARRAY(I,1))
       J = 1
       DØ 69 K = 2, 10
       IF (ABSF(ARRAY(I,K)) - BIG) 69, 69, 70
   70  BIG = ABSF(ARRAY(I,K))
       J = K
   69  CØNTINUE
       RETURN
       END
```

FIGURE 9.5   An example of a SUBROUTINE subprogram.

ment following the CALL. If, later, it is necessary to find the largest
element in row M + 2 of an array named DETAIL, storing its absolute
value as SIZE and the column number as KWHICH, we can write

CALL LARGE (DETAIL, M + 2, SIZE, KWHICH)

To emphasize the independence of the variable names between the
main program and any subprograms, we note that it would be possible
to write the statement

CALL LARGE (ARRAY, I, BIG, J)

If this is done, all of the variables here must still be defined *in the calling
program*. The name I in the calling program and the name I in the
subprogram are unrelated. And this must logically be so: the name I
in the subprogram tells what to do with a value from the calling program, whereas the name I in the calling program must specify a value
that has previously been computed by the calling program.

9.5   Summary of the differences between the types of functions

FORTRAN provides for four types of functions: those supplied with
the system, arithmetic statement functions, FUNCTION subprograms,
and SUBROUTINE subprograms. The differences between them are
summarized in Table 9.1.

Table 9.1

	Supplied	Arithmetic Statement	FUNCTION	SUBROUTINE
Naming	4–7 characters; first character a letter which is X if and only if function value is fixed point; last character must be F	4–7 characters; first character a letter which is X if and only if function value is fixed point; last character must be F	1–6 characters; first character a letter which is I, J, K, L, M, or N if and only if function value is fixed point; last character must not be F if name is more than three characters	1–6 characters; first character a letter; last character must not be F if name is more than three characters
Definition	Provided with the system	One arithmetic statement before first usage of function	Any number of statements after word FUNCTION	Any number of statements after word SUB-ROUTINE
How called	Writing name where function value is desired	Writing name where function value is desired	Writing name where function value is desired	CALL statement
Number of arguments	One or more, as defined	One or more, as defined	One or more, as defined	Any number, including *none*, as defined
Number of outputs	One	One	One is associated with function name; others may be specified as arguments	Any number

9.6   The EQUIVALENCE and COMMON statements

These two nonexecutable statements make possible certain conveniences in the naming of variables and the assignment of storage locations to them.

The EQUIVALENCE statement causes two or more variable names to be assigned to the same storage location, which is useful in two rather different ways.

In one usage the EQUIVALENCE statement allows the programmer to define two or more variable names as meaning the same thing. It might be that after writing a long program the programmer will realize that he has inadvertently changed variable names and that X, X1, and RST6 should refer to the same variable. Rather than going back and changing the variable names in the program, a time-consuming and error-prone process, he can write

$$\text{EQUIVALENCE (X, X1, RST6)}$$

and the mistake is corrected.

The other application is in making use of the same storage location to contain two or more variables that are never needed at the same time. Suppose that in the initial READ statement of a program the variable I27 appears but is never used after that. During the program a DO parameter NP1 is established, but only for that loop. Later, the variable JJM2 is applied to a similar purpose. At the end the variable NEXT1 is used in the final PRINT statement. As it stands, four storage locations will be allocated to these variables, which is pointless, since their usage never overlaps. If the programmer is short of storage space, he can assign all four variables to one location by writing

$$\text{EQUIVALENCE (I27, NP1, JJM2, NEXT1)}$$

The same thing could, of course, be accomplished by changing the variable names, but using an EQUIVALENCE is obviously simpler.

These two applications of EQUIVALENCE differ only in viewpoint; the statement and its treatment by the compiler are the same in either case.

One EQUIVALENCE statement can establish equivalence between any number of sets of variables. For instance, if A and B are to be made equivalent, as are X and Y, we can write

$$\text{EQUIVALENCE (A, B), (X, Y)}$$

Seldom is storage space so "tight" that the EQUIVALENCE statement is *really* needed for non-subscripted variables. The real value comes in establishing equivalence between arrays. Unfortunately, however, usage here varies somewhat among the different versions of FORTRAN. We accordingly refer the reader to the appropriate manual and leave the subject.

The COMMON Statement

It has been stated that each subprogram has its own variable names: the name X in the main program is not necessarily taken to be the same as the name X in a subprogram. However, if the programmer wishes them to mean the same, he can write the statement

$$\text{COMMON X}$$

in *both* places. The statement does considerably more, actually. Suppose, for instance, that we have the following statements:

$$\begin{aligned} &\text{main program:} \quad \text{COMMON X, Y, I} \\ &\text{subprogram:} \quad\quad \text{COMMON A, B, J} \end{aligned}$$

Then X and A are assigned to the same memory location, as are Y and B and I and J. This not only saves storage locations but also provides a way to establish correspondence between variables in a main program and in subprograms, without actually naming them as arguments in the definitions.

Probably the most frequent application of the COMMON statement is to cause variable names to mean the same thing in a main program and one or more subprograms. In this usage *identical* COMMON statements are written in all segments. If this is done, such variables may be used freely throughout the main programs and the various subprograms without ever making them arguments of the subprograms if it is convenient not to do so. This usage of the COMMON statement is exemplified in the following case study.

9.7 Case study 11: Quadratic equation solution with subprograms

This case study illustrates some of the ideas about subprograms and the COMMON statement that we have been discussing. The numerical aspects of the example are quite simple; the solution of quadratic equations by the familiar formula presents no new concepts. The emphasis is on program organization and input-output formats. Some of the material on input-output includes techniques not discussed in the text, although they are covered in Appendix 1. These techniques are described briefly here; the reader who wishes to concentrate on the subprogram concepts will have little difficulty skipping over the input-output topics.

A program is to be set up to solve the quadratic equation $Ax^2 + Bx + C = 0$. The program is to be able to read from cards the coefficients of many such equations—possibly hundreds—and to produce an easily readable report showing for each equation the coefficients and the roots. A data card contains the coefficients of two equations, six values in all. However, each equation is to be written out on a line by itself. The roots can be real or complex. A heading is to be printed at the top of each page, the pages are to be numbered, and the lines are to be counted as they are printed, so that each page will contain only 20 lines of output, double spaced.

The program is to be written to use two SUBROUTINE subprograms. Each subprogram can be called twice for each data card, avoiding duplication and perhaps making the complete program easier to modify and correct. The main routine will handle the reading of data cards, the printing of page headings, page numbering, line counting, and the detection of the end of the deck, which is signaled by a blank card, placed at the end of the deck for the purpose. The detection of this card can be set up as a test for a data card in which $A = 0$. A can never be zero with valid data; if $A = 0$, the equation is not quadratic.

The first subprogram will get the solutions, taking into account that if the discriminant $B^2 - 4AC$ is negative the roots are complex. The input to this subprogram, named SOLVE, consists of the names of the three coefficients; these are named as arguments of the subprogram. The output consists of the real and imaginary parts of the two roots, which are named X1REAL, X1IMAG, X2REAL, and X2IMAG. These four variables are needed in the main program and in both subprograms. They are named in COMMON statements in all three places, making it unnecessary to write them as arguments of the subprograms.

The second subprogram, named OUTPUT, writes the coefficients and the roots. It is desired to print the results so that the reader can tell at a glance if the roots are pure real or pure imaginary. If the roots are real, the space for the imaginary parts is to be left blank, and if they are pure imaginary the space for the real parts is to be left blank. We recall that complex roots always occur as complex conjugates; it can never happen that only one root is complex or that two complex roots have different real parts.

A block diagram of the main program is shown in Figure 9.6, which is seen to be straightforward. There is one new feature: upon detec-

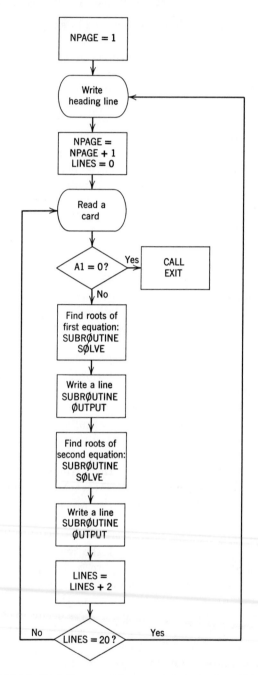

FIGURE 9.6   Block diagram of the main program for Case Study 11.

tion of the blank sentinel card we do not write a STOP statement, but a CALL EXIT. This is done on the assumption that the complete program will be run under control of a *monitor program* that runs the machine between jobs. CALL EXIT has the effect of returning control to the monitor, just as the RETURN statement in a subprogram returns control to the program that called it.

The block diagram of the subprogram for finding the roots is shown in Figure 9.7. The procedure shown steers a middle course between the bare minimum required to distinguish between real and complex roots and the more complicated tests that could be made to take advantage of every special situation. The bare minimum would be to go to the complex section if the discriminant is negative and to the real section if it is zero or positive. Since the IF statement automatically gives us a three-way branch, it seems reasonable to take special action if the discriminant is zero to avoid computing the square root of zero. We could go further with this testing for special conditions, however. If C is zero, then both roots are real, one being zero and the other $-B/A$. If B is zero, the formulas simplify slightly. If B and C are both zero, then of course both roots are zero—but it is hard to see why such a case would ever be entered.

In any such case it is necessary to draw a line somewhere. Time can indeed be saved by taking advantage of the special situations—

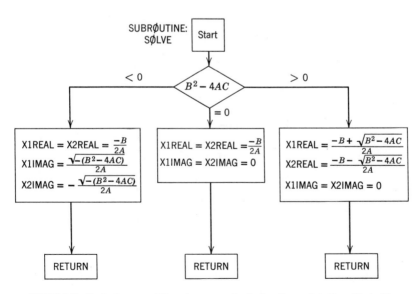

FIGURE 9.7   Block diagram of the subprogram for finding the roots in Case Study 11.

unless testing for them wastes all the savings. Even where there is a net savings, though, a thorough series of tests may simply not be worth the trouble and the program complexity.

The block diagram of the output subprogram, Figure 9.8, is also fairly simple. Note that it is not necessary to test both imaginary components for zero values, since both will always be zero or both nonzero. This is not true of the real parts.

The main program is shown in Figure 9.9. We begin with a COMMON statement naming the real and imaginary parts of the two roots. The same statement appears in both subprograms, so that these four variable names have identical meanings throughout the complete program. This would not be true, of course, without the COMMON statement.

Next we set the page number equal to 1 and print the heading line, the bulk of which consists of the column identifications; in fact, the only variable in the line is the page number itself. The printing of actual text, as distinguished from numeric values of variables, is accomplished with a field specification that has not been discussed: the

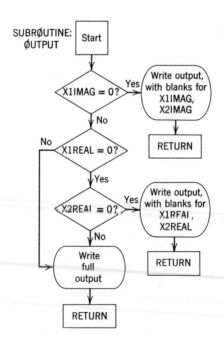

FIGURE 9.8   Block diagram of the subprogram for printing the results in Case Study 11.

```
┌─C FOR COMMENT
│ STATEMENT   ┊
│ NUMBER      ┊ Cont.              FORTRAN STATEMENT
│1        5 6│7
├─────────────┼──────────────────────────────────────────────────────────
│             │ COMMON X1REAL, X1IMAG, X2REAL, X2IMAG
│             │ NPAGE = 1
│          5  │ PRINT 8, NPAGE
│          8  │ FORMAT (1H1, 9X, 1HA, 14X, 1HB, 14X, 1HC, 1IX,
│          1  │      7HX1 REAL, 8X, 7HX1 IMAG, 8X, 7HX2 REAL, 8X,
│          2  │      17HX2 IMAG,      PAGE, I4/1/)
│             │ NPAGE = NPAGE + 1
│             │ LINES = 0
│         14  │ READ 15, A1, B1, C1, A2, B2, C2
│         15  │ FORMAT (6F10.0)
│             │ IF (A1) 16, 17, 16
│         17  │ CALL EXIT
│         16  │ CALL SOLVE (A1, B1, C1)
│             │ CALL OUTPUT (A1, B1, C1)
│             │ CALL SOLVE (A2, B2, C2)
│             │ CALL OUTPUT (A2, B2, C2)
│             │ LINES = LINES + 2
│             │ IF (LINES - 40) 14, 5, 5
│             │ END
```

FIGURE 9.9   The main program for Case Study 11.

Hollerith field specification.* With this field specification we first write an integer that specifies the number of characters of Hollerith text, then the letter H, then the text itself. The text may consist of any of the characters available on the printer, including the "character" *blank*.

The first Hollerith field in FORMAT statement 8 has a quite different purpose. The first character of each line is *not* printed, but instead controls the spacing of the carriage on the printer: a blank calls for normal single spacing, a zero calls for double spacing, and a 1 calls for skipping to the first printing position on the next page before the line is printed. Thus, when we write 1H1 we specify that the paper should be advanced to the next page before this line is printed. The next field specification is also a new type, the blank, for which the letter is X. Here, 9X calls for nine blanks to be inserted in the line at this point. The same thing can be done with a Hollerith field specification, of course, by actually leaving the blanks in writing the FORMAT state-

---

* Named after Herman Hollerith, who invented the method of representing alphabetic characters on a punched card for the United States Census of 1890.

```
C FOR COMMENT
STATEMENT
NUMBER
1      5 6 7                          FORTRAN STATEMENT

       SUBROUTINE SOLVE (A, B, C)
       COMMON X1REAL, X1IMAG, X2REAL, X2IMAG
       DISC = B**2 - 4.0 * A * C
       IF (DISC) 50, 60, 70
   50  X1REAL = -B / (2.0 * A)
       X2REAL = X1REAL
       X1IMAG = SQRTF(-DISC) / (2.0 * A)
       X2IMAG = -X1IMAG
       RETURN
   60  X1REAL = -B / (2.0 * A)
       X2REAL = X1REAL
       X1IMAG = 0..0
       X2IMAG = 0..0
       RETURN
   70  S = SQRTF(DISC)
       X1REAL = (-B + S) / (2.0 * A)
       X2REAL = (-B - S) / (2.0 * A)
       X1IMAG = 0..0
       X2IMAG = 0..0
       RETURN
       END
```

FIGURE 9.10   The subprogram for finding the roots in Case Study 11.

ment, but the X is a little simpler and less prone to error.   Reading
through this statement, we find the rest of the information for the
heading line.   Note that when a blank printing position is desired in a
Hollerith field it must actually be left blank and it must be counted in
determining the width of the field.   We see several examples of this
factor, especially in the last Hollerith field, in which it seemed simpler
to include the six blanks than to write the 6X.   Such decisions are at
the programmer's discretion, of course.

The I4 finally gets us back to a familiar field specification.   This
identifies the page number as an integer and allots four printing
positions to it.   At the end of the FORMAT statement we find one
more new item: the two slashes have the effect here of forcing a blank
line between the heading and the first line of results.   (As explained in
Appendix 1, the slash can do somewhat more than this.)

The appearance of the heading line produced by this FORMAT
statement may be seen in the sample output of Figure 9.12.

After incrementing the page counter and initializing the line counter,
we read a data card.   The READ statement must have different names
for the three coefficients of the two equations.   A test of first value for

A detects the sentinel card and takes us to the CALL EXIT that terminates the program execution.

Now we are ready to find the roots for the first set of coefficients, so we call into operation the SUBROUTINE that solves the equation. The arguments are the first set of coefficients. When control returns from SOLVE, values will have been given to X1REAL, X1IMAG, X2REAL, and X2IMAG. Now we call the SUBROUTINE for printing the output, naming only the three coefficients; the four parts of the roots are communicated via the COMMON statements. Another call of each of the subprograms computes and prints the roots for the second set of coefficients from the data card. After incrementing the line counter by two, an IF statement determines whether the page is full and goes back to print the heading line if it is.

The coding of the two subprograms, shown in Figures 9.10 and 9.11, should not be hard to follow. Two new variables, DISC and S, are set up in the SOLVE subroutine to avoid computing certain expressions repeatedly. Advantage is taken of the fact that complex roots occur only as complex conjugates, once again to avoid computing an expression twice.

The OUTPUT subprogram is not complicated, but the FORMAT statements should be studied carefully. The blank spaces for the two special cases of pure real and pure imaginary roots are introduced by

```
      SUBROUTINE OUTPUT (A, B, C)
      COMMON X1REAL, X1IMAG, X2REAL, X2IMAG
      IF (X1IMAG) 90, 91, 90
   91 PRINT 95, A, B, C, X1REAL, X2REAL
   95 FORMAT (1H0, 1P4E15.4, 15X, 1PE15.4)
      RETURN
   90 IF (X1REAL) 100, 101, 100
  101 IF (X2REAL) 100, 102, 100
  102 PRINT 103, A, B, C, X1IMAG, X2IMAG
  103 FORMAT (1H0, 1P3E15.4, 15X, 1PE15.4, 15X, 1PE15.4)
      RETURN
  100 PRINT 110, A, B, C, X1REAL, X1IMAG, X2REAL, X2IMAG
  110 FORMAT (1H0, 1P7E15.4)
      RETURN
      END
```

FIGURE 9.11 The subprogram for printing the results in Case Study 11.

A	B	C	X1 REAL	X1 IMAG	X2 REAL	X2 IMAG
1.0000E 00	-2.0000E 00	1.0000E 00	1.0000E 00		1.0000E 00	
1.0000E 00	-1.0000E 01	2.5000E 01	5.0000E 00		5.0000E 00	
1.0000E 00	-3.0000E 00	2.0000E 00	2.0000E 00		1.0000E 00	
2.0000E 00	-6.0000E 00	4.0000E 00	2.0000E 00		1.0000E 00	
1.0000E 00	1.0000E 00	-2.5500E 03	5.0000E 01		-5.1000E 01	
1.0000E 01	-2.0000E 01	1.0000E 01	1.0000E 00		1.0000E 00	
1.0000E 03	-2.0000E 03	1.0000E 03	1.0000E 00		1.0000E 00	
2.0000E-02	-4.0000E-02	2.0000E-02	1.0000E 00		1.0000E 00	
1.4320E 00	9.8750E 00	-4.5670E 00	4.3500E-01		-7.3316E 00	
8.8130E 00	-1.3104E 01	0.	1.4869E 00		0.	
2.3009E 01	1.9917E 01	0.	-5.1810E-09		-8.6562E-01	
1.0000E 00	0.	-1.0000E 00	1.0000E 00		-1.0000E 00	
1.0000E 00	0.	1.0000E 00		1.0000E 00		-1.0000E 00
9.0000E 00	0.	3.6000E 01		2.0000E 00		-2.0000E 00
1.0000E 00	2.0000E 00	5.0000E 00	-1.0000E 00	2.0000E 00	-1.0000E 00	-2.0000E 00
6.3190E 00	4.3380E 00	2.3294E 01	-3.4325E-01	1.8891E 00	-3.4325E-01	-1.8891E 00
-9.0000E 00	2.3000E 01	3.7000E 01	-1.1189E 00		3.6744E 00	
6.1000E 01	0.	8.7000E 01		1.1942E 00		-1.1942E 00
6.1000E 01	2.0000E 00	8.7000E 01	-1.6393E-02	1.1941E 00	-1.6393E-02	-1.1941E 00
6.1000E 01	1.5900E 02	8.7000E 01	-7.8145E-01		-1.8251E 00	

FIGURE 9.12 Representative output of the programs of Figures 9.9, 9.10, and 9.11. (Case Study 11.)

15X field specifications.   Note that each FORMAT begins with a
Hollerith field specification, 1HO.   The zero, as noted above, causes
double spacing, making the report easier to read.

Figure 9.12 shows part of a page of output that might be produced
by this program.   It is, of course, somewhat reduced from normal size.

Exercises

*1. Define an arithmetic statement function to compute

$$\text{DENOMF(X)} = X^2 + \sqrt{1 + 2X + 3X^2}$$

Then use the function to compute

$$\text{ALPHA} = \frac{6.9 + Y}{Y^2 + \sqrt{1 + 2Y + 3Y^2}}$$

$$\text{BETA} = \frac{2.1Z + Z^4}{Z^2 + \sqrt{1 + 2Z + 3Z^2}}$$

$$\text{GAMMA} = \frac{\sin Y}{Y^4 + \sqrt{1 + 2Y^2 + 3Y^4}}$$

$$\text{DELTA} = \frac{1}{\sin^2 Y + \sqrt{1 + 2\sin Y + 3\sin^2 Y}}$$

2. Define an arithmetic statement function to compute

$$\text{SLGF(A)} = 2.549 \log\left(A + A^2 + \frac{1}{A}\right)$$

Then use the function to compute

$$R = X + \log X + 2.549 \log\left(X + X^2 + \frac{1}{X}\right)$$

$$S = \cos X + 2.549 \log\left(1 + X + (1 + X)^2 + \frac{1}{1 + X}\right)$$

$$T = 2.549 \log\left[(A - B)^3 + (A - B)^6 + \frac{1}{(A - B)^3}\right]$$

$$U = [B(I) + 6]^2 + 2.549 \log\left[\frac{1}{B(I)} + \frac{1}{B(I)^2} + B(I)\right]$$

*3. Define an arithmetic statement function to compute

$$\text{S34F(X,A)} = \sqrt{X^2 - A^2}$$

Then use it to compute

$$\text{SFK} = \frac{V \cdot \sqrt{V^2 - R^2}}{2} - \frac{R^2}{2} \log |V + \sqrt{V^2 - R^2}|$$

$$\text{PSB} = \frac{[X(I)^2 - B^2]^{7/2}}{7} + \frac{2B^2[X(I)^2 - B^2]^{5/2}}{5} + \frac{B^4[X(I)^2 - B^2]^{3/2}}{3}$$

4. Write an arithmetic statement function to compute

$$\text{SQUADF(A,B,C,X)} = \sqrt{AX^2 + BX + C}$$

Then use it to compute

$$\text{ETX} = \frac{4PZ + 2Q}{(4PR - Q^2)\sqrt{PZ^2 + QZ + R}}$$

$$\text{AVP} = \sqrt{RY^2 + SY + \sqrt{DY^2 + EY + 16}}$$

*5. Write a FUNCTION subprogram to compute

$$Y(X) = \begin{cases} 1 + \sqrt{1 + X^2} & \text{if } X < 0 \\ 0 & \text{if } X = 0 \\ 1 - \sqrt{1 + X^2} & \text{if } X > 0 \end{cases}$$

Then write statements to compute the following formulas, which use the mathematical function notation: "Y as a function of $A + Z$," etc.

$$F = 2 + Y(A + Z)$$

$$G = \frac{Y[X(K)] + Y[X(K + 1)]}{2}$$

$$H = Y[\cos (2\pi X)] + \sqrt{1 + Y(2\pi X)}$$

6. Write a FUNCTION subprogram to compute

$$\text{RHO(A,B,N)} = \frac{A}{2\pi} \sum_{i=1}^{N} B_i$$

where B is a one-dimensional array of 50 elements $N(\leq 50)$.

Then use it to compute $\dfrac{1}{2\pi}$ times the sum of the first 18 elements of an array named A; call this SOME.

*7. If A is any two-dimensional array with 20 rows and 20 columns, write a FUNCTION subprogram to get the sum of the absolute values of the elements in the Kth row of A, except for A(K,K), that is,

$$\text{SUMNR(A,K)} = \sum_{j \neq K} |A_{Kj}|$$

Hint. This is the same as $\displaystyle\sum_{\text{all } j} |A_{Kj}| - |A_{KK}|$.

8. A is any 20 by 20 array. Write a FUNCTION subprogram to compute

$$\text{PD(A,I,J)} = \frac{A(I-1,J) + A(I+1,J) + A(I,J-1) + A(I,J+1)}{4}$$

Then use it to compute

$$B_{ij} = (1-A)B_{ij} + A\,\frac{B_{i-1,j} + B_{i+1,j} + B_{i,j-1} + B_{i+1,j}}{4}$$

(Could an arithmetic statement function be used here?)

*9. A is a one-dimensional array with a maximum of 50 elements. Write a SUBROUTINE subprogram to compute the average of the first N elements and a count of the number of these elements that are zero. Call the subprogram AVERNZ(A, N, AVER, NZ).

Then use the subprogram to get the average of the first 20 elements of an array named ZETA, place the average in ZMEAN and the count of zero elements in NZCNT.

10. Given single variables A, B, X, and L, write a SUBROUTINE subprogram to compute R, S, and T from

$$R = \sqrt{A + BX + X^L}$$

$$S = \cos\,(2\pi X + A) \cdot e^{BX}$$

$$T = \left(\frac{A + BX}{2}\right)^{L+1} - \left(\frac{A - BX}{3}\right)^{L-1}$$

*11. Write five arithmetic statement functions, all named DEQF(X,Y), to compute the following expressions:

a. $y - 2e^{-x}$

b. $2x + (x^2 - y) \tan x$

c. $y^3 - \dfrac{y}{x}$

d. $\cos x - \sin x - y$

e. $\dfrac{2y}{x} + x^2 e^x$

12. Write five arithmetic statement functions, all named SOLNF(X), to compute the following expressions:

a. $e^{-x} + e^x$

b. $x^2 + \cos x$

c. $\dfrac{1}{2x^2} + 2x$

d. $\cos x + e^{-x}$

e. $x^2 \cdot (e^x - e^1)$

*13. Write a FUNCTION subprogram to carry out the following operations.

$$\text{YNEXT(X,Y,H)} = Y + \frac{H}{6} (k_1 + 2k_2 + 2k_3 + k_4)$$

where $k_1 = \text{DEQF(X,Y)}$

$$k_2 = \text{DEQF} \left(X + \frac{H}{2}, Y + \frac{Hk_1}{2} \right)$$

$$k_3 = \text{DEQF} \left(X + \frac{H}{2}, Y + \frac{Hk_2}{2} \right)$$

$$k_4 = \text{DEQF}(X + H, Y + k_3)$$

For the arithmetic statement function DEQF(X,Y) use any of the functions written for Exercise 11.

14. Write a FUNCTION to evaluate

$$\text{SQUARE(X,L)} = \sin x + \tfrac{1}{3} \sin 3x + \cdots + \frac{1}{L} \sin Lx$$

For $L = 29$, evaluate and print SQUARE for all X values from zero to 7.0, in steps of 0.2.

This is the Fourier series for a square wave of height $\pi/4$ and period 2π.

15. Write a FUNCTION that accepts as input three values A, B, and N, and finds the integral between A and B of some function that is supplied by the programmer, using N intervals. The function being integrated is written as an arithmetic statement function and physically combined with the FUNCTION before compiling.

16. Devise a FUNCTION to find a root of a quartic equation, given the coefficients, a starting guess, a tolerance, the name of the root, and a limit to the number of iterations that should be allowed.

17. Make the least squares curve-fitting program of Figure 8.15 into a SUBROUTINE. Write your own specifications for the use of the program.

—10

Ordinary Differential Equations

10.1 Introduction

Equations involving the derivative of a function of one variable occur in virtually every branch of applied mathematics. Broadly speaking, any physical situation that concerns the rate of change of one variable with respect to another leads to a differential equation, and such situations are clearly very common.

For a simple example, suppose that the rate of change of y with respect to x is proportional to y:

$$(10.1) \qquad \frac{dy}{dx} = y$$

(We shall often use a prime to denote differentiation and thus write this equation: $y' = y$.) Elementary techniques lead to the classical solution

$$y = ae^x$$

where a is an arbitrary constant. Different values of a lead to a family of curves, all of which satisfy the given differential equation (10.1), which is simply a statement that at each point on the curve the value of the function and the value of its derivative are to be equal. If in addition to the differential equation we are given a value of y for some x, the constant a can be determined. It might be specified, for instance, that the solution to (10.1) is to pass through the point $x = 0$, $y = 1$, which we would ordinarily write

$$(10.2) \qquad y(0) = 1$$

Then we find easily that $a = 1$ and that the particular curve from the general family is

$$y = e^x$$

Many techniques exist for finding the solutions to differential equations in terms of elementary functions or in terms of special functions, such as Bessel functions. We would not wish to minimize the importance of this basic field of mathematics, but it should nevertheless be realized that often practical problems either cannot be solved at all by the classical methods or lead to solutions that are so difficult to obtain or so cumbersome to evaluate that they are not worth the trouble. For instance, the simple-appearing equation

$$y' = x^2 + y^2$$

has no elementary solution. In a great many instances of practical work some of the coefficients or functions in a differential equation are strongly nonlinear or are given only as a tabulated set of experimental data, the latter ruling out a classical solution from the outset.

For a variety of reasons, then, we are led to search for methods of solution that will apply when the classical methods are of no help to us. (We should emphasize once again, however, that the existence of problems that cannot conveniently be solved by classical methods does not mean that the modern student should overlook the classical methods. The numerical approaches we shall discuss do not relieve the analyst of the responsibility of formulating the equation properly; they do not relieve him of the responsibility of recognizing an equation that has a reasonable solution in terms of special functions, some of which are widely used; and they do not change the fact that an informed analyst can frequently improve the initial formulation of a problem. Numerical methods are no excuse for poor analysis.)

In this chapter we shall concentrate on the methods of solving a single first-order ordinary (no partial derivatives) differential equation with one initial condition:

$$(10.3) \qquad y' = f(x, y)$$

$$(10.4) \qquad y(x_0) = y_0$$

The methods we shall consider are easily generalized to handle systems of simultaneous first-order equations. (See for instance the Case Study of Section 10.8.) Moreover, higher order equations may be reduced to a system of simultaneous first-order equations. For instance, the second-order equation

$$y'' = g(y', y, x)$$

can be rewritten

$$z' = g(z, y, x)$$

$$y' = z$$

where z is a new dependent variable defined by the second equation. These are now two simultaneous equations in y and z; their solution gives both the function and its derivative. The methods we shall study will therefore have considerably broader application than the simplicity of the fundamental equation might suggest.

Let us consider now what we mean by a solution to (10.3) and (10.4) and what we mean by a numerical solution. Equation 10.3 is a relation that may be viewed as a partial definition of a curve in the x-y plane; at each point on the curve we are told the value of its derivative in terms of x and y. There will in general be a family of curves that satisfies (10.3); (10.4) specifies the particular curve that passes through a given point. For example, (10.1) leads to a family of curves, some of which are shown in Figure 10.1; (10.2) picks out the one identified in the figure.

A solution is an expression for y in terms of x. To find numerical values of the function, we simply substitute any particular values of x into the expression and compute the corresponding values of y.

In broad outline a numerical solution is obtained as follows. The differential equation gives the slope of the curve at any point as a function of x and y; at the outset we know only one point through which the curve passes, namely x_0, y_0. We therefore begin there. We compute the slope of the curve at $x = x_0$ and proceed a small distance along the corresponding tangent. If the increment in x is called h, as we shall do, we arrive at a new point $x_1 = x_0 + h$, and from the slope of the tangent, obtained from the differential equation, we get a new value of y, y_1. Continuing in this way, we get a sequence of short straight lines, which, we hope, approximates sufficiently accurately the true curve that is the solution.

Obviously there are pitfalls in this simplest approach to numerical solution (which, as we shall see, is known as Euler's method). We are approximating a *curve* by a sequence of straight *lines*, which suggests difficulties at the outset. It can easily enough happen that the sequence of lines deviates considerably from the true curve, as suggested in Figure 10.2. This is the problem of *stability*, to which we shall have to devote considerable attention.

Clearly, we must find some way to take into account the curvature of the true solution rather than simply approximating it by a sequence of straight lines, as in Euler's method. We are led to two basic categories of methods.

1. One-step methods, in which we use information about the curve at one point and do not iterate the solution. A Taylor-series solution provides a fundamental method of this type; we base much of our analysis on this theoretical method, but, as we shall see, it is not usually practical. Practical techniques of this type, of which there are many, include the Runge-Kutta methods. We shall see that they are *direct* methods (no iteration), which seems to imply less effort, but they do in practical cases require more evaluations of the function. Furthermore, they have the serious disadvantage that it is difficult to estimate the error.

2. Multistep methods, in which the next point on the curve can be

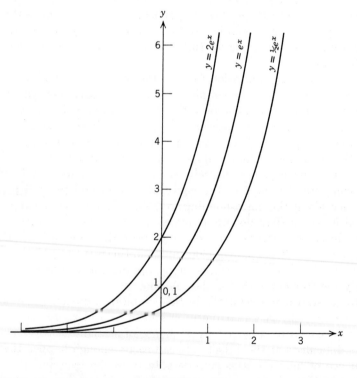

FIGURE 10.1 Three members of the family of curves represented by the differential equation $y' = y$. The initial condition $y(0) = 1$ picks out a particular member of the family.

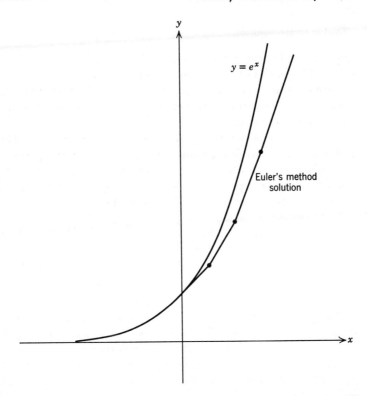

FIGURE 10.2 Graphical representation of the meaning of a numerical solution of a differential equation. The process described in the text is essentially Euler's method.

found with fewer evaluations of the function but which require iteration to arrive at a sufficiently accurate value. Most methods of this type are called *predictor-corrector*. Offsetting the effort of the iteration and a certain problem in getting the solution "started" is the fact that an estimate of the error is obtained as a by-product of the calculation.

As we have seen in many other situations, these contrasting methods have their strengths and weaknesses, and, as before, we shall be led to a judicious combination of the two.

There are a great many methods in both categories; the numerical solution of differential equations has received intensive study, especially in recent years. The methods we shall present will include approaches that the reader may use in solving practical problems and will serve to introduce the basic ideas of most other current methods.

10.2 Taylor series solution

We begin our study with a method that theoretically provides a solution to any differential equation but is nevertheless of little practical computational value. Its importance to us lies in the fact that it provides a basis for evaluating and comparing the methods that are of considerable practical worth.

We write the Taylor series expansion of the solution, $y(x)$, about some point $x = x_m$. In other words, we assume that the process of solution has proceeded to some specified point, and we ask what happens in going to the next point. This will be a frequent starting point for discussions of the various methods of solution.

$$(10.5) \quad y(x) = y_m + y_m'(x - x_m)$$
$$+ \frac{y_m''}{2}(x - x_m)^2 + \frac{y_m'''}{6}(x - x_m)^3 + \cdots$$

where $y_m^{(j)}$ is the jth derivative of $y(x)$ evaluated at $x = x_m$.

Now suppose that we have found an approximate solution for $m + 1$ points along the x-axis, $x_0, x_1, x_2, \ldots, x_m$. [Recall that the solution at x_0 is given by (10.4).] The successive x values here are all a distance h from that preceding; that is, $x_i = x_0 + ih$. We can approximate the solution at the next point x_{m+1} by substituting x_{m+1} for x in (10.5).

$$(10.6) \qquad y_{m+1} = y_m + hy_m' + \frac{h^2}{2}y_m'' + \frac{h^3}{6}y_m''' + \cdots$$

The more terms we take in the series the better the approximation will be. In any case, it is necessary to evaluate the various derivatives. From (10.3)

$$(10.7) \qquad y_m' = f(x_m, y_m)$$

Differentiating (10.3) with respect to x, we get

$$(10.8) \qquad y'' = \frac{\partial f}{\partial x}(x, y) + f(x, y)\frac{\partial f}{\partial y}(x, y)$$

so that

$$(10.9) \qquad y_m'' = f_x + ff_y$$

where the letter subscripts denote partial derivatives with respect to the variable given by the subscript:

$$f_x = \frac{\partial f}{\partial x}$$

It is assumed that all functions and derivatives are evaluated at $x = x_m$, $y = y_m$.

Equation 10.6 then becomes

(10.10) $$y_{m+1} = y_m + h\left(f + \frac{h}{2}(f_x + ff_y)\right) + O(h^3)$$

where $O(h^3)$, which is read "of order h^3," means that all succeeding terms contain h to the third or higher powers. This is another way of saying that if we used the formula in (10.10) without the $O(h^3)$ term the truncation error would be approximately Kh^3, where K is some constant.

The Taylor-series solution is classified as a one-step method because finding y_{m+1} requires the information at only one preceding point, x_m, y_m.

The practical difficulty of this method is that it may be hard—in fact, in some cases impossible—to find f_x and f_y. Moreover, if we wish to get a better approximation, that is, with a smaller truncation error, then we need to evaluate y_m''', which is

$$y_m''' = f_{xx} + 2ff_{xy} + f^2 f_{yy} + f_x f_y + ff_y{}^2$$

Succeeding derivatives become even more complicated.

The method is therefore generally impractical from a computational point of view. However, as we now turn to methods that are practical, we have a yardstick for judging them: the extent to which they agree with the Taylor series expansion. Some methods will agree only as far as terms in h, others will agree out through terms in h^4, etc. This way of judging a method will apply even though the methods of practical interest do not involve computing the value of any derivatives of $f(x, y)$.

10.3   Runge-Kutta methods

Our study of practical computing methods begins with a broad class of techniques known as *Runge-Kutta methods*. As we might expect, the different methods in this category involve more or less computation and accordingly have more or less accuracy. To establish the pattern of the methods, we shall in fact consider one (Euler's method) that is seldom used but is of historical interest and, like the Taylor-series solution, provides a necessary starting point for other discussions.

The Runge-Kutta methods have three distinguishing properties:

1. They are one-step methods: to find y_{m+1}, we need only the information available at the preceding point, x_m, y_m.

2. They agree with the Taylor series through terms in h^p, where p is different for different methods and is called the *order* of the method.

3. They do not require the evaluation of any derivatives of $f(x, y)$, but only of the function f itself.

It is the third property that makes these methods more practical than the Taylor series. We should expect, however, that we will have to evaluate $f(x, y)$ for more than one value of x and y; this is the price we pay for not having to evaluate the derivatives. It is a price well worth paying.

Let us begin, as usual, by considering what we can learn from geometrical intuition, after which we shall justify the results analytically.

Suppose we have a solution y_m at the point $x = x_m$. Then we can draw the line with the slope

$$y_m{}' = f(x_m, y_m)$$

which passes through the point x_m, y_m. The situation is pictured in Figure 10.3, where the curve is the exact (but unknown, of course)

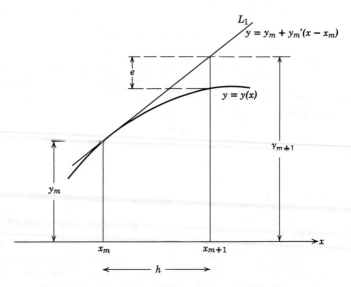

FIGURE 10.3   Geometrical representation of Euler's method.

solution and the line just described is identified as L_1. We can then let y_{m+1} be the point where L_1 intersects the ordinate erected at $x = x_{m+1} = x_m + h$.

The equation of the line L_1 is

$$y = y_m + y_m'(x - x_m)$$

but

$$y_m' = f(x_m, y_m)$$

and

$$x_{m+1} - x_m = h$$

so

(10.11) $$y_{m+1} = y_m + h\,f(x_m, y_m)$$

The error at $x = x_{m+1}$ is shown as e. This, of course, agrees with the Taylor-series expansion (10.10) through terms in h, so the truncation error is

$$e_T = Kh^2$$

We should note that although y_m is shown in Figure 10.3 as lying on the solution $y = y(x)$ in practice y_m is, of course, approximate and does not lie exactly on the curve.

Equation 10.11, which is *Euler's method*, is one of the oldest and best known numerical methods for integrating differential equations.

Besides having a relatively large truncation error, Euler's method is often unstable; that is, a small error—roundoff, truncation, or inherent —becomes magnified as the value of x increases. We will, therefore, not discuss the method any further but pass on to more accurate approaches. We might note, however, that according to our definitions Euler's method is a Runge-Kutta method, specifically, one of the first-order, since it agrees with the Taylor series through terms in h.

Euler's method uses only the slope at the point x_m, y_m in computing the value of y_{m+1}. The method can be improved in a number of different ways. We shall investigate two, called the *improved Euler method* and the *modified Euler method*, and then show that they are but two of a family of second-order Runge-Kutta methods.

In the improved Euler method* we work with the average of the slopes at x_m, y_m and $x_m + h$, $y_m + hy_m'$. The latter point is the one we called x_{m+1}, y_{m+1} in Euler's method. Geometrically (see Figure 10.4), we use Euler's method to find the point $x_m + h$, $y_m + hy_m'$, which is on line L_1 in the diagram. At this point we compute the slope of the curve, leading to line L_2. We average the two slopes and

---

* Also known as Heun's method.

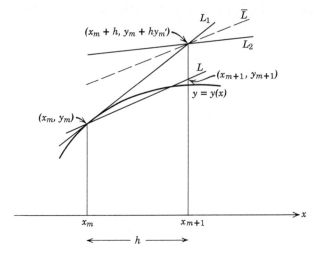

FIGURE 10.4   Geometrical representation of the improved Euler method.

get the dashed line $\bar{L}$.   Finally, we draw a line L parallel to $\bar{L}$ through the point x_m, y_m.   The point at which this line intersects the ordinate $x = x_{m+1} = x_m + h$ is taken to be the point x_{m+1}, y_{m+1}.
The slope of the line $\bar{L}$, and also that of the line L, is

$$(10.12) \quad \Phi(x_m, y_m, h) = \tfrac{1}{2}[f(x_m, y_m) + f(x_m + h, y_m + hy_m')]$$

where

$$(10.13) \qquad\qquad y_m' = f(x_m, y_m)$$

The equation of L is then

$$y = y_m + (x - x_m)\, \Phi(x_m, y_m, h)$$

so

$$(10.14) \qquad\qquad y_{m+1} = y_m + h\, \Phi(x_m, y_m, h)$$

Equations 10.12, 10.13, and 10.14 define the *improved Euler method*.
To see how well this agrees with the Taylor series, recall that the series expansion of $f(x, y)$ can be written

$$(10.15) \quad f(x, y) = f(x_m, y_m) + (x - x_m)\frac{\partial f}{\partial x} + (y - y_m)\frac{\partial f}{\partial y} + \cdots$$

where the partial derivatives are evaluated at $x = x_m$ and $y = y_m$.
Substituting $x = x_m + h$ and $y = y_m + hy_m'$ into (10.15) and using

(10.13) for y_m' we get

$$f(x_m + h, y_m + hy_m') = f + hf_x + hff_y + O(h^2)$$

where again f and all derivatives are evaluated at x_m, y_m.   Substituting this result into (10.12) and rearranging, we get

$$\Phi(x_m, y_m, h) = f + \frac{h}{2}(f_x + ff_y) + O(h^2)$$

Finally, this expression can be used in equation (10.14), providing a direct comparison with the Taylor series:

$$y_{m+1} = y_m + hf + \frac{h^2}{2}(f_x + ff_y) + O(h^3)$$

This agrees with the Taylor series through terms in h^2, so that the improved Euler method is a second-order Runge-Kutta method.   We are required to evaluate $f(x, y)$ *twice* (at x_m, y_m and $x_m + h, y_m + hy_m'$). In a comparison of the computational effort for the same order of accuracy, the Taylor series required three function evaluations: $f, f_x,$ and f_y.

   In the improved Euler method we averaged *slopes*.   Another approach is to average *points*, in the following sense.   In Figure 10.5 we start as before with the line L_1, which passes through x_m, y_m and has a slope given by $f(x_m, y_m)$.   We proceed along this line only until

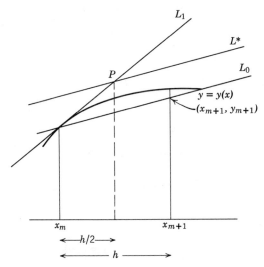

FIGURE 10.5   Geometrical representation of the modified Euler method.

its intersection with the ordinate erected at $x_m + h/2$; this is the point P in the diagram, where $y = y_m + (h/2)y_m'$. We calculate the slope there:

$$(10.16) \qquad \Phi(x_m, y_m, h) = f\left(x_m + \frac{h}{2}, y_m + \frac{h}{2}y_m'\right)$$

where

$$(10.17) \qquad y_m' = f(x_m, y_m)$$

The line through P with this slope is shown as L^*. We next draw a line parallel to L^* passing through x_m, y_m, which is shown as L_0. Now let y_{m+1} be the intersection of L_0 with $x = x_m + h$. The equation of L_0 is

$$y = y_m + (x - x_m)\,\Phi(x_m, y_m, h)$$

where Φ is given by (10.16). Thus

$$(10.18) \qquad y_{m+1} = y_m + h\,\Phi(x_m, y_m, h)$$

Equations 10.16, 10.17, and 10.18 define what is known as the *modified Euler method* or the *improved polygon method*. We leave the reader to show that it agrees with the Taylor series (10.10) through terms in h^2 and is therefore another second-order Runge-Kutta method.

Since we now have two rather different second-order Runge-Kutta methods, it might be interesting to see what the two have in common and whether they can be generalized.

We note that both are given by an expression of the form

$$(10.19) \qquad y_{m+1} = y_m + h\,\Phi(x_m, y_m, h)$$

and that in both cases Φ is of the form

$$(10.20) \quad \Phi(x_m, y_m, h) = a_1 f(x_m, y_m) + a_2 f(x_m + b_1 h, y_m + b_2 h y_m')$$

where

$$(10.21) \qquad y_m' = f(x_m, y_m)$$

In particular, for the improved Euler method

$$a_1 = a_2 = \tfrac{1}{2}$$

$$b_1 = b_2 = 1$$

whereas for the modified Euler method

$$a_1 = 0, \qquad a_2 = 1$$

$$b_1 = b_2 = \tfrac{1}{2}$$

Now (10.19), (10.20), and (10.21) represent a Runge-Kutta type formula. Let us see what order formula they can yield, at best, and what the permissible values for the parameters a_1, a_2, b_1, and b_2 are.

To obtain agreement with the Taylor series through terms in h will in general require one parameter. To obtain agreement through terms in h^2 will require two more parameters, since there are the terms $h^2 f_x$ and $h^2 f f_y$ to consider. Because we have only four parameters at our disposal, and three of them will be used to approximate the Taylor series through terms in h^2, a second-order formula will be the best we can do. With four parameters available and only three conditions to be met, we should expect to be able to derive many different second-order formulas, varying the one free parameter. This is indeed the case.

In the series expansion for $f(x, y)$ about x_m, y_m (10.15) let

$$x = x_m + b_1 h$$

$$y = y_m + b_2 h f$$

Then

$$f(x_m + b_1 h, y_m + b_2 h f) = f + b_1 h f_x + b_2 h f f_y + O(h^2)$$

where the functions on the right are evaluated at x_m, y_m. Then (10.19) can be expressed as

$$y_{m+1} = y_m + h(a_1 f + a_2 f + h\{a_2 b_1 f_x + a_2 b_2 f f_y\}) + O(h^3)$$

We compare this with the Taylor series (10.10). If terms in hf are to agree, then we require that

$$a_1 + a_2 = 1$$

From comparing terms in $h^2 f_x$, we require that

$$a_2 b_1 = \tfrac{1}{2}$$

And finally, from comparing terms in $h^2 f f_y$, we require that

$$a_2 b_2 = \tfrac{1}{2}$$

Since we have three equations in four parameters, we may choose one of the parameters arbitrarily, excluding zero perhaps, depending on which parameter is taken as the free one. For instance, let

$$a_2 = \omega \neq 0$$

Then

$$a_1 = 1 - \omega$$

$$b_1 = b_2 = \frac{1}{2\omega}$$

and (10.19), (10.20), and (10.21) reduce to

$$(10.22) \quad y_{m+1} = y_m + h \left[(1 - \omega) f(x_m, y_m) \right.$$

$$\left. + \omega f \left(x_m + \frac{h}{2\omega}, y_m + \frac{h}{2\omega} f(x_m, y_m) \right) \right] + O(h^3)$$

This is the most general second-order Runge-Kutta method. For $\omega = \frac{1}{2}$ we get the improved Euler method (Heun's method). For $\omega = 1$ we get the modified Euler method. The truncation error for any nonzero choice of ω is

$$(10.23) \qquad e_T = K h^3$$

It is possible to obtain bounds on $|K|$. A paper by Ralston* shows that the smallest upper bound is obtained when $\omega = \frac{2}{3}$.

Before going on to higher order Runge-Kutta methods, we may pause to consider a simple example (10.1):

$$y' = y$$

with the initial condition

$$y(0) = 1$$

As pointed out earlier, the exact solution is

$$y = e^x$$

The second-order Runge-Kutta method, from (10.22), is

$$y_{m+1} = y_m + h \left[(1 - \omega)y_m + \omega \left(y_m + \frac{h}{2\omega} y_m \right) \right]$$

which, for any nonzero choice of ω at all, reduces to

$$y_{m+1} = y_m \left(1 + h + \frac{h^2}{2} \right)$$

It follows that

$$y_{m+1} = \left(1 + h + \frac{h^2}{2} \right)^{m+1}$$

The term in parentheses is the same as the first three terms of the

---

* "Runge-Kutta Methods with Minimum Error Bounds," Anthony Ralston, Mathematics of Computation, **16**, 431–437 (1962).

Taylor series for e^h, and

$$y_{m+1} \simeq e^{h(m+1)} = e^{x_{m+1}}$$

as we should expect.

If we let $h = 0.1$, the computed values of y are as shown in Table

Table 10.1

i	x_i	y_i	error
1	0.1	1.105	0.000
2	0.2	1.221	0.000
3	0.3	1.349	0.001
4	0.4	1.491	0.001
5	0.5	1.648	0.001
6	0.6	1.821	0.001
7	0.7	2.012	0.002
8	0.8	2.223	0.003
9	0.9	2.456	0.004
10	1.0	2.714	0.004

10.1, which also lists the errors, $e^{x_i} - y_i$. It is clear that the error grows as x increases. By the time $x = 2$ ($i = 20$), the error will have grown to 0.021. Notice that the error is always positive, since

$$1 + h + \frac{h^2}{2} < e^h \qquad \text{for } h > 0$$

Third- and fourth-order Runge-Kutta methods can be developed in ways that are entirely analogous to those we have used to get first- and second-order methods.* We shall not follow the derivations but content ourselves with stating the fourth-order formula, which is one of the most commonly used methods of integrating differential equations. (It is so widely used, in fact, that in the literature of numerical computation it is often referred to simply as "the Runge-Kutta method," without any qualification of the order or type.) This classical Runge-Kutta method can be defined by the following five equations:

$$(10.24) \qquad y_{m+1} = y_m + \frac{h}{6}(k_1 + 2k_2 + 2k_3 + k_4)$$

---

* See, for example, the article by Ralston cited earlier.

where

(10.25) $\qquad k_1 = f(x_m, y_m)$

(10.26) $\qquad k_2 = f\left(x_m + \dfrac{h}{2}, y_m + \dfrac{hk_1}{2}\right)$

(10.27) $\qquad k_3 = f\left(x_m + \dfrac{h}{2}, y_m + \dfrac{hk_2}{2}\right)$

(10.28) $\qquad k_4 = f(x_m + h, y_m + hk_3)$

The truncation error here is

$$e_T = Kh^5$$

so we have a fourth-order method. Bounds for K are given in the paper by Ralston referred to earlier, in which the fourth-order method that produces a minimum upper bound on K may also be found.

Notice that in this method the function must be evaluated *four* times.

It will be interesting to compare this method, which integrates a function of x and y, with the methods we discussed in Chapter 6 for integrating a function of x alone. For this purpose let us suppose that f is a function of x only; that is,

$$f(x, y) = F(x)$$

and

(10.29) $\qquad y(x) = \displaystyle\int_{x_0}^{x} F(x)\, dx$

Let

$$p = \frac{h}{2}$$

and define

$$F_j = F(x_0 + jp)$$

Now

$$y_m = y(x_0 + mh) = y(x_0 + 2mp)$$

We define

$$Y_j = y(x_0 + jp)$$

so that

$$y_m = Y_{2m}$$

Thus (10.24) becomes

$$Y_{2m+2} - Y_{2m} = \frac{p}{3}\left(F_{2m} + 4F_{2m+1} + F_{2m+2}\right)$$

where we allow $m = 0, 1, 2, \ldots, n - 1$.   Thus

$$Y_2 - Y_0 = \frac{p}{3} \left(F_0 + 4F_1 + F_2 \right)$$

$$Y_4 - Y_2 = \frac{p}{3} \left(F_2 + 4F_3 + F_4 \right)$$

$$\cdots \cdots \cdots \cdots \cdots \cdots \cdots$$

$$Y_{2n} - Y_{2n-2} = \frac{p}{3} \left(F_{2n-2} + 4F_{2n-1} + F_{2n} \right)$$

Adding all these equations, we get

$$Y_{2n} - Y_0 = \frac{p}{3} \left(F_0 + 4F_1 + 2F_2 + 4F_3 + \cdots + 2F_{2n-2} \right.$$
$$\left. + 4F_{2n-1} + F_{2n} \right)$$

This is precisely Simpson's rule for the evaluation of (10.29), where $x = x_0 + 2nh$.

Thus the classical fourth-order Runge-Kutta method given by (10.24) to (10.28) is a generalization of Simpson's rule, the generalization being that we are not restricted to functions of x.   For this reason the method is often referred to as the *Runge-Kutta-Simpson rule*.

Let us return again to the simple example

$$y' = y, \, y(0) = 1$$

Then (10.25) to (10.28) yield

$$k_1 = y_m$$

$$k_2 = y_m + \frac{h}{2} y_m$$

$$k_3 = y_m + \frac{h}{2} \left(y_m + \frac{h}{2} y_m \right)$$

$$k_4 = y_m + h \left[y_m + \frac{h}{2} \left(y_m + \frac{h}{2} y_m \right) \right]$$

Using these in (10.24), we get

$$y_{m+1} = \left(1 + h + \frac{h^2}{2} + \frac{h^3}{6} + \frac{h^4}{24} \right) y_m$$

The term in parentheses is now the same as the first *five* terms of the Taylor series of e^h.

10.4 Error analysis for Runge-Kutta methods

We have noted that the truncation error in a pth-order Runge-Kutta method is Kh^{p+1}, where K is some constant. Bounds on K for $p = 2, 3,$ and 4 are given in Ralston's paper. The derivation of these bounds is not a simple matter, and, moreover, their evaluation requires quantities that do not appear in (10.24) through (10.28). One of the serious drawbacks of Runge-Kutta methods is the lack of simple means for estimating the error. The methods of the following section owe part of their attractiveness to the fact that error estimates are an easy by-product of the calculation of a new point.

Without some measure of the truncation error, it is difficult to choose the proper step size, h. A rough rule-of-thumb has been given by Collatz.* If

$$\frac{|k_2 - k_3|}{|k_1 - k_2|}$$

becomes large (more than a few hundredths), then h should be decreased.†

Merson has shown that an estimate of the truncation error can be obtained at the expense of one additional evaluation of $f(x, y)$. This may be costly if $f(x, y)$ is at all complicated. For further information see Section 16 of Chapter 2 of Fox's book.‡

A more precise estimate can be obtained at the expense of considerable extra effort by using Richardson's deferred approach to the limit, which we discussed in Chapter 6.

To do this, let Y_m be the "true" value of the solution at $x = x_0 + mh$. Then for the classical fourth-order method

(10.30) $$Y_m = y_m^{(h)} + Kh^5$$

where the superscript (h) on y_m indicates that Y_m was calculated with a step size of h. We then recompute the solution with a step size of $h/2$, so that

(10.31) $$Y_m = y_m^{(h/2)} + K\left(\frac{h}{2}\right)^5$$

---

* L. Collatz, *Numerische Behandlung von Differential-gleichungen*, Springer Verlag, Berlin, 1951, p. 34.
† See also Chapter 9 of Ralston and Wilf, *Mathematical Methods for Digital Computers*, Wiley, 1960.
‡ L. Fox, *Numerical Solution of Ordinary and Partial Differential Equations*, Pergamon, New York, 1962.

Subtracting (10.30) from (10.31) we get

$$y_m^{(h)} - y_m^{(h/2)} = -\tfrac{31}{32}Kh^5$$

and the truncation error in (10.29) is

(10.32) $\qquad E_T = Kh^5 = \tfrac{32}{31}[y_m^{(h/2)} - y_m^{(h)}]$

If the fifth derivative of y is reasonably constant, we have a fairly good estimate. The problem, of course, is that the solution must be computed *twice;* the information in the result (10.32) is not usually worth the effort.

Similar results can be obtained with second-order Runge-Kutta methods, in which the truncation error is Kh^3.

Even if the truncation error is small, a Runge-Kutta method may produce extremely inaccurate results under unfavorable conditions. Such erroneous results can arise because small errors (roundoff or truncation) may become magnified as the solution is carried out for larger and larger x.

For example, consider the simple equation

$$y' = -10y$$

with the initial condition

$$y(0) = 1$$

The exact solution is

$$y = e^{-10x}$$

From an analysis completely analogous to that leading to Table 10.1 we find that any second-order method leads to

$$y_{m+1} = (1 - 10h + 50h^2)^m$$

But now notice that the term in parentheses is greater than 1 if $h > 0.2$. For large m, therefore, y becomes indefinitely large. The exact solution, on the other hand, becomes small.

This phenomenon is called *partial instability* by Mayers.* It is distinguished from other instabilities by the fact that it depends on h. The instabilities discussed in Section 10.6 are independent of h.

The reader is warned that such partial instability exists for Runge-Kutta methods even when the exact solution does not decay exponentially, as in the foregoing example.

---

* See Section 7 in Chapter 4 of Fox's text.

10.5   Predictor-corrector methods

A distinguishing feature of Runge-Kutta methods is that in getting the next point, x_{m+1}, y_{m+1}, we use the information provided by x_m, y_m, but no prior points.   In second-order or higher methods we have to evaluate the function at one or more additional points.   This appears to be unreasonable on the face of it, for once the integration process has proceeded a few steps we already have available additional information without *any* function evaluations, namely, the value of y at the prior points.   The fact that Runge-Kutta methods do not use the readily available prior information, plus the lack of a convenient error estimate, makes us look for additional methods.   We shall see, however, that these methods cannot "start" themselves, since they not only *use* prior points but *demand* them.   Some other method must be used to get the new processes started or to change the step size.   We will be led, therefore, to a judicious combination of methods.

These methods, of which there are many variations, go by the name of *predictor-corrector*.   As implied by the name, we first "predict" a value for y_{m+1}.   We then use a different formula to "correct" this value.   We may then, if it appears desirable, employ the corrector formula again to "recorrect" the value of y_{m+1}.   This process can be iterated as many times as we wish, although we shall see that there are efficiency considerations that suggest choosing a step size that avoids going through a great many iterations.

Among the many possible formulas for the predictor and for the corrector, we shall choose an example of each that the reader will find applicable to many practical problems.   With the basic ideas clearly understood, there will then be no difficulty in applying the many other methods found in the literature.

For the predictor we shall use a second-order method:

$$(10.33) \qquad y_{m+1}^{(0)} = y_{m-1} + 2hf(x_m, y_m)$$

where the superscript (0) indicates that this is our first "guess" at y_{m+1}—a predicted value.   This suggests immediately that this method cannot be used to compute y_1, since to do so would require a point prior to the initial point x_0.   A Runge-Kutta method is often used to start a predictor-corrector method, a matter to which we shall return later.

One might think that this requirement for x_{m-1}, y_{m-1} could be avoided by using Euler's method.   This turns out not to be practical because the truncation error is too large.   It is this use of prior information without additional function evaluations that leads to the classification as *multistep* methods.

Geometrically (see Figure 10.6), the predictor amounts to finding the slope at x_m, y_m and drawing a line L_1 with that slope through x_m, y_m. We then draw a line L, parallel to L_1, through x_{m-1}, y_{m-1}. Where this line intersects the line $x = x_{m+1}$ is the predicted value, $y_{m+1}^{(0)}$.

We now need a method of improving our predicted value. Since we know y_{m+1} approximately, we can calculate an approximate slope at x_{m+1}, $y_{m+1}^{(0)}$. This is exhibited as the line L_2 in Figure 10.7. The line L_1 is the same as L_1 in Figure 10.6, having the slope given by $f(x_m, y_m)$. We now average the slopes of the lines L_1 and L_2, giving the line $\bar{L}$. Finally, a line L is drawn parallel to $\bar{L}$ through the point x_m, y_m. Its intersection with the line $x = x_{m+1}$ yields a new approximation to y_{m+1}. We call this the *corrected* value $y_{m+1}^{(1)}$. It is given by

$$y_{m+1}^{(1)} = y_m + \frac{h}{2}[f(x_m, y_m) + f(x_{m+1}, y_{m+1}^{(0)})]$$

We can now get another and presumably better estimate of $f(x_{m+1}, y_{m+1})$ by using $y_{m+1}^{(1)}$ and recorrecting the value of y_{m+1}. Thus, in general, the ith approximation to y_{m+1} is given by

(10.34) $$y_{m+1}^{(i)} = y_m + \frac{h}{2}[f(x_m, y_m) + f(x_{m+1}, y_{m+1}^{(i-1)})]$$

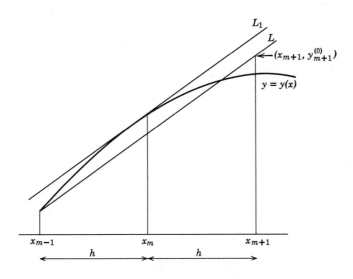

FIGURE 10.6   Geometrical representation of the second order predictor described in the text.

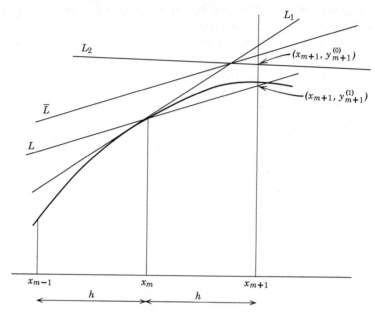

FIGURE 10.7 Geometrical representation of the second order corrector described in the text.

for $i = 1, 2, 3, \ldots$. The iterations are stopped when

(10.35)
$$\left| y_{m+1}^{(i+1)} - y_{m+1}^{(i)} \right| < \epsilon$$

for a specified positive ϵ.

The observant reader will notice a similarity between this corrector method and the improved Euler method given by (10.12) to (10.14). The essential difference is that Euler's method was used before as the "predictor" and we did not iterate, whereas here we use the more accurate (10.33).

The question that naturally arises is, will (10.35) ever be satisfied? In other words, does the process converge?

To answer this crucial question, we begin by noting that

$$y_{m+1}^{(i+1)} - y_{m+1}^{(i)} = \frac{h}{2} \left[f(x_{m+1}, y_{m+1}^{(i)}) - f(x_{m+1}, y_{m+1}^{(i-1)}) \right]$$

Using the mean value theorem,

(10.36)
$$y_{m+1}^{(i+1)} - y_{m+1}^{(i)} = \frac{h}{2} \left(\frac{\partial f}{\partial y} \right) \left[y_{m+1}^{(i)} - y_{m+1}^{(i-1)} \right]$$

where $\partial f / \partial y$ is evaluated for $x = x_{m+1}$ and for some y between $y_{m+1}^{(i)}$ and $y_{m+1}^{(i+1)}$.

We now assume that $\partial f / \partial y$ is bounded, that is, there is some M such that

$$\left| \frac{\partial f}{\partial y} \right| \leq M$$

Then it follows from (10.36) that

$$\left| y_{m+1}^{(i+1)} - y_{m+1}^{(i)} \right| \leq \frac{hM}{2} \left| y_{m+1}^{(i)} - y_{m+1}^{(i-1)} \right|$$

Similarly

$$\left| y_{m+1}^{(i)} - y_{m+1}^{(i-1)} \right| \leq \frac{hM}{2} \left| y_{m+1}^{(i-1)} - y_{m+1}^{(i-2)} \right|$$

Substituting this in the preceding inequality,

$$\left| y_{m+1}^{(i+1)} - y_{m+1}^{(i)} \right| \leq \left(\frac{hM}{2} \right)^2 \left| y_{m+1}^{(i-1)} - y_{m+1}^{(i-2)} \right|$$

Continuing in this way, we arrive finally at

$$\left| y_{m+1}^{(i+1)} - y_{m+1}^{(i)} \right| \leq \left(\frac{hM}{2} \right)^i \left| y_{m+1}^{(1)} - y_{m+1}^{(0)} \right|$$

Thus if the step size h is chosen so that

(10.37) $$h < \frac{2}{M}$$

the difference in the corrected values approaches zero and the process thus converges.

It should be clearly understood what we have just proved. Subject to the condition stated, the method has been shown to converge to *some* definite value, but not necessarily to the *true* solution. The difference between the two is the truncation error, which we consider in Section 10.6.

We shall discuss how rapid the convergence should be in Section 10.6. Obviously, the smaller h is, the more rapidly the process will converge.

First let us look a little more closely at the correction formula (10.34). Suppose that f is a function of x only, that is,

$$f(x, y) = F(x)$$

so that

(10.38) $$y(x) = \int_{x_0}^{x} F(x)\, dx$$

Then

$$y_{m+1} = y_m + \frac{h}{2}[F(x_m) + F(x_{m+1})]$$

where now we have dropped the superscripts on y_{m+1}, since the first corrected value is exact except for truncation and roundoff error. It follows then that

$$y_n - y_0 = \frac{h}{2}[F(x_0) + 2F(x_1) + \cdots + 2F(x_{n-1}) + F(x_n)]$$

This is simply the trapezoidal rule for the evaluation of (10.38) where $x = x_0 + nh$. This correction formula is therefore a generalization of the trapezoidal rule, just as the classical Runge-Kutta method is a generalization of Simpson's rule. This naturally implies that the improved Euler method is also a generalization of the trapezoidal rule.

Notice finally that the corrector formula

$$y_{m+1} = y_m + \frac{h}{2}[f(x_m, y_m) + f(x_{m+1}, y_{m+1})]$$

is *implicit* in the sense that y_{m+1} appears on both sides of the equation, the one on the left being a new value computed from the formula and the one on the right being the prior approximation. We therefore cannot solve for y_{m+1} directly. All of the other formulas in this chapter have been *explicit*. That is to say, y_{m+1} was given explicitly in terms of y_m and perhaps y_{m-1}, and, of course, some x values that are known. We shall encounter this same division into explicit and implicit types in the next chapter on partial differential equations.

10.6   Error analysis of predictor-corrector methods

The analysis of errors and related matters in predictor-corrector methods can conveniently be broken into several distinct investigations. We shall first discuss the truncation errors in the predictor (10.33) and the corrector (10.34). The results will be expressed easily in terms of quantities already computed in getting the solution. We shall then discuss the proper choice of the step size h. Finally, we shall consider the problem of stability: whether errors—inherent, roundoff, or truncation—grow as x increases.

To find the truncation error in the predictor (10.33), recall that the Taylor series for $y(x)$ about the point $x = x_m$ is

$$y(x) = y_m + y_m'(x - x_m) + \frac{y_m''}{2}(x - x_m)^2 + \frac{1}{6}(x - x_m)^3 y'''(\xi)$$

where ξ lies between x and x_m. Letting $x = x_{m+1}$, we get

$$y_{m+1} = y_m + hy_m' + \frac{h^2}{2}y_m'' + \frac{h^3}{6}y'''(\xi_1), \qquad x_m \leq \xi_1 \leq x_{m+1}$$

Similarly, letting $x = x_{m-1}$, we get

$$y_{m-1} = y_m - hy_m' + \frac{h^2}{2}y_m'' - \frac{h^3}{6}y'''(\xi_2), \qquad x_{m-1} \leq \xi_2 \leq x_m$$

If we subtract these two equations and note that

$$\frac{y'''(\xi_1) + y'''(\xi_2)}{2} = y'''(\xi), \qquad x_{m-1} \leq \xi \leq x_{m+1}$$

it follows that

$$y_{m+1} = y_{m-1} + 2hy_m' + \frac{h^3}{3}y'''(\xi)$$

The truncation error is then

$$(10.39) \qquad E_T^{(p)} = \frac{h^3}{3}y'''(\xi), \qquad x_{m-1} \leq \xi \leq x_{m+1}$$

If the third derivative is reasonably constant, then the truncation error is Kh^3, as implied in Section 10.5 when we stated that this predictor was a second-order method.

We have already noted that the corrector (10.34) is a generalization of the trapezoidal rule. In Chapter 6 we found the truncation error for the trapezoidal rule to be

$$(10.40) \qquad E_T^{(c)} = -\frac{h^3}{12}y'''(\eta), \qquad x_{m-1} \leq \eta \leq x_{m+1}$$

This too is $O(h^3)$.

The fact that the truncation errors in both predictor and corrector are of the same order allows us to develop a simple method of estimating y''', hence $E_T^{(c)}$. The technique is closely allied to the deferred approach to the limit used in Chapter 6 and in Section 10.4.

We let Y_m be the true value of the solution at $x = x_m$. Then

$$Y_m = y_m^{(0)} + \frac{h^3}{3} y'''(\xi)$$

and

$$Y_m = y_m^{(i)} - \frac{h^3}{12} y'''(\eta)$$

where $y_m^{(0)}$ and $y_m^{(i)}$ are given by (10.33) and (10.34). Subtracting these equations we get

$$0 = y_m^{(i)} - y_m^{(0)} - \frac{h^3}{12} [y'''(\eta) + 4y'''(\xi)]$$

If we assume that y''' is reasonably constant for $x_{m-1} \le x \le x_{m+1}$, then

$$\frac{5h^3}{12} y''' = y_m^{(i)} - y_m^{(0)}$$

and

(10.41) $$E_T^{(c)} = -\frac{h^3}{12} y''' = \frac{1}{5} [y_m^{(0)} - y_m^{(i)}]$$

The values needed for this estimate are already available from the calculation. Thus, in contrast to the Runge-Kutta methods, we have an easily computed estimate for the truncation error. Notice that the argument depended on both truncation errors being of the same order. It is therefore desirable that any predictor-corrector pair have this property.

We are now ready to discuss the choice of the step size h. There is no formula for choosing the initial value of h, with the possible exception of (10.37), which is usually not much help: M may be hard to estimate, and if it varies over the interval of integration (10.37) will be unduly conservative at most points. Once the calculation has started, however, we can compute the truncation error by (10.41). If this number is too large, we decrease the step size (often by halving it). If the number is smaller than we need, we increase the step size (often by doubling it).

We can make one further remark on the choice of h. Recall from (10.37) that the method converges if

$$h < \frac{2}{M}$$

But we do not know the value of M. However, the smaller h is, the more rapid the convergence will be. We thus have an economic choice. If we choose a small h, not many iterations will be required per point, but there will be many points. If we choose a larger h, there will be fewer points but more iterations per point. There is strong empirical evidence* to indicate that the most *efficient* number of iterations is usually *two*. (Here efficiency is used in the sense of minimum computation for a given accuracy.) In other words, if the step size is chosen so that the convergence criterion (10.35) is satisfied in two iterations, the total amount of computation will be minimized.

This approach is readily programmed. We count the iterations; if more than two iterations are required, we reduce the step size, but if one iteration is sufficient we increase it.

We have not yet discussed the actual process of changing the step size. It is clear that some thought must be given to the matter because once the step size is changed the predictor formula no longer applies directly. If the step size is to be doubled, it would theoretically be possible to go back *two* steps (in terms of the preceding step size) in order to get started with the larger interval, but in practice a more direct attack is quite adequate. What we actually do is to stop the calculation by the predictor-corrector method and take x_m, y_m to be a new starting point. The predictor-corrector method is then restarted with the new step size, using a Runge-Kutta method.

Finally, we turn to the manner in which an error is propagated ("grows"), that is, the question of *stability*.

The error is governed by the corrector formula (10.34). Thus the final choice of y_{m+1} satisfies

$$(10.42) \qquad y_{m+1} = y_m + \frac{h}{2}[f(x_m, y_m) + f(x_{m+1}, y_{m+1})]$$

apart from roundoff error. If Y_m is the exact solution, then

$$(10.43) \qquad Y_{m+1} = Y_m + \frac{h}{2}[f(x_m, Y_m) + f(x_{m+1}, Y_{m+1})] + e_m$$

where e_m includes the truncation error and the roundoff error in (10.42). If we subtract (10.42) from (10.43) and let

$$\epsilon_i = Y_i - y_i$$

---

* T. E. Hull and A. L. Creemer, "Efficiency of Predictor-Corrector Procedures," *J. ACM*, **10**, 291–301 (1963).

it follows that

$$\epsilon_{m+1} = \epsilon_m + \frac{h}{2} \{[f(x_m, Y_m) - f(x_m, y_m)]$$
$$+ [f(x_{m+1}, Y_{m+1}) - f(x_{m+1}, y_{m+1})]\} + e_m$$

From the mean value theorem

$$\epsilon_{m+1} = \epsilon_m + \frac{h}{2} [f_y(x_{m+1}, \xi_{m+1}) \cdot \epsilon_{m+1} + f_y(x_m, \xi_m) \cdot \epsilon_m] + e_m$$

where ξ_i lies between y_i and Y_i. Thus

(10.44) $$\epsilon_{m+1} = \mu \epsilon_m + \delta$$

where

(10.45) $$\mu = \frac{1 + \dfrac{hf_y}{2}}{1 - \dfrac{hf_y}{2}}$$

and

(10.46) $$\delta = \frac{e_m}{1 - \dfrac{hf_y}{2}}$$

The arguments have been omitted from the f_y terms, and we assume that e_m is independent of m.

Equation 10.44 is called a *difference equation*. We shall discuss its solution for ϵ_m shortly. First, recall that (10.37) required that

(10.47) $$\left| \frac{hf_y}{2} \right| < 1$$

for convergence. Suppose that

(10.48) $$f_y < 0$$

Then, if h satisfies (10.47), it follows that

$$0 < \mu < 1$$

Thus the error ϵ_m in y_m is not magnified in ϵ_{m+1}. That is to say, the errors do not grow, and the method is therefore said to be *stable*, or, more precisely, it possesses *absolute stability*.*

---

* The absolute errors do not grow.

On the other hand, if

$$f_y > 0$$

then

$$\mu > 1$$

and the method is unstable, but this does not mean that we cannot then use the method.   We shall see that even in this case the *relative* errors do not grow.

Suppose, for the moment, that f_y is constant, that is, the differential equation is

$$y' = Ay$$

where A is a constant.   Then

$$Y = ae^{Ax}$$

and

(10.49) $$Y_m = ae^{A(x_0 + mh)} = a^* e^{(hA)m}$$

where a^* is a new constant incorporating the constant factor e^{Ax_0}. If $A > 0$, then Y_m grows exponentially with m.   Even if ϵ_m grows, the relative error (ϵ_m/Y_m) may not grow.   In fact, it is unreasonable to ask that the absolute error remain bounded in this case.

In order to investigate the growth of the relative error, we note that the solution of the difference equation (10.44) is

(10.50) $$\epsilon_m = a_0 \mu^m + \frac{\delta}{1 - \mu}$$

where a_0 is an arbitrary constant.   The reader may verify this result by substituting (10.50) in (10.44).

Now, carrying out the division indicated in (10.45) and recalling that $f_y = A$, we have

$$\mu = \left(1 + \frac{hA}{2}\right)\left[1 + \left(\frac{hA}{2}\right) + \left(\frac{hA}{2}\right)^2 + \left(\frac{hA}{2}\right)^3 + \cdots\right]$$

$$= 1 + hA + \frac{(hA)^2}{2} + \frac{(hA)^3}{4} + \cdots$$

and the series converges for $|hA| < 2$, which is the condition of convergence of the predictor-corrector method (10.47).   Now

$$e^{hA} = 1 + hA + \frac{(hA)^2}{2} + \frac{(hA)^3}{6} + \cdots$$

so that

$$\mu = e^{hA} + O(h^3)$$

That is to say, $\mu = e^{hA}$ to the same accuracy as the truncation error in the method.   Thus from (10.50)

(10.51) $$\epsilon_m \simeq a_0 e^{(hA)m} + \frac{\delta}{1 - e^{hA}}$$

The latter term is independent of m, and thus the first term dominates as m increases.

Comparing (10.49) and (10.51)

$$\frac{\epsilon_m}{Y_m} \simeq \frac{a^*}{a_0} = \text{constant}$$

and the relative error remains fixed.

Similarly for $A < 0$, e_m and Y both behave as e^{-hA}.   Again the relative error does not grow.

We may say then that the method described in Section 10.5 has *relative stability*.

Now we must recall that the arguments leading to relative stability assumed that f_y was a constant.   In any case of interest this is not true.   There is strong empirical evidence, however, that the relative errors do not—on the average—grow in a relatively stable process. The same may be said of the absolute errors in an absolutely stable process.

In summary, then, our simple predictor-corrector method (10.33) and (10.34) is a relatively stable process.   Moreover, it is absolutely stable if $f_y < 0$.

We may make one final remark.   Recall from (10.41) that

$$Y_m - y_m^{(i)} = E_T^{(c)} = \tfrac{1}{5}(y_m^{(0)} - y_m^{(i)})$$

Thus a more accurate solution may be found by making one final correction:

(10.52) $$y_m = y_m^{(i)} + \tfrac{1}{5}(y_m^{(0)} - y_m^{(i)})$$

10.7   Attainable accuracy

We cannot give a detailed analysis of the effect of uncertainty in the parameters in the differential equation (10.3) or the initial condition (10.4) because of the wide variety of possible equations.   We can, however, indicate the serious consequences of errors in data on the solution with a simple example.

Following Mayers,* we consider the differential equation

$$y' = y - x$$

For the initial condition

$$y(0) = 1$$

the solution is

$$y = x + 1$$

Suppose now that the error in the initial condition may be as great as 1%. The solution then may vary between

$$y^{(1)} = 0.01e^x + x + 1$$

and

$$y^{(2)} = -0.01e^x + x + 1$$

We see that at $x = 5$, y may be in error by as much as $0.01e^5$, or about 30%, as a result of a 1% error in the initial condition. The percentage error in the result grows rapidly with x.

No numerical method can produce a solution more accurate than 30% at $x = 5$ because this size error is inherent in the original problem. For this reason Mayers refers to this type of error growth as *inherent instability*.

10.8 Comparison of methods

We have noted at various points in the preceding discussion the relative merits and deficiencies of one-step (Runge-Kutta) and multistep (predictor-corrector) methods. We summarize the results here and suggest an appropriate way to combine the two types of methods to take advantage of the strengths of each.

Runge-Kutta methods

1. Since they do not use information from previously calculated points, Runge-Kutta methods are self-starting.

2. For the same reason, however, they require several evaluations of the function $f(x, y)$ and are therefore time-consuming.

3. Being self-starting, they permit an easy change in the step size.

4. They provide no easily obtainable information about truncation error.

---

* Section 6 of Chapter 4 of Fox's book.

Predictor-corrector methods

The characteristics are complementary to those of Runge-Kutta methods.

1. Since they do use information about prior points, they are not self-starting.

2. They substitute information about prior points for repeated evaluation of $f(x, y)$ and are therefore more efficient (unless, of course, the step size is so large that many iterations of the corrector formula are needed).

3. Except in special circumstances that are usually not of practical usefulness, a change in step size requires a temporary reversion to a Runge-Kutta method.

4. A good estimate of the truncation error flows naturally out of the computation.

The complementary nature of the two types of methods suggests immediately that a combination of the two will prove useful. We suggest the following course of action.

1. Start the solution of a Runge-Kutta method, such as (10.22), to find y_1.

2. Use the predictor-corrector pair (10.33) and (10.34) to compute succeeding y_m.

3. If more than two iterations of the corrector are needed to obtain the desired accuracy *or* if the truncation error given by (10.41) is too large, decrease the step size (see 4 below). If, on the other hand, the truncation error is exceedingly small, the step size can be increased.

4. To change the step size, consider the last value of y_i that was sufficiently accurate, to be an initial point. Restart the solution from that point, using a Runge-Kutta method as in 1 above.

5. In any case, when $y_m^{(i)}$ has been obtained from the corrector, use (10.52) to compute the final value of y_m.

Naturally, there are many other predictor-corrector formulas that give higher accuracy. They are catalogued in most texts on numerical analysis,* and some of them are sketched in the exercises. However, more accurate Runge-Kutta methods, such as (10.24) to (10.28), should be used to start them.

---

* See, for instance, Chapter 5 of Peter Henrici, *Discrete Variable Methods in Ordinary Differential Equations*, Wiley, New York, 1962, or Chapter 15 of Richard W. Hamming, *Numerical Methods for Scientists and Engineers*, McGraw-Hill, New York, 1962.

10.9   Case study 12: Flight of supersonic aircraft

We consider the problem of determining the flight path of a supersonic turbojet aircraft.   Only a basic outline of the formulation of the problem is given.   For details the reader is referred to Angelo Miele, "Flight Mechanics," Vol. I, *Theory of Flight Paths*, Addison-Wesley, Reading, Mass., 1962.

We shall assume a flat earth and a constant-weight aircraft with fixed control surfaces, which we represent by a point mass.   If the path lies in a vertical plane, the forces acting on the aircraft can be represented as in Figure 10.8, where W is the weight, T is the thrust, D is the drag, and L is the lift.

We let V be the velocity along the path, θ the angle the path makes with the horizon, and Z the altitude.

The equations of motion of the aircraft along directions parallel and perpendicular to the flight path are

(10.53)
$$\frac{dV}{dZ} = F(V, \theta)$$

(10.54)
$$\frac{d\theta}{dZ} = G(V, \theta)$$

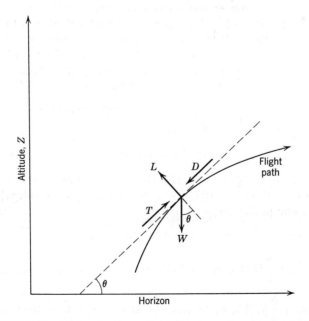

FIGURE 10.8   The forces acting on the idealized aircraft in Case Study 12.

with the initial conditions

(10.55) $$V(0) = V_0, \qquad \theta(0) = \theta_0$$

The functions F and G are given by

(10.56) $$F(V, \theta) = \frac{g(T - W \sin \theta - D)}{WV \sin \theta}$$

(10.57) $$D = \tfrac{1}{2} C_D \rho S V^2$$

(10.58) $$G(V, \theta) = \frac{g(L - W \cos \theta)}{WV^2 \sin \theta}$$

(10.59) $$L = \tfrac{1}{2} C_L \rho S V^2$$

We define the constants as follows and also give typical values that will be used in the numerical computation to be described shortly.

(10.60)
$$\begin{cases} g = 32.174 \text{ ft/sec}^2 & \text{(gravitational constant)} \\ W = 20,000 \text{ lb} & \text{(weight of aircraft)} \\ C_D = 0.02 & \text{(drag coefficient)} \\ C_L = 0.1 & \text{(lift coefficient)} \\ S = 160 \text{ ft}^2 & \text{(wing area)} \end{cases}$$

The other two quantities that have not been defined are the thrust T and the air density ρ. We shall assume that thrust is a function of velocity and altitude. Density is taken to be a function of altitude only; a more accurate analysis would have to consider variations with temperature. The relations below are rough curve fits to empirical data.

(10.61) $$T = (1 + \tfrac{1}{2} e^{-(V \times 10^{-3} - 1.5)^2})(10^4 - 0.27z) \text{ lb}$$

(10.62)
$$\begin{cases} \rho = \rho_0 e^{-Z/2.36 \cdot 10^4} \text{ lb-sec}^2/\text{ft}^4 \\ \rho_0 = 2.3769 \cdot 10^{-3} \text{ lb-sec}^2/\text{ft}^4 \end{cases}$$

We shall solve (10.53) and (10.54) simultaneously, where F and G are given by (10.56) to (10.62) and the initial conditions are given by (10.55). The procedure is as follows:

1. Use the improved Euler method to compute V_1, θ_1.

$$V_1 = V_0 + \frac{h}{2} [F(V_0, \theta_0) + F(V_0 + hF(V_0, \theta_0), \theta_0 + hG(V_0, \theta_0))]$$

$$\theta_1 = \theta_0 + \frac{h}{2} [G(V_0, \theta_0) + G(V_0 + hG(V_0, \theta_0), \theta_0 + hG(V_0, \theta_0))]$$

The equation for V contains both V and θ, and the equation for θ also contains both. This is, of course, the essence of the fact that these are simultaneous equations. On the right-hand sides of both equations, however, V and θ appear only with zero subscripts; that is, we are always working with preceding and therefore fixed values.

2. For $m = 1, 2, \ldots$, we predict values of V_{m+1}, θ_{m+1} from

$$V_{m+1}^{(0)} = V_{m-1} + 2hF(V_m, \theta_m)$$

$$\theta_{m+1}^{(0)} = \theta_{m-1} + 2hG(V_m, \theta_m)$$

This is analogous to (10.33).

3. We correct the values of V_{m+1}, θ_{m+1} from

$$V_{m+1}^{(i)} = V_m + \frac{h}{2}[F(V_m, \theta_m) + F(V_{m+1}^{(i-1)}, \theta_{m+1}^{(i-1)})]$$

$$\theta_{m+1}^{(i)} = \theta_m + \frac{h}{2}[G(V_m, \theta_m) + G(V_{m+1}^{(i-1)}, \theta_{m+1}^{(i-1)})]$$

This is analogous to (10.34). At this stage there is an interaction between the two equations, requiring that the two formulas be applied *alternately*. If we were to try to get a final solution for V, iterating on it alone, we would have to work exclusively with the predicted value of θ, which is only an approximation. When we then iterated to get a more accurate θ, we would naturally develop a value different from that used in computing V. In short, the equations are simultaneous. (The observant reader will note the strong parallel with the Gauss-Seidel iteration method for solving simultaneous algebraic equations, where it is obvious that continued iteration on one equation by itself would ignore the simultaneity.)

In a complete treatment of this subject we would, of course, have to prove that this process of iteration with interaction converges. Without carrying out the lengthy analysis, we can state that for a wide range of problems the process does indeed converge.

4. We estimate the truncation error from

$$E_T(V_{m+1}) = \tfrac{1}{5}(V_m^{(0)} - V_m^{(i)})$$

$$E_T(\theta_{m+1}) = \tfrac{1}{5}(\theta_m^{(0)} - \theta_m^{(i)})$$

These estimates are printed and also used to correct the final values of V and θ, according to (10.52).

The block diagram shown in Figure 10.9 is in a slightly different style from most of the others in the book. Here we have not attempted to show every detail of the calculation but rather have tried to give a clear picture of the major features of the approach. The

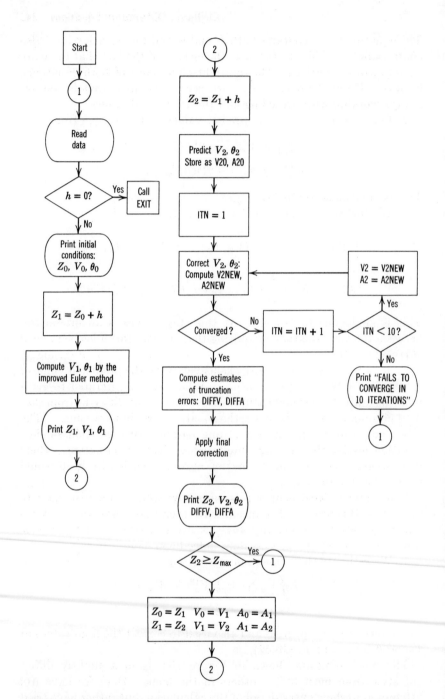

FIGURE 10.9 Block diagram of the method of solving two simultaneous differential equations of flight. (Case Study 12.)

effect of the shift in emphasis is to give more importance to the decisions and the flow of control than to the computational steps.

We begin by reading the values of the parameters that describe the aircraft and the flight. The flight is described by Z_0 and Z_{max}, the initial and maximum altitudes, θ_0, the initial flight angle, and V_0, and initial velocity. The aircraft is described by its weight, wing area, S, lift coefficient, C_L, and drag coefficient, C_D. Finally, the numerical method requires values for h, the step size, and TOLER, the convergence tolerance. An h of zero signals the end of the deck. We print the various parameters, a heading line, and the initial conditions.

Next we use the improved Euler method to find V_1 and θ_1 and we print them.

Now we are able to move into the predictor-corrector method. The notational convention used is as follows: Z_0 in the block diagram (and program) corresponds to x_{m-1} in the text, Z_1 in the block diagram corresponds to x_m in the text, and Z_2 in the block diagram corresponds to x_{m+1} in the text.

It will be seen that the block diagram follows the text description of the predictor-corrector method quite closely, with the difference that here we have two equations to be solved successively. We have also introduced an iteration counter, ITN, to prevent the program from spinning its wheels in a nonconvergent case. Equation 10.41 is used to compute estimates of the truncation errors; these are printed. Equation 10.52 is employed to make a final correction to the values of V and θ. After printing the values and testing for the end of the range, we are ready to go back to apply the predictor-corrector method again. Before doing so, however, it is necessary to give Z_0 the value previously assigned to Z_1 and to give Z_1 the value previously assigned to Z_2; similar actions are required for V and θ. With these changes in values, the predictor-corrector steps will compute the next point on the curve.

The program in Figure 10.10 follows the block diagram quite closely, with the addition of a few measures taken for programming convenience. The program is presented as a listing of the source program deck. Statement numbers have been assigned to certain statements that do not otherwise need them in order to simplify the description of the program.

The first four statements are arithmetic statement functions to compute air density, engine thrust, and the two differential equations as functions of the appropriate arguments. The differential equation functions involve a number of variables such as weight and thrust, that are not listed as arguments.

```
      DENSTYF(Z) = 2.3769E-3 * EXPF(-Z/2.36E4)
      THRUSTF(V,Z)=(1.0+0.5*EXPF(-(V*0.001-1.5)**2))*(10000.0-0.27*Z)
      FFNCF(V, A) = GRAV * (T - WEIGHT * SINF(A)
     1   - 0.5 * CD * RHO * S * V**2) / (WEIGHT * V * SINF(A))
      GFNCF(V, A) = GRAV *(0.5*CL*RHO*S*V**2 - WEIGHT*COSF(A)) /
     1   (WEIGHT * V**2 * SINF(A))
      GRAV = 32.174
    5 READ INPUT TAPE 7, 1, Z0, ZMAX, THETAO, V0, WEIGHT, S, CL, CD,
     1   H, TOLER
    1 FORMAT (8F10.0/2F10.0)
      IF(H) 3, 3, 2
    3 CALL EXIT
    2 WRITE OUTPUT TAPE 10, 4, Z0, ZMAX, THETAO, V0, WEIGHT, S, CL,
     1   CD, H, TOLER
    4 FORMAT (4H1Z0=, F7.0, 7H  ZMAX=, F7.0, 9H   THETAO=, F6.2,
     1   5H  V0=, F6.0//8H WEIGHT=, F7.0, 5X, 10HWING AREA=, F5.0//
     2   18H LIFT COEFFICIENT=, F6.3, 5X, 17HDRAG COEFFICIENT=, F6.3//
     3   3H H=, F7.2, 5X, 10HTOLERANCE=, F7.4///9H ALTITUDE, 2X,
     4   8HVELOCITY,4X, 5HANGLE, 6X, 5HDIFFV, 5X,5HDIFFA, 3X,3HITN//)
      WRITE OUTPUT TAPE 10, 105, Z0, V0, THETAO
  105 FORMAT (F8.0, F11.2, F10.3, F10.5, F10.5, I4)
   14 Z1 = Z0 + H
      RHO = DENSTYF(Z0)
      T = THRUSTF(V0, Z0)
      A0 = THETAO /57.29578
      F = FFNCF(V0, A0)
      G = GFNCF(V0, A0)
      VV = V0 + H * F
      AA = A0 + H * G
      RHO = DENSTYF(Z1)
      T = THRUSTF(VV, Z1)
      V1 = V0 + 0.5 * H * (F + FFNCF(VV, AA))
      A1 = A0 + 0.5 * H * (G + GFNCF(VV, AA))
      THETA = A1 * 57.29578
  114 WRITE OUTPUT TAPE 10, 105, Z1, V1, THETA
   16 Z2 = Z1 + H
      RHO = DENSTYF(Z1)
      T = THRUSTF(V1, Z1)
      F = FFNCF(V1, A1)
      G = GFNCF(V1, A1)
      V2 = V0 + 2.0 * H * F
      A2 = A0 + 2.0 * H * G
      V20 = V2
  116 A20 = A2
   17 RHO = DENSTYF(Z2)
      ITN = 1
   12 T = THRUSTF(V2, Z2)
      V2NEW = V1 + 0.5 * H * (F + FFNCF(V2, A2))
      A2NEW = A1 + 0.5 * H * (G + GFNCF(V2, A2))
      IF(ABSF((V2 - V2NEW)/V2NEW) - TOLER)  10, 11, 11
   10 IF(ABSF((A2 - A2NEW)/A2NEW) - TOLER) 20, 11, 11
   11 ITN = ITN + 1
      IF (ITN - 10) 19, 18, 18
   19 V2 = V2NEW
      A2 = A2NEW
      GO TO 12
   18 WRITE OUTPUT TAPE 10, 9876
 9876 FORMAT (35H FAILS TO CONVERGE IN 10 ITERATIONS)
  117 GO TO 5
   20 DIFFV = 0.2 * (V20 - V2NEW)
      DIFFA = 0.2 * (A20 - A2NEW)
      V2 = V2NEW + DIFFV
      A2 = A2NEW + DIFFA
      THETA = 57.29578 * A2
      DIFFA = 57.29578 * DIFFA
      WRITE OUTPUT TAPE 10, 105, Z2, V2, THETA, DIFFV, DIFFA, ITN
      IF (Z2 + 1.0 - ZMAX) 15, 5, 5
   15 A0 = A1
      A1 = A2
      Z0 = Z1
      Z1 = Z2
      V0 = V1
      V1 = V2
      GO TO 16
      END
```

FIGURE 10.10   A program for solving two simultaneous differential equations of flight, as diagrammed in Figure 10.9.   (Case Study 12.)

The statements from 5 to 105 are concerned with reading the parameters, printing them, and printing the initial conditions. We see that READ INPUT TAPE is used in place of READ, and WRITE OUTPUT TAPE in place of PRINT. The reason for these statements is that the program was run on a large computer in which input is normally placed on magnetic tape before entering it into the computer. The transfer to tape is done with a much smaller computer while the large machine is doing something else. Output from the large machine is likewise placed on tape and later printed by a small computer while the large one goes on with something else. The purpose is to avoid slowing down the large computer to the relative crawl of the input and output devices. Almost all large computers are operated in this mode.

The printing of the parameters is done with a fairly complicated FORMAT statement that inserts identifications of the various variables, spaces numbers on the line, and spaces the lines; a final section of the statement causes printing of a heading line. The reader who has delved into Appendix 1 may study this statement; the reader who is not interested in the matter may skip it. In the FORMAT statement 105 there are three field specifications that are not used by the output statement preceding; such field specifications are simply ignored. They come into play when the same FORMAT is used by a later WRITE OUTPUT TAPE in which there are three additional numbers to be printed.

Statements 14 to 114 apply the improved Euler method to the initial conditions. We note the necessity of a conversion between degrees (for input and output) and radians (for internal calculations). Since both differential equation functions involve thrust and density, they must be computed before entering the differential equations functions.

The statements from 16 to 116 predict values of V2 and A2. These values are stored as V20 and A20 so that after the corrector has converged we will know what the predicted values were.

The statements from 17 to 117 apply the corrector formula until convergence is reached, if this is possible within 10 iterations. The calculation of the air density is not included in this loop; since it depends only on altitude, which does not change during the iteration, it can be computed once at the beginning. The thrust, on the other hand, must be recomputed, since it depends on the velocity—which is one of the results of the iterative scheme. The convergence test is made on the basis of the relative difference between successive iterates. Note that both V and θ must have converged before we go on to print the values.

The statements from 20 to the end of the program apply the correction (10.52), print the various results, test for the end of the range of altitudes, and set up the next iteration.   Note in the test of Z2 against ZMAX the 1.0; this is inserted to cover the possibility that because of roundoff error the value of Z2 might be slightly less than ZMAX, although extremely close to it.   We assume, of course, that H would never be as small as 1.0.   If more points remain to be calculated, we go to statement 15 and following, where the variables are made ready for the next step.   If the last point has been calculated we go back to statement 5 to read another set of parameters.   Eventually, an h value of zero breaks this loop.

It was mentioned in the text that a program can be written so that the step size is automatically halved if too many iterations are required and doubled if there are too few.   We have not done this here to avoid the complexity that a thorough program of this kind would need.   It might be instructive to point out some of the things that would have to be considered if automatic step-size changing were to be employed.

1. It could happen, unless suitably prevented, that the program would try to halve and double at the same point; the two actions would put us back where we started, ready to do both of them over again—indefinitely.

2. Many differential equations have singularities, points at which a solution does not exist.   We shall see this in the numerical examples that follow.   On approaching such a point, an automatic interval halving routine might halve indefinitely, never reaching the singularity. A counter would have to be provided to set a limit on the number of halvings.

3. It would be highly desirable to write the program so that automatic interval changing could be disabled.   For instance, it might be necessary to plot a graph from the results, in which case it might be more important to have results at specified points than to save a little time.   (This applies more to doubling.)

4. If halving should be called for the very first time the corrector is called into action, how far do we go back?   If we accept the point computed from the improved Euler method, we have doubtful accuracy.   If we return to the beginning, we have to think about the line of output already printed, based on the larger interval.

All of these problems can be solved; in some cases it is quite feasible to develop automatic interval changing.   For our purposes it seems inappropriate.

Figure 10.11 reproduces the printout from the program, with the

```
ZO=   5000.   ZMAX= 25000.   THETAO= 15.00   VO= 1500.

WEIGHT= 20000.      WING AREA= 160.

LIFT COEFFICIENT= 0.100      DRAG COEFFICIENT= 0.020

H= 500.00      TOLERANCE= 0.0001
```

ALTITUDE	VELOCITY	ANGLE	DIFFV	DIFFA	ITN
5000.	1500.00	15.000			
5500.	1501.29	16.146			
6000.	1501.69	17.175	-0.01588	-0.00195	2
6500.	1501.38	18.108	-0.01127	-0.00118	2
7000.	1500.49	18.959	-0.00818	-0.00094	2
7500.	1499.10	19.738	-0.00611	-0.00071	2
8000.	1497.29	20.452	-0.00469	-0.00057	2
8500.	1495.11	21.109	-0.00367	-0.00046	2
9000.	1492.60	21.712	-0.00299	-0.00037	1
9500.	1489.79	22.267	-0.00247	-0.00031	1
10000.	1486.71	22.777	-0.00199	-0.00026	1
10500.	1483.38	23.245	-0.00164	-0.00022	1
11000.	1479.81	23.674	-0.00135	-0.00019	1
11500.	1476.04	24.065	-0.00112	-0.00016	1
12000.	1472.05	24.420	-0.00093	-0.00014	1
12500.	1467.88	24.741	-0.00078	-0.00012	1
13000.	1463.52	25.030	-0.00065	-0.00010	1
13500.	1458.98	25.286	-0.00054	-0.00008	1
14000.	1454.27	25.512	-0.00045	-0.00007	1
14500.	1449.39	25.709	-0.00037	-0.00006	1
15000.	1444.34	25.876	-0.00030	-0.00005	1
15500.	1439.14	26.014	-0.00024	-0.00004	1
16000.	1433.78	26.124	-0.00019	-0.00003	1
16500.	1428.27	26.206	-0.00014	-0.00002	1
17000.	1422.60	26.261	-0.00010	-0.00001	1
17500.	1416.78	26.287	-0.00007	-0.00000	1
18000.	1410.81	26.287	-0.00003	0.00001	1
18500.	1404.68	26.258	0.	0.00001	1
19000.	1398.41	26.202	0.00002	0.00002	1
19500.	1391.98	26.117	0.00005	0.00003	1
20000.	1385.40	26.003	0.00007	0.00004	1
20500.	1378.67	25.861	0.00010	0.00005	1
21000.	1371.78	25.688	0.00012	0.00007	1
21500.	1364.74	25.485	0.00014	0.00008	1
22000.	1357.54	25.249	0.00016	0.00009	1
22500.	1350.18	24.981	0.00018	0.00011	1
23000.	1342.66	24.678	0.00020	0.00013	1
23500.	1334.97	24.339	0.00021	0.00015	1
24000.	1327.12	23.961	0.00023	0.00018	1
24500.	1319.10	23.544	0.00025	0.00021	1
25000.	1310.91	23.083	0.00026	0.00025	1

FIGURE 10.11   Output of the program of Figure 10.10, with parameter values as shown.   (Case Study 12.)

parameter values as shown at the top of the page.   Note that $h = 500$ and that the tolerance is 0.0001.   Since the convergence test is based on the relative difference between successive iterates, a tolerance of 0.0001 means that two successive velocities must agree within about 0.15 ft/sec and two successive angles within about 0.017°, for the values at 6000 ft.   These values are somewhat larger than the estimates of the truncation errors, so it is no surprise to see that only one iteration of the corrector was required after the first half dozen lines.

Figure 10.12 is a plot of velocity and angle as functions of altitude. We see that the velocity rises very slightly at first, then falls off.   The angle increases steadily at first; this increasing climb, of course, is part of the cause of the drop in velocity, since the steeper the climb, the greater the effect of the $W \sin \theta$ term in opposing the forward motion of the aircraft.   But as the velocity drops and the aircraft reaches higher altitudes, both the thrust and the lift fall off.   A drop in thrust tends to make the velocity fall even further, and a drop in lift tends to diminish the rate of increase of the angle.   Eventually the angle stops increasing and decreases instead.   (Bear in mind what we are plotting. The falling curve does not mean that the aircraft has nosed over, but only that the angle is decreasing although still positive.)

Although it may be obvious, we emphasize again that this is a highly simplified model of flight.   In particular, we are assuming no movement of the control surfaces and no change in the engine power setting.   In actual flight it is, of course, possible to make a trade off between velocity and rate of climb.

Returning to the viewpoint of numerical methods, we may find it interesting to experiment with the step size to see what we can learn

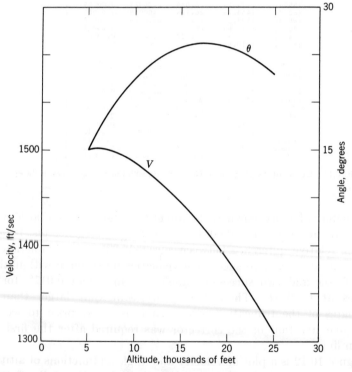

FIGURE 10.12   A plot of the results in Figure 10.11, showing the dependence of velocity and angle on altitude.   (Case Study 12.)

```
ZO=  5000.   ZMAX= 25000.   THETAO= 15.00   VO= 1500.

WEIGHT= 20000.      WING AREA= 160.

LIFT COEFFICIENT= 0.100      DRAG COEFFICIENT= 0.020

H=1000.00      TOLERANCE= 0.0001
```

ALTITUDE	VELOCITY	ANGLE	DIFFV	DIFFA	ITN
5000.	1500.00	15.000			
6000.	1501.66	17.181			
7000.	1500.43	18.961	-0.08774	-0.01163	2
8000.	1497.23	20.454	-0.04428	-0.00496	2
9000.	1492.53	21.713	-0.02823	-0.00362	2
10000.	1486.64	22.778	-0.01780	-0.00238	2
11000.	1479.75	23.674	-0.01203	-0.00171	2
12000.	1471.99	24.420	-0.00826	-0.00124	2
13000.	1463.45	25.029	-0.00576	-0.00091	2
14000.	1454.20	25.512	-0.00402	-0.00066	2
15000.	1444.28	25.875	-0.00286	-0.00046	1
16000.	1433.72	26.123	-0.00196	-0.00029	1
17000.	1422.54	26.259	-0.00114	-0.00015	1
18000.	1410.74	26.285	-0.00052	-0.00001	1
19000.	1398.35	26.200	0.00000	0.00013	1
20000.	1385.34	26.001	0.00044	0.00028	1
21000.	1371.72	25.686	0.00083	0.00045	1
22000.	1357.48	25.246	0.00107	0.00066	2
23000.	1342.60	24.675	0.00128	0.00093	2
24000.	1327.06	23.958	0.00153	0.00129	2
25000.	1310.85	23.078	0.00173	0.00179	2

FIGURE 10.13   Same as Figure 10.11, except that $h = 1000$. (Case Study 12.)

about truncation errors and the number of iterations required. Figure 10.13 is the output with the same parameters, except $h = 1000$. We see that the truncation error estimates have risen considerably—much more than the two-to-one ratio of the steps. However, since we are applying a correction based on these error estimates, there is not much change in the final values of the variables. (The fact that there is any change at all is proof that we have *estimates* of the errors. If the estimates were exact, then exact values could be computed based on any step size whatsoever.)

In keeping with the increased truncation errors we find that more iterations are required for most points than were required with $h = 500$.

If we go to an even larger value, $h = 2000$, we get the results of Figure 10.14. Doubling the step size once again increased the truncation errors by a factor somewhere between 5 and 10. Now all but one point required several iterations of the corrector formula.

If this calculation were to be done a great many times for parameter values in this general range, $h = 2000$ would probably be a fairly good choice. We see that in most cases just two iterations are required; this, we stated before, is a more or less ideal number from the standpoint of minimizing the amount of computation for a given accuracy. The truncation errors are reasonable, and the differences between the computed values here and the more accurate values found with a smaller step size are in keeping with the accuracy of the data.

```
ZO=  5000.   ZMAX= 25000.   THETAO= 15.00   VO= 1500.
WEIGHT= 20000.      WING AREA= 160.
LIFT COEFFICIENT= 0.100      DRAG COEFFICIENT= 0.020
H=2000.00      TOLERANCE= 0.0001


ALTITUDE  VELOCITY    ANGLE      DIFFV      DIFFA    ITN
 5000.    1500.00    15.000
 7000.    1500.34    19.011
 9000.    1492.20    21.729   -0.39923   -0.05955    3
11000.    1479.41    23.688   -0.10399   -0.01357    2
13000.    1463.09    25.039   -0.06668   -0.01030    2
15000.    1443.91    25.882   -0.02809   -0.00482    2
17000.    1422.16    26.264   -0.01347   -0.00221    2
19000.    1397.97    26.202   -0.00316    0.00013    1
21000.    1371.34    25.685    0.00340    0.00252    2
23000.    1342.22    24.670    0.00833    0.00574    2
25000.    1310.47    23.068    0.01190    0.01115    3
```

FIGURE 10.14   Same as Figure 10.11, except that $h = 2000$.   (Case Study 12.)

This case study, although not totally realistic, is an excellent example of something that might not have become clear so far. The purpose of running a problem on a computer is seldom to get one set of answers for one set of data. Much more commonly the purpose is to investigate the behavior of a proposed system under a wide variety of conditions. Frequently it is necessary to find the conditions under which the system would operate optimally.

In the case of aircraft performance the characteristics of common interest are such things as the time required to climb from one altitude to another, the time required to fly a given distance at a given altitude or sequence of altitudes, and the range under specified operating conditions. We might find ourselves asking such questions as this. As a long flight progresses, the combined weight of aircraft and fuel drops; the altitude for least fuel consumption is a function of weight; how should altitude be changed as the flight progresses to minimize fuel consumption?

Questions like this can result in the use of hundreds of hours of computer time. Together with related questions of aircraft and engine design, they constitute a major application area of computers.

The main point, however, is that once we have a mathematical description of a system—of any type—we have a tool for investigating a wide range of matters of interest in the design and evaluation of the system.

In order to get into practical cases in the aircraft example at hand, we would need several additional variables: control of the aircraft, control of the engine thrust, information on fuel consumption, etc. All of these matters are quite within our capability at this point, but they would complicate the case study beyond its value to us in this book. We shall therefore content ourselves with two small examples based on the present formulation.

Let us ask: what happens to the velocity and angle in a climb of 10,000 feet from various starting altitudes, always beginning at 1500 ft/sec and 15°? The program allows easy investigation of the matter. All we have to do is punch up data cards in which Z_0 and Z_{max} range over different 10,000-ft intervals. The results of five such runs are plotted in Figure 10.15. We see that in all cases, whether the climb started at sea level or 20,000 ft, the velocity drops off in about the same fashion. The angle, however, is strongly dependent on the starting altitude. Starting from sea level and from 5000 ft, the angle is still increasing after a 10,000 ft climb; starting from 10,000 and 15,000 ft, it increases at first, then decreases; starting from 20,000 ft, it decreases from the start. Furthermore, according to this formulation, the aircraft cannot climb from 20,000 to 30,000 ft under these operating conditions. The physical problem presumably is that the thrust drops off rather strongly with altitude. Mathematically, the symptom is that we approach level flight, and this formulation does not permit level flight because of the $\sin \theta$ in the denominator of both differential equations.

Figure 10.16 shows the last few lines of the output for an attempted climb from 20,000 to 30,000 ft. We see the truncation error increasing as $\sin \theta$ gets small and thereby causes the differential equation expressions to become large. The number of iterations rises accordingly, until convergence is not possible with the tolerance of 0.0001. Even with a smaller step size and a larger tolerance, however, the solution could not be continued much further: the angle is decreasing steadily toward zero.

Let us try another type of investigation: what happens to the velocity and angle as we vary the initial velocity, always climbing from 5000 to 25,000 ft and always starting with an initial angle of 15°? Figure 10.17 is a plot of the behavior for $V_0 = 900$ ft/sec. As the climb begins, there is too little velocity to provide much lift. The low velocity means a low thrust and the angle drops rapidly. There is, however, enough thrust to provide an increase in velocity, which means more lift, and, as the angle drops, more of the thrust goes into increasing the velocity. Therefore the more the angle drops, the more the velocity increases. At about 8500 ft the angle drops to about 1.2°, which causes the number of iterations to jump to six for a few steps, even though only one had been required earlier. At this point of almost level flight, almost all of the thrust goes into increased velocity, which therefore rises rapidly and in turn raises the lift. The

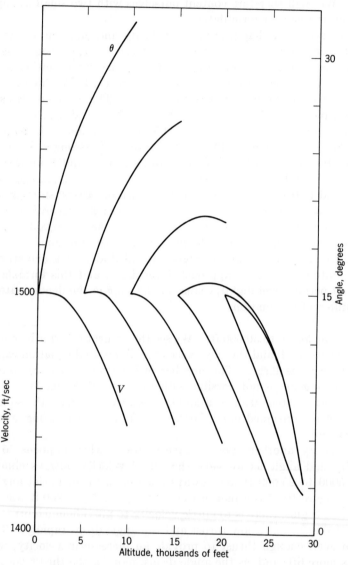

FIGURE 10.15 A plot of the results of a series of 10,000 ft climbs, all starting at the same velocity and angle, but beginning from different initial altitudes. (Case Study 12.)

```
28000.    1419.91    5.845   -0.00013    0.00004   1
28050.    1419.51    5.657   -0.00014    0.00005   1
28100.    1419.14    5.463   -0.00017    0.00006   1
28150.    1418.78    5.260   -0.00020    0.00007   1
28200.    1418.44    5.048   -0.00026    0.00009   1
28250.    1418.13    4.825   -0.00033    0.00011   2
28300.    1417.84    4.591   -0.00042    0.00015   2
28350.    1417.60    4.342   -0.00054    0.00019   2
28400.    1417.39    4.078   -0.00074    0.00025   2
28450.    1417.24    3.794   -0.00103    0.00035   2
28500.    1417.16    3.485   -0.00150    0.00050   2
28550.    1417.16    3.145   -0.00235    0.00079   2
28600.    1417.28    2.762   -0.00409    0.00136   3
28650.    1417.60    2.314   -0.00832    0.00275   3
28700.    1418.25    1.751   -0.02315    0.00760   5
FAILS TO CONVERGE IN 10 ITERATIONS
```

FIGURE 10.16   The last few lines of the printout for an attempted climb from 20,000 to 30,000 ft. (Case Study 12.)

net effect is that the angle begins to increase.   It continues to do so until about 18,000 ft, after which the decreasing velocity, thrust, and air density combine to reduce the lift.   The solution was stopped at 25,000 ft, but it is doubtful whether the climb could have been continued much higher.

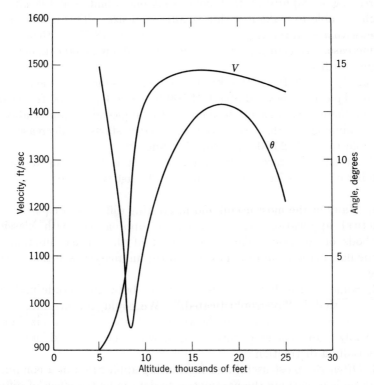

FIGURE 10.17   A plot of a run identical to that of Figure 10.11, except that $V_0 = 900$. (Case Study 12.)

The performance can be described thus: the only reason the aircraft was able to get to 25,000 ft was that it nearly leveled off early in the climb, long enough to gain some velocity. This raises the possibility that if the initial velocity had been a little higher the leveling off might not have occurred and the plane might not have been able to make it to 25,000 ft, even though it started out faster. Running the program with all parameters the same as before, except $V_0 = 1000$, we see that this is indeed the case. Now, instead of almost leveling off and thus gaining velocity rapidly, the angle decreases steadily but gradually from 15°. The result is that at 24,200 ft the angle has dropped to 1.2° and the corrector formula will not converge. Restarting the solution from the value at 24,000 feet with a tolerance of 0.0003 and an h of 5 ft, the solution can be continued out to 24,320 ft, but once again we cannot converge. The solution definitely calls at least for leveling off and perhaps nosing over.

The behavior is somewhat different for $V_0 = 1100$ ft/sec. With $h = 100$, the method fails to converge at 18,400 ft, but the velocity is increasing so rapidly at that point that one wonders if the aircraft might be able to make it with a smaller step size. This is indeed the case; with $h = 5$, the angle decreases to 0.087° at 18,550 ft, then begins to increase. It continues increasing up to about 23,000 ft, before it begins to drop.

For $V_0 = 1200$ ft/sec the situation is as it was for 1000: the solution cannot be carried beyond about 21,500 ft. For $V_0 = 1300$ ft/sec and higher there is enough lift to increase the angle fairly appreciably at the beginning, so that when the angle later starts to decrease it is possible to reach 25,000 ft before leveling off.

What has this case study taught us? It is to be hoped that a number of lessons have been learned or at least suggested.

1. Many of the most useful and interesting differential equations in practical applications cannot even be approached with classical methods of solution. The empirical fit of the thrust function, in particular, made it quite impossible to get an analytic solution in this case.

2. Some kind of balance must be struck between a crude program and one that is "oversophisticated." We could, for instance, have inserted program features to halve and double the step size automatically. In some cases this might be wise; here it would have been essentially a distraction.

3. Often the most useful and fascinating application of a computer program is in varying the parameters to determine the effect of differ-

ent conditions (or combinations of conditions) on the various performance characteristics of the system.   Sometimes the search for optimum operating conditions can be programmed.   This branch of applied mathematics is the subject of extensive research at the present time.*

Exercises

1. Given that $y' = 0.04y$ and that $y(0) = 1000$.

   a. Compute $y(1)$, using Euler's method with $h = 1$.
   b. Compute $y(1)$, using Euler's method with $h = 0.5$.
   c. Compute $y(1)$, using Euler's method with $h = 0.25$.
   d. Compute $y(1)$ from the solution to the equation $y = 1000e^{0.04t}$.
   e. Interpret parts (a) to (d) in terms of a familiar banking operation.

*2. The rate of emission of radioactivity of a substance is proportional to the amount of the substance remaining.   The differential equation is therefore $y' = -ky$, where the minus sign reflects the fact that the radioactivity decreases with time.   Suppose that $k = 0.01$ and that there are 100 g of the material at $t = 0$; how much will remain when $t = 100$?

   The solution of the equation is $y = 100e^{-kt}$; the exact answer is 36.788 g.   Solve the equation numerically, using

   a. Euler's method, $h = 25$;
   b. Euler's method, $h = 10$;
   c. Euler's method, $h = 5$;
   d. Euler's method, $h = 1$;
   e. improved Euler method, $h = 20$;
   f. improved Euler method, $h = 10$;
   g. modified Euler method, $h = 20$;
   h. modified Euler method, $h = 10$;
   i. fourth-order Runge-Kutta method, $h = 100$;
   j. fourth-order Runge-Kutta method, $h = 50$;
   k. the second order predictor-corrector method in the text, with $h = 20$, given that $y(20) = 81.8731$ exactly;
   l. predictor-corrector, with $h = 10$, given that $y(10) = 90.4837$.

3. A body with an initial mass of 200 slugs is accelerated by a constant force of 2000 lb.   The mass decreases at a rate of 1 slug/sec.   If the body is at rest at $t = 0$, find its velocity at the end of 50 sec.   The differential equation is $dV/dt = 2000/(200 - t)$; the solution is $V = 2000 \log [200/(200 - t)]$, so that $V(50) = 575.36$.   Solve the equation numer-

---

* See, for instance, Richard E. Bellman and Stuart E. Dreyfus, *Applied Dynamic Programming*, Princeton University Press, 1962.

ically, using

  a. Euler's method, $h = 10$;
  b. Euler's method, $h = 5$;
  c. Euler's method, $h = 2$;
  d. improved Euler method, $h = 10$;
  e. modified Euler method, $h = 10$;
  f. fourth-order Runge-Kutta method, $h = 10$;
  g. text predictor-corrector method, $h = 10$.

4. Suppose that the body described in Exercise 3 is subject to an air resistance equal to twice the velocity. The differential equation is now $dV/dt = (2000 - 2V)/(200 - t)$. If the body is at rest at $t = 0$, the solution is $V = 10t - t^2/40$, so that $V(50) = 437.5$. Solve the equation numerically, using

  a. Euler's method, $h = 10$;
  b. improved Euler method, $h = 10$;
  c. modified Euler method, $h = 10$;
  d. fourth-order Runge-Kutta method, $h = 10$;
  e. text predictor-corrector method, $h = 10$.

5. Given $y' = 4 - 2x$, $y(0) = 2$, solve by the improved Euler method and the modified Euler method, using $h = 0.5$ and continuing to $x = 5$. Compare with the solution, $y = -x^2 + 4x + 2$. Would you expect Euler's method to be exact also? For what kind of equation would you expect Euler's method to be exact?

6. Given that $y' = -x/y$, $y(0) = 20$, evaluate $y(24)$ using

  a. modified Euler method, $h = 2$;
  b. fourth-order Runge-Kutta method, $h = 4$. What happens?

7. Given that $y' = (6y + 2x + 1)/x$, $y(1) = -\frac{17}{30}$, find $y(4)$, using the text predictor-corrector method with $h = 1$. Repeat with $y(1) = -\frac{16}{30}$.

8. Given that $y' = xy^2 + 3xy$, $y(0) = -0.5$, find $y(3)$, using the text predictor-corrector method with $h = 0.5$.

9. Given $y' = \cos x - \sin x - y$, $y(0) = 2$, solve by the text predictor-corrector with $h = 0.5$ to $x = 10$. Show that the solution possesses absolute stability. The analytic solution is $y = \cos x + e^{-x}$.

10. Given that $y' = 2y/x + x^2 e^x$, $y(1) = 0$. Solve by the text predictor-corrector with $h = 0.2$ to $x = 5$. Show that although the absolute error grows the relative error does not grow. The solution is $y = x^2(e^x - e)$.

*11. Draw block diagrams and write programs to solve differential equations by the methods of Euler, improved Euler, modified Euler, fourth-order Runge-Kutta, and the text predictor-corrector. Each program should have as its first statement an arithmetic statement function defining the differential equation; this can be changed to solve different equations. Each program should read a card containing values of x and y (the initial condition), h (the step size), and x last (the final value of x). The program for the predictor-corrector should use the fourth-order Runge-Kutta method to find the necessary second value of y; it should not modify the step size, but it should include an iteration counter to stop the program if convergence has not been achieved after 10 iterations.

12. Extend the predictor-corrector program of Exercise 11 to provide a printout of the estimate of truncation error at each step.

13. Extend the predictor-corrector program of Exercise 11 to halve or double the step size as dictated by the iteration counter.

14. Show that the second-order Runge-Kutta method (10.22), when applied to $y' = -y$, $y(0) = 1$, yields

$$y_m = \left(1 - h + \frac{h^2}{2}\right)^m \simeq e^{-x_m}$$

Would you expect the error in using this approximation always to have the same sign?

15. For the equation $y' = ky$ the corrector formula (10.31) can be solved explicitly for y_{m+1}. (We may therefore drop the superscripts.) Show that the resulting expression agrees with the Taylor series through terms in h^2.

16. Consider the following predictor-corrector pair:

$$y_{m+1}^{(0)} = y_m + \frac{h}{2}[y_m' + f(x_m + h, y_m + hy_m')]$$

and

$$y_{m+1}^{(i+1)} = y_m + \frac{h}{2}[y_m' + f(x_{m+1}, y_{m+1}^{(i)})] \qquad i = 0, 1, 2, \ldots$$

where $y_m' = f(x_m, y_m)$.

a. What is the name of this predictor?
b. What are the orders of the two formulas?
c. What advantage does this predictor have over (10.33)?
d. What is the disadvantage of using this predictor rather than (10.33)?

*17. Reduce $y'' + y = F(x)$ to a pair of first-order equations. Show that the right-hand member of each equation is independent of the differentiated variable on the left. Does this mean that no iterations of the corrector formula are required?

18. Reduce $y''' + a(x, y)y'' + b(x, y)y' = c(x, y)$ to a set of three first-order equations and describe a numerical method of solution.

19. If Euler's method is used as a predictor,

$$y_{m+1}^{(0)} = y_m + h\, f(x_m, y_m)$$

then an appropriate corrector is

$$y_{m+1}^{(i)} = y_m - h\, f(x_{m+1}, y_{m+1}^{(i-1)})$$

a. Show that the truncation error in the predictor is

$$E_T^{(p)} = \frac{h^2}{2} y''(\xi) \qquad x_m \leq \xi \leq x_{m+1}$$

and in the corrector is

$$E_T^{(c)} = \frac{-h^2}{2} y''(\eta) \qquad x_m \leq \eta \leq x_{m+1}$$

Assuming that y'' is constant, find an estimate of $E_T^{(c)}$ in terms of $y_{m+1}^{(0)}$ and $y_{m+1}^{(i)}$. Derive a correction term that can be used to improve $y_{m+1}^{(i)}$.

b. Show that the corrector converges if $h < 1/M$,

where $\qquad |\partial f / \partial y| < M$

c. Show that the corrector possesses absolute and relative stability if $f_y > 0$ but that it is unstable—in both a relative and an absolute sense—if $f_y < 0$.

20. Consider the second-order equation $y'' + ay' + by = c$, where a, b, and c are functions of x. Suppose it is given that $y(0) = K_0$, $y(1) = K_1$. Propose a numerical method for finding $y(x)$ for $0 \leq x \leq 1$. *Hint.* Take a "guess" at $y(h)$ and see if this yields $y(1) = K_1$. If not, modify the "guess."

21. Show that the difference equation

$$\epsilon_{n+1} - 2a\epsilon_n - \epsilon_{n-1} = 0$$

has the solution

$$\epsilon_n = c_1 \lambda_1{}^n + c_2 \lambda_2{}^n$$

where

$$\lambda_1 = a + \sqrt{a^2 + 1}$$

$$\lambda_2 = a - \sqrt{a^2 + 1}$$

and c_1 and c_2 are arbitrary constants. By making use of these results, show that the predictor (10.33) is unstable.

*22. Consider the general predictor formula

$$y_{m+1} = A_0 y_m + A_1 y_{m-1} + h B_0 y_m'$$

This is usually referred to as a *Milne type predictor** and it is characterized by the fact that on the right there is one more value of y than of y'.

a. Determine the equations that A_0, A_1, and B_0 must satisfy if the predictor is to be exact for $y = 1$, $y = x$, and $y = x^2$.

b. Show that the solution of the equations above yields the predictor given by (10.33).

c. By using $y = x^3$ show that the truncation error is of order h^3.

---

* See Hamming, Section 15.6.

23. Consider the predictor formula

$$y_{m+1} = A_0 y_m + h(B_0 y_m' + B_1 y_{m-1}')$$

This is called an *Adams-Bashforth type predictor*,* characterized by the presence of one more value of y' on the right than of y.

a. Determine the equations that A_0, B_0, and B_1 must satisfy if the predictor is to be exact for $y = 1$, $y = x$, and $y = x^2$.

b. Show that the resulting predictor is

$$y_{m+1} = y_m + \frac{h}{2} (3y_m' - y_{m-1}')$$

c. By using $y = x^3$ show that the truncation error is of order h^3. This predictor may therefore be used with the corrector (10.34).

24. Consider the corrector formula

$$y_{m+1} = a_0 y_m + h(b_{-1} y_{m+1}' + b_0 y_m')$$

a. Why is this a corrector formula and not a predictor?

b. Determine the equations that a_0, b_{-1}, and b_0 must satisfy if the formula is to be exact for $y = 1$, $y = x$, and $y = x^2$.

c. Show that the resulting formula is the corrector of (10.34).

d. Using $y = x^3$ show that the truncation error is of order h^3.

*25. Consider the predictor formula

$$y_{m+1} = A_0 y_m + A_1 y_{m-1} + A_2 y_{m-2} + h(B_0 y_m' + B_1 y_{m-1}')$$

a. Is this a Milne or an Adams-Bashforth type predictor?

b. Determine the equations that A_0, A_1, A_2, B_0, and B_1 must satisfy if the formula is to be exact for $y = 1$, $y = x$, $y = x^2$, $y = x^3$, and $y = x^4$.

c. Show that the resulting formula is

$$y_{m+1} = -9y_m + 9y_{m-1} + y_{m-2} + 6h(y_m' + y_{m-1}')$$

d. What power of h appears in the truncation error term?

26. Consider the predictor formula

$$y_{m+1} = A_0 y_m + A_1 y_{m-1} + h(B_0 y_m' + B_1 y_{m-1}' + B_2 y_{m-2}'')$$

a. Is this a Milne or an Adams-Bashforth type predictor?

b. Determine the equations that A_0, A_1, B_0, B_1, and B_2 must satisfy if the formula is to be exact for $y = 1$, $y = x$, $y = x^2$, $y = x^3$, and $y = x^4$.

c. Solve these equations for A_0, A_1, B_0, B_1, and B_2.

d. By using $y = x^5$ show that the truncation error is of order h^5.

---

* See Hamming, Section 15.7.

*27. Consider the corrector formula

$$y_{m+1} = a_0 y_m + a_1 y_{m-1} + h(b_{-1} y'_{m+1} + b_0 y'_m + b_1 y'_{m-1})$$

a. Is this an explicit or implicit formula?

b. Determine the equations that a_0, a_1, b_{-1}, b_0, and b_1 must satisfy if the formula is to be exact for $y = 1$, $y = x$, $y = x^2$, $y = x^3$, $y = x^4$.

c. Why cannot these equations be solved for a_0, a_1, b_{-1}, b_0, b_1?

d. Solve the first four of the equations for a_0, b_{-1}, b_0, b_1 in terms of a_1.

e. Show that the truncation error is of order h^4 if $a_1 \neq 1$.

f. Show that for $a_1 = 1$ the truncation error is of order h^5.

Note. Despite this result, $a_1 = 1$ is not the best choice even though it produces a smaller truncation error, since the choice of a_1 strongly affects the stability of the method. For certain differential equations it may be necessary to choose $a_1 \neq 1$ in order to achieve the desired stability.

—11

Partial Differential Equations

11.1   Introduction and definitions

Partial differential equations constitute one of the most rapidly developing of all the branches of numerical analysis.   The fields of application in which partial differential equations occur (nuclear physics and aerodynamics, to name only two) are increasing in importance.   Furthermore, the advent of modern computers has made it feasible to attack problems that are simply out of the question without a computer.

We shall not be able, of course, to give a full development of the subject.   We can, however, introduce the student to the broad outlines of the material and present some numerical methods that will serve in many cases.*

The discussion is limited to linear, second-order partial differential equations in two independent variables.   These can be written in the form

(11.1) $A u_{xx} + B u_{xy} + C u_{yy} + D u_x + E u_y + F u = G$

where A, B, C, D, E, F, and G are functions of x and y (the two independent variables) only.   The dependent variable is u and the subscripts denote partial derivatives; for instance,

$$u_{xy} = \frac{\partial^2 u}{\partial x\, \partial y}$$

We recall that an ordinary differential equation (10.1) has a whole

---

* For serious study we recommend the excellent text *Finite Difference Methods for Partial Differential Equations*, by George E. Forsythe and Wolfgang R. Wasow, Wiley, New York, 1960.

family of solutions, a particular one of which is picked out by the initial condition (10.2). Similarly, here, some additional information must be supplied along with (11.1) in order to pick out a specific solution. Now, however, since we are dealing with two independent variables, the added conditions will have to be given along some *curve* in the x-y plane. The information may relate to u and/or its derivatives. In some cases the curve along which the information is given will be closed and in other cases it will not; this depends on the *type* of equation.

We define three types of second-order partial differential equations.

1. The equation is *elliptic* if $B^2 - 4AC < 0$.
2. The equation is *parabolic* if $B^2 - 4AC = 0$.
3. The equation is *hyperbolic* if $B^2 - 4AC > 0$.

It is possible for an equation to be of more than one type, depending on the values of the coefficients. For example,

$$yu_{xx} + u_{yy} = 0$$

is elliptic for $y > 0$, parabolic for $y = 0$, and hyperbolic for $y < 0$. The equations with which we shall deal, however, which include many common applications, have constant coefficients and are therefore of only one type.

In the following sections we shall present representative examples of each of the three types, with appropriate subsidiary conditions, and exhibit practical methods of solution for each.

11.2 Difference equations

The classical definition of the derivative of a function of a single variable is often stated as

$$\frac{dy}{dx} = \lim_{h \to 0} \frac{y(x + h) - y(x)}{h}$$

In a digital computer we cannot take the limit. We can, however, set h at some small (but obviously nonzero) value and attempt to prove that the approximation is sufficiently close (accuracy) and that the error does not grow as we continue the process (stability).

The method can be described as replacing a *derivative* with a *difference*. Although we did not describe the process in these terms, this is precisely what we did in Chapter 10 in solving ordinary differential equations. Here we shall take the same approach to partial differential equations, working with approximations that will be displayed as differences.

Since we now have two independent variables, the difference equations will have to reflect both. Let us begin, however, by considering only differences in the x direction.

Recall that the Taylor series for $u(x, y_0)$ about the point x_0, y_0 can be written

$$u(x, y_0) = u(x_0, y_0) + (x - x_0)\, u_x(x_0, y_0) + \frac{(x - x_0)^2}{2}\, u_{xx}(\xi, y_0)$$

where ξ lies between x and x_0. If we now let $x = x_0 + h$, we get, after some rearrangement,

$$u_x(x_0, y_0) - \frac{u(x_0 + h, y_0) - u(x_0, y_0)}{h} = -\frac{h}{2}\, u_{xx}(\xi, y_0)$$

In other words, if we approximate u_x by

$$(11.2) \qquad u_x(x_0, y_0) = \frac{u(x_0 + h, y_0) - u(x_0, y_0)}{h}$$

the truncation error is

$$E_T = -\frac{h}{2}\, u_{xx}(\xi, y_0) \qquad x_0 \le \xi \le x_0 + h$$

Equation 11.2 was obtained by substituting $x = x_0 + h$ in the Taylor series; the result is called a *forward difference*. We can obtain a different approximation, called a *backward difference*, by letting $x = x_0 - h$. The result is

$$(11.3) \qquad u_x(x_0, y_0) = \frac{u(x_0, y_0) - u(x_0 - h, y_0)}{h}$$

We shall have occasion to use both forward and backward differences, as we see now in deriving an approximation for u_{xx}. The technique is to write a difference equation for u_{xx} in terms of u_x, then substitute suitable difference approximations for u_x. The difference equation for u_{xx}, using a forward difference, is

$$(11.4) \qquad u_{xx}(x_0, y_0) = \frac{u_x(x_0 + h, y_0) - u_x(x_0, y_0)}{h}$$

If we were now to substitute forward differences for u_x, the result would be biased in the forward direction; we therefore use backward differences to avoid this effect. The backward difference for $u_x(x_0, y_0)$ is given by (11.3) and

$$(11.5) \qquad u_x(x_0 + h, y_0) = \frac{u(x_0 + h, y_0) - u(x_0, y_0)}{h}$$

[This is, of course, the same expression as for the forward difference for $u(x_0, y_0)$.] Substituting (11.3) and (11.5) in (11.4), we get

$$(11.6) \quad u_{xx}(x_0, y_0) = \frac{u(x_0 + h, y_0) - 2u(x_0, y_0) + u(x_0 - h, y_0)}{h^2}$$

This is an important result and one that we shall use repeatedly in the remainder of the chapter. Notice the symmetry of the formula.

To determine the truncation error, we recall that

$$u(x, y_0) = u(x_0, y_0) + (x - x_0) u_x(x_0, y_0) + \frac{(x - x_0)^2}{2} u_{xx}(x_0, y_0)$$

$$+ \frac{(x - x_0)^3}{6} u_{xxx}(x_0, y_0) + \frac{(x - x_0)^4}{24} u_{xxxx}(\xi, y_0)$$

Now we let $x = x_0 + h$ and then $x = x_0 - h$ and subtract the two resulting equations. The truncation error is seen to be

$$E_T = -\frac{h^2}{12} u_{xxxx}(\xi, y_0), \qquad x_0 - h \le \xi \le x_0 + h$$

So far we have dealt only with derivatives in the x direction. An entirely analogous development leads to a difference equation for u_{yy}, where we take the step size in the y direction to be k:

$$(11.7) \quad u_{yy}(x_0, y_0) = \frac{u(x_0, y_0 + k) - 2u(x_0, y_0) + u(x_0, y_0 + k)}{k^2}$$

The truncation error is

$$E_T = -\frac{k^2}{12} u_{yyyy}(x_0, \eta), \qquad y_0 - k \le \eta \le y_0 + k$$

We now have difference expressions for u_x, u_{xx}, and u_{yy}. The equation for u_y is the exact analogy of (11.2), and we leave the derivation of u_{xy} to the reader in an exercise (No. 39). With these expressions, the partial differential equation (11.1) can be completely rewritten in terms of differences. For instance, a particularly common equation is *LaPlace's equation:*

$$u_{xx} + u_{yy} = 0$$

We rewrite it as

$$\frac{u(x_0 + h, y_0) - 2u(x_0, y_0) + u(x_0 - h, y_0)}{h^2}$$

$$+ \frac{u(x_0, y_0 + k) - 2u(x_0, y_0) + u(x_0, y_0 - k)}{k^2} = 0$$

This difference equation may now be approached by the methods that we shall discuss in the next two sections.

11.3 Elliptic equations

As a typical example of a physical problem that leads to an elliptic partial differential equation consider the elastic torsion of a long cylindrical bar. The cross section may be any shape; a schematic picture is presented in Figure 11.1. The cross section is considered to be bounded by a curve C; its interior is called the region R.

We consider the z-axis to lie parallel to the axis of the cylinder and to pass through the center of mass, 0, of the cross section. The cross sections are thus parallel to the x-y plane. Finally, let the angle of twist per unit length be θ, that is, the angle of twist in the plane $z = z_0$ is θz_0.

The only nonzero stresses are the shear stresses τ_x and τ_y in the x and y directions in the x-y plane. (Subscripts do *not* indicate partial dif-

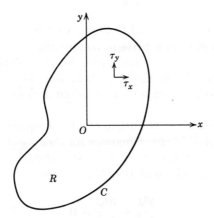

FIGURE 11.1   Cross section of a cylindrical bar in elastic torsion.

ferentiation here!) If we define a function ψ by

(11.8)
$$
\begin{cases}
\tau_x = \dfrac{E\theta}{2(1+\nu)} \dfrac{\partial \psi}{\partial y} \\[4mm]
\tau_y = -\dfrac{E\theta}{2(1+\nu)} \dfrac{\partial \psi}{\partial x}
\end{cases}
$$

where E is Young's modulus and ν is Poisson's ratio for the material, then ψ is the solution of

(11.9)
$$
\frac{\partial^2 \psi}{\partial x^2} + \frac{\partial^2 \psi}{\partial y^2} = -2
$$

in the region R and

$$
\psi = \text{constant}
$$

on the boundary C of the cross section. Since the physical properties involved here depend only on derivatives of ψ, the value of the constant is immaterial. It is customary to take

(11.10)
$$
\psi = 0
$$

on C.

Equation 11.9 is called *Poisson's equation*. It is often written

$$
\Delta \psi = -2
$$

or

$$
\nabla^2 \psi = -2
$$

Many physical problems lead to Poisson's equation. The potential or voltage distribution in a plate of conducting material with a fixed potential on its boundary is also given by the solution of Poisson's equation. Finally, the steady-state heat flow in a two-dimensional body satisfies Poisson's equation, as we shall discuss in Case Study 13 in Section 11.9.

With this brief sketch of the origin of elliptic equations, we now turn to the derivation of difference equations for their solution. The actual process of solution is taken up in the next section.

Let us consider the classical *Dirichlet problem*

(11.11)
$$
\frac{\partial^2 \psi}{\partial x^2} + \frac{\partial^2 \psi}{\partial y^2} = 0
$$

ı some region R and

(11.12) $$\psi = f(x, y)$$

on the boundary C of R. Equation 11.11, as noted earlier, is called *LaPlace's equation*. It is a special case of Poisson's equation.

We now restrict the curve C to something that is easily handled: straight lines parallel to the x- and y-axes. Other curves can certainly be handled by numerical techniques and can be programmed for a computer, but the explanation of the basic techniques, which is all we are attempting here, do not require this complete generality.

In particular, we consider a rectangle of width A and height B. We shall see that the extensions to handle any region bounded by straight lines parallel to the axes are easy mathematically (as in the case study), although some interesting programming problems are created.

We first divide the width A into n intervals, each of width $h = A/n$. Similarly, we divide the height B into m intervals, each of height $k = B/m$. There are $(n - 1)(m - 1)$ mesh intersections inside the rectangle. We shall write a difference equation for each interior mesh point and then solve the resulting system of simultaneous equations.

First, we should agree on how to name the intersections. We start numbering them in the horizontal direction with zero at the left; the right-hand side is then numbered n. Similarly, we number from the bottom to the top from zero to m. The mesh intersection labeled i, j is the ith from the left end and the jth from the bottom. For example, in Figure 11.2 the intersection P is 3, 2 and Q is 2, 8.

Now let the origin be at 0, 0 and introduce the notation

$$u(ih, jk) = u_{i,j}$$

Similarly, we write

$$f(ih, jk) = f_{i,j}$$

Using this notation, the boundary conditions (11.12) can be written

(11.13) $$\begin{cases} u_{i,0} = f_{i,0} & i = 0, 1, 2, \ldots, n \\ u_{i,m} = f_{i,m} & i = 0, 1, 2, \ldots, n \\ u_{0,j} = f_{0,j} & j = 0, 1, 2, \ldots, m \\ u_{n,j} = f_{n,j} & j = 0, 1, 2, \ldots, m \end{cases}$$

If we now let i, j be the point x_0, y_0 in (11.6) and (11.7) and write $\lambda = k/h$, the differential equation (11.11) becomes the difference

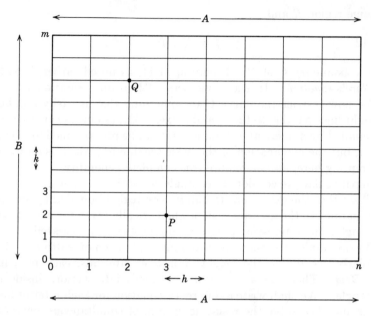

FIGURE 11.2   A mesh of points laid over a rectangular region.

equation:

(11.14) $\lambda^2 u_{i+1,j} + \lambda^2 u_{i-1,j} + u_{i,j+1} + u_{i,j-1} - 2(1 + \lambda^2)u_{i,j} = 0$

for $i = 1, 2, \ldots , n - 1$ and $j = 1, 2, \ldots , m - 1$.

For $\lambda = 1$, that is, for equal step sizes in the x and y directions, this says that the value of $u_{i,j}$ is the average of its four neighbors to the north, south, east, and west.

The important point is that we now have a system of simultaneous linear algebraic equations. There are $(m - 1)(n - 1)$ equations in $(m + 1)(n + 1)$ unknowns, $u_{i,j}$. The boundary conditions (11.13) can be used to eliminate $2(m + n)$ unknowns. We then have a system of $(m - 1)(n - 1)$ equations in the same number of unknowns, which we know how to solve by the methods of Chapter 8. In doing so, however, it will be worth our while to investigate the system of equations carefully for special properties that may simplify the solution; this is the subject of the next section.

We may note a few things about the difference equation formulation before going on to solve the system.

For any point i, j we can represent (11.14) schematically by drawing the five points that are related by the equation and showing for each point its coefficient in (11.14).   The result is called the *stencil* of the method.

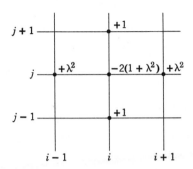

Note finally that we are leaving one crucial question to more advanced works.   We did indicate earlier that as $h \to 0$ and $k \to 0$ the difference equation approaches the differential equation.   We have not, however, taken up the following question, which is quite different: as h, $k \to 0$, does the *solution* of the difference equation approach the *solution* of the differential equation?   The answer is "yes" for the elliptic equation, although we shall not present the proof.   We shall see, however, that for parabolic and hyperbolic equations it is necessary to observe certain restrictions to guarantee this obviously essential convergence.

11.4   The solution of elliptic difference equations

Let us write out some of the equations of (11.14) in detail.   For convenience we shall take $\lambda = 1$, representing equal spacing in the x and y directions, but the conclusions will be valid for a general $\lambda > 0$.   We start at $i = 1$, $j = 1$, and with j held fixed run through $i = 1, 2, \ldots, n - 1$.

$$4u_{1,1} - u_{2,1} - u_{1,2} = f_{1,0} + f_{0,1}$$

$$-u_{1,1} + 4u_{2,1} - u_{3,1} - u_{2,2} = f_{2,0}$$

$$-u_{2,1} + 4u_{3,1} - u_{4,1} - u_{3,2} = f_{3,0}$$

$$\cdot \cdot \cdot \cdot \cdot \cdot \cdot \cdot \cdot \cdot \cdot \cdot \cdot \cdot \cdot \cdot \cdot \cdot \cdot \cdot \cdot \cdot \cdot$$

$$-u_{n-2,1} + 4u_{n-1,1} - u_{n-1,2} = f_{n-1,0} + f_{n,1}$$

Now we increase j to 2 and again run through $i = 1, 2, \ldots, n - 1$.

$$-u_{1,1} + 4u_{1,2} - u_{2,2} - u_{1,3} = f_{0,2}$$

$$-u_{2,1} - u_{1,2} + 4u_{2,2} - u_{3,2} - u_{2,3} = 0$$

$$-u_{3,1} - u_{2,2} + 4u_{3,2} - u_{4,2} - u_{3,3} = 0$$

$$\cdots\cdots\cdots\cdots\cdots\cdots\cdots$$

$$-u_{n-2,1} - u_{n-3,2} + 4u_{n-2,2} - u_{n-1,2} - u_{n-2,3} = 0$$

$$-u_{n-1,1} - u_{n-2,2} + 4u_{n-1,2} - u_{n-1,3} = f_{n,2}$$

We continue in this way, each time increasing j and running through $i = 1, 2, \ldots, n - 1$. The final value of j is $m - 1$.

The important things to notice about this system, in terms of finding a solution to it, are these:

1. The system is *sparse*, that is, most of the coefficients in each equation are zero.
2. In each equation one coefficient is $+4$. If there are five nonzero coefficients, the other four add up to -4; if there are fewer than five nonzero coefficients, the others add up to -2 or -3.

Thus the conditions for convergence of the Gauss-Seidel iteration method are satisfied, by virtue of the second characteristic. And the first characteristic makes it undesirable to use Gauss elimination: our originally sparse system becomes a full triangular system in the elimination. Considering that m and n are frequently quite large (in the hundreds range), elimination is particularly unattractive.

It may be helpful to display some of the equations in the form in which they will be iterated. Using superscripts to indicate the number of the iteration, and with $u_{i,j}^{(0)}$ arbitrarily set to zero for all i, j, we have the following representative equations to be solved, in the same order as before.

$$u_{1,1}^{(1)} = \tfrac{1}{4}[f_{1,0} + f_{0,1} + u_{2,1}^{(0)} + u_{1,2}^{(0)}]$$

$$u_{2,1}^{(1)} = \tfrac{1}{4}[f_{2,0} + u_{1,1}^{(1)} + u_{3,1}^{(0)} + u_{2,2}^{(0)}]$$

$$u_{3,1}^{(1)} = \tfrac{1}{4}[f_{3,0} + u_{2,1}^{(1)} + u_{4,1}^{(0)} + u_{3,2}^{(0)}]$$

$$\cdots\cdots\cdots\cdots\cdots\cdots\cdots$$

$$u_{n-1,1}^{(1)} = \tfrac{1}{4}[f_{n-1,0} + f_{n,1} + u_{n-2,1}^{(1)} + u_{n-1,2}^{(0)}]$$

$$u_{1,2}^{(1)} = \tfrac{1}{4}[f_{0,2} + u_{1,1}^{(1)} + u_{2,2}^{(0)} + u_{1,3}^{(0)}]$$

$$u_{2,2}^{(1)} = \tfrac{1}{4}[u_{2,1}^{(1)} + u_{1,2}^{(1)} + u_{3,2}^{(0)} + u_{2,3}^{(0)}]$$

$$\cdots\cdots\cdots\cdots\cdots\cdots\cdots$$

This set of equations undoubtedly has a forbidding appearance; actually, it is quite easily set up for computer solution. One small problem occurs in using FORTRAN for the purpose, and even that is more an annoyance than a real difficulty: zero subscripts are not permitted in FORTRAN. We have followed the conventional notation here rather than avoiding the problem by numbering from 1 instead of zero, which would be one solution. Another solution, and the one we shall use, is to pretend for the time being that zero subscripts are permitted and then make a trivial conversion in the actual program.

If we pretend that zero subscripts are allowed, the basic scheme is as follows. We set up a two-dimensional array, with $m + 1$ rows and $n + 1$ columns. Rows zero and m and columns zero and n are initially loaded with the boundary values, using any convenient technique. In some cases they are read from cards; in others it is feasible to compute them from the algebraic statement of the conditions. We then enter a loop controlled by two DO statements, one running through j values from one to $m - 1$, the other through i values from one to $n - 1$. Each i, j pair identifies a mesh point; at each point we solve (11.14) for $u_{i,j}$. As each new value is computed, it is compared with the value for that point in the preceding iteration; the largest difference found anywhere in the mesh is compared with an ϵ to determine convergence. If the process has not converged, the whole iteration scheme is repeated.

This is almost more easily done than said. The block diagram of Figure 11.3 describes the entire process. A program for a slightly more complex boundary appears in the Case Study of Section 11.9.

The Gauss-Seidel method applied to elliptic difference equations is often called the *method of successive displacements* or the *Liebmann method*.

Now recall that we found it advantageous in Chapter 5 to over-correct or undercorrect when calculating a new approximation to the root of an equation; we mentioned at the end of Section 8.6 that an analogous technique would be found useful in the Gauss-Seidel method. It is, in fact, particularly valuable in the Liebmann method.

To do this we change the contents of the block marked with an asterisk in Figure 11.3 to make it read

$$u_{i,j} = \omega x + (1 - \omega)u_{i,j}$$

in which x is the value of $u_{i,j}$ calculated from (11.4). The parameter ω is called the *relaxation parameter*. In general, we shall require that $1 < \omega < 2$. If $\omega = 1$, then we have the usual Liebmann method. For $\omega \neq 1$ we have the *extrapolated Liebmann method*. With a good choice of ω it can produce dramatic savings in computing time—reduc-

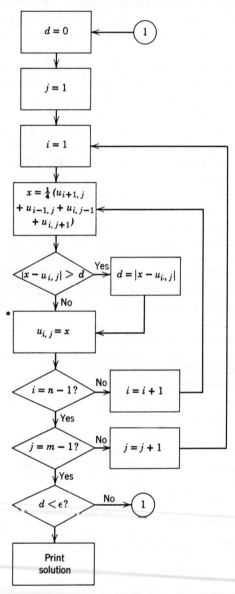

FIGURE 11.3 Block diagram of the Liebmann method of solving elliptic difference equations. The box marked with an asterisk is modified to get the extrapolated Liebmann method. Boundary values and ϵ are assumed to be set up by a separate program segment.

tions of as much as 20 to 1 are possible. In the case study in Section 11.9 we plot the number of iterations required for a particular example versus various values of ω. For a square the optimum value is approximately 1.9, for reasonably large n.

We have discussed the extrapolated Liebmann method so far only for the LaPlace equation. More generally, any elliptic equation that has no u_{xy} term leads to a system of equations satisfying the conditions for convergence.

All of the preceding further assumes a linear equation. Little of a theoretical nature is known about convergence for nonlinear equations. However, many experiments have been conducted with quasi-linear equations,* using the extrapolated Liebmann method, with great success. The general approach is to guess a value of ω and note the rate of convergence. Then, by changing ω and observing the change in convergence, the succeeding changes can be predicted. Convergence has in fact been obtained even for equations with a u_{xy} term, although there is no theoretical foundation for expecting convergence.

There are many other ways of solving the difference equations (11.14). Those used most frequently are line relaxation (see Exercise 31), block relaxation, and the alternating direction method (see Exercise 32). They are frequently more efficient than the Liebmann method.

Finally, it is possible to use the deferred approach to the limit here, just as we have done on other occasions. If $U_{i,j}$ is the true solution and $u_{i,j}$ the calculated solution then

$$U_{i,j} = u_{i,j} + K_{i,j}h^2$$

if the fourth derivatives are reasonably constant. For another interval size, p, let the calculated solution be $v_{i,j}$, so that

$$U_{i,j} = v_{i,j} + K_{i,j}p^2$$

and

$$K_{i,j} = \frac{v_{i,j} - u_{i,j}}{h^2 - p^2}$$

11.5 Hyperbolic equations

As before, we begin our study of this type of partial differential equation with a brief statement of a physical situation in which it occurs.

---

* Quasi-linear equations are linear in the second derivatives, u_{xx}, u_{yy}, and u_{xy}, but may be nonlinear in u_x, u_y, u, x, and y.

We stretch a string of length L between two points on the x-axis, $x = 0$ and $x = L$. The tension in the string is T. If we displace the string by a small amount and then release it, it will vibrate. The displacement of a point on the string thus depends not only on where the point is but also on the time t. We shall not derive the equation that the displacement u satisfies. The result is

$$u_{xx} - a^2 u_{tt} = 0$$

for $0 \leq x \leq L$ and $t > 0$. The coefficient a takes into account the physical characteristics

$$a^2 = \frac{w}{Tg}$$

where w is the weight per unit length of the string, T is the tension, and g is the gravitational constant.

This is usually referred to as the *wave equation*. For simplicity in the following we shall take $a = 1$, giving as our problem to solve

(11.15) $\qquad u_{xx} - u_{tt} = 0, \qquad 0 \leq x \leq L, \qquad t > 0$

This is really no loss of generality, since a simple change of variables reduces the general equation to the case $a = 1$.

Since the end points are held fixed, we have

(11.16) $\qquad u(0, t) = u(L, t) = 0, \qquad t \geq 0$

The initial conditions are the original displacement:

(11.17) $\qquad u(x, 0) = f(x), \qquad 0 \leq x \leq L$

and the initial velocity

(11.18) $\qquad u_t(x, 0) = g(x), \qquad 0 < x < L$

For example, if we pluck the string at its center, as shown in Figure 11.1, and release it without imparting any initial velocity, the initial conditions are

$$f(x) = \begin{cases} \dfrac{2\delta}{L} x & 0 \leq x \leq \dfrac{L}{2} \\[3mm] \dfrac{2\delta}{L}(L - x) & \dfrac{L}{2} \leq x \leq L \end{cases}$$

$$g(x) = 0 \qquad\qquad 0 \leq x \leq L$$

Notice that we have stated *initial* conditions, not *boundary* conditions. Indeed, if a hyperbolic equation were stated with boundary

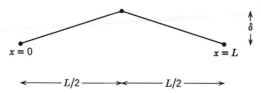

FIGURE 11.4   A possible initial condition for a vibrating string described by the wave equation.

conditions, we would discover that no unique solution could be found. Such a problem is called *ill-posed*. It is essential that each type of equation have the proper type of subsidiary conditions.

To find difference equations corresponding to (11.15), we turn once again to (11.6) and (11.7), except that we are now writing t in place of y. We again lay down a mesh, but now it is of indefinite extension in the time direction; we may continue the solution for a time period as great as we wish. We shall use a spacing of h in the x direction and k in the t direction. There will thus be $n = L/h$ steps along the x-axis and any number along the t-axis.

If we let

$$u_{i,j} = u(ih, jk)$$

and

$$\lambda = \frac{k}{h}$$

then the difference equation at $x = ih$, $t = jk$ is

(11.19) $u_{i,j+1} = 2(1 - \lambda^2)u_{i,j} + \lambda^2(u_{i+1,j} + u_{i-1,j}) - u_{i,j-1}$

for $i = 1, 2, \ldots, n$ and $j = 1, 2, 3, \ldots$.   The stencil is

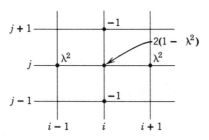

The boundary condition (11.16) is easily written as

(11.20) $u_{0,j} = u_{n,j} = 0, \qquad j = 1, 2, 3, \ldots$

The initial conditions (11.17) may be expressed

(11.21) $\qquad u_{i,0} = f(ih), \qquad i = 1, 2, \ldots, n - 1$

To difference the initial condition (11.18), we make use of (11.2) and write

$$\frac{u_{i,1} - u_{i,0}}{k} = g(ih)$$

Then, using (11.21), we get

(11.22) $\qquad u_{i,1} = f(ih) + kg(ih)$

11.6 Solution of hyperbolic difference equations

Notice now that (11.21) and (11.22) give the value of u on the first two rows, $j = 0$ and $j = 1$. Setting $j = 1$ in (11.19) yields

$$u_{i,2} = 2(1 - \lambda^2)u_{i,1} + \lambda^2(u_{i+1,1} + u_{i-1,1}) - u_{i,0}$$

The terms on the right involve values of u on only the first two lines; all are known from the initial conditions. Hence there is only one unknown in the equation above, and the third line may be calculated explicitly. Once this has been done, the fourth line, $u_{i,3}$, can be calculated from the second and third and so on for as many time steps as desired. No simultaneous equations ever need be solved.

Thus (11.19) represents an *explicit* scheme for the solution of the wave equation. By way of contrast, recall that (11.14) represented a scheme for elliptic equations in which more than one $u_{i,j}$ was unknown in each difference equation; it was thus an *implicit* method.

We now come to the important questions of convergence and stability. We shall not be able to derive the results, which, however, are easily stated. We can guarantee that the solution of (11.19) will converge to the solution of (11.15) if

$$\lambda < 1$$

or, equivalently, if

(11.23) $\qquad k < h$

This is a sufficient condition for convergence; it is not necessary. In other words, there may be equations and spacings that violate (11.23) and still converge, but we cannot guarantee convergence in such a case. In general, we will wish to ensure convergence rather than merely hoping for it and will require that (11.23) be satisfied.

Thus, once we have chosen the step size h in the x direction, we are limited as to the step size we can take in time.* If the problem requires carrying the solution out to a large value of t, a great many time steps may be needed.

Another important factor is that if $\lambda > 1$ the method is unstable, both absolutely and relatively. This means, as it did with ordinary differential equations, that any errors become magnified as the solution progresses.

It is obviously essential that (11.23) be satisfied. A characteristic of explicit methods is that a restriction such as (11.23) must be satisfied in order to ensure convergence and stability.

There are also *implicit* methods for solving hyperbolic equations. These do not suffer from instabilities as do the explicit methods. We postpone a discussion of implicit schemes and their solution until Section 11.8 on parabolic equations since the general discussion there applies to hyperbolic equations as well.

11.7   Parabolic equations

As an example of this type of equation, consider a long thin bar lying along the x-axis between $x = 0$ and $x = L$. Suppose the temperature at $x = 0$ is held fixed at T_0 and the temperature at $x = L$ is held fixed at T_L. Suppose also that at time $t = 0$ the temperature of the rod is given by $f(x)$. If $u(x, t)$ is the temperature at the point x at time t, then u is given by the solution to

$$(11.24) \qquad u_{xx} = au_t$$

Here $a = c\rho/k$, where c is the specific heat of the material, ρ is the density, and k is the thermal conductivity. For simplicity we will take $c = 1$, so that the equation we wish to solve will be

$$(11.25) \qquad u_{xx} = u_t$$

The boundary conditions are

$$(11.26) \qquad \begin{cases} u(0, t) = T_0 \\ u(L, t) = T_L \end{cases}$$

and the initial condition is

$$(11.27) \qquad u(x, 0) = f(x)$$

Equation 11.25 is a parabolic partial differential equation, referred to as the *heat equation* or the *diffusion equation*.

---

* It is assumed, of course, that consistent units have been used throughout.

Many other important physical problems give rise to parabolic equations. For example, the so-called telegraph equations that occur in studies of transmission lines are parabolic.

The boundary conditions (11.26) in difference form are

$$(11.28) \qquad \begin{cases} u_{0,j} = T_0 & j = 1, 2, \ldots \\ u_{n,j} = T_L & j = 1, 2, \ldots \end{cases}$$

The initial condition (11.27) is

$$(11.29) \qquad u_{i,0} = f(ih) \qquad i = 1, 2, \ldots, n - 1$$

To difference (11.25) we once again lay a mesh over the area $0 \le x \le L$ and $t > 0$ with a spacing h in the x direction and k in the time direction. Using (11.2) and (11.6), we get

$$(11.30) \qquad u_{i,j+1} = \lambda u_{i+1,j} + (1 - 2\lambda)u_{i,j} + \lambda u_{i-1,j}$$

where

$$(11.31) \qquad \lambda = \frac{k}{h^2}$$

and $i = 1, 2, \ldots, n - 1$ and $j = 1, 2, 3, \ldots$. Note carefully the new definition of λ. The stencil is

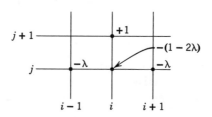

The truncation error at i, j is bounded by

$$(11.32) \qquad |T_{i,j}| \le \frac{\lambda(6\lambda - 1)}{12} Mh^4$$

where

$$|u_{xxxx}| < M$$

provided $\lambda \ne \frac{1}{6}$, for in that case the bound vanishes. When $\lambda = \frac{1}{6}$, the bound becomes

$$(11.33) \qquad |T_{i,j}| \le \frac{N}{3240} h^6$$

where
$$|u_{xxxxxx}| < N$$

Thus it is clearly best—from the point of view of minimizing truncation error—to choose

(11.34) $$k = \tfrac{1}{6}h^2$$

This may not always be convenient.

The discussion so far in this chapter may have created the impression that we have no choices in setting up a differencing scheme. To show that this is by no means the case and to demonstrate that different methods have their advantages and disadvantages, we now develop two other differencing schemes for parabolic equations.

The method just presented used forward differences (11.2) for the time derivative. If we use backward differences (11.3), the difference formula for (11.25) becomes

(11.35) $$-\lambda u_{i+1,j} + (1 + 2\lambda)u_{i,j} - \lambda u_{i-1,j} = u_{i,j-1}$$

where λ is given still by (11.31). The stencil now is

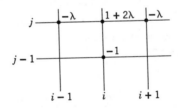

The truncation error is bounded by

(11.36) $$|T_{i,j}| \leq \frac{\lambda(6\lambda + 1)}{12} Mh^4$$

where again
$$|u_{xxxx}| < M$$

This is larger than (11.32). Notice, moreover, that we cannot reduce $T_{i,j}$ to $O(h^6)$ by a judicious choice of λ.

Finally, we consider one more possible difference equation for (11.25). Recall that from (11.6) at the point i, j

$$u_{xx} \simeq \frac{u_{i+1,j} - 2u_{i,j} + u_{i-1,j}}{h^2}$$

Similarly at the point $i, j + 1$

$$u_{xx} \simeq \frac{u_{i+1,j+1} - 2u_{i,j+1} + u_{i-1,j+1}}{h^2}$$

Averaging these approximations, we get

$$u_{xx} \simeq \frac{1}{2h^2} (u_{i+1,j+1} - 2u_{i,j+1} + u_{i-1,j+1} + u_{i+1,j} - 2u_{i,j} + u_{i-1,j})$$

If we now use the forward difference for u_t, we have

$$u_t \simeq \frac{1}{k} (u_{i,j+1} - u_{i,j})$$

The difference equation for (11.25) becomes

$$(11.37) \quad \frac{\lambda}{2} u_{i-1,j+1} - (\lambda + 1)u_{i,j+1} + \frac{\lambda}{2} u_{i+1,j+1}$$

$$= -\frac{\lambda}{2} u_{i+1,j} + (\lambda - 1)u_{i,j} - \frac{\lambda}{2} u_{i-1,j}$$

This difference scheme is often called the *Crank-Nicholson method*. The stencil for (11.37) is

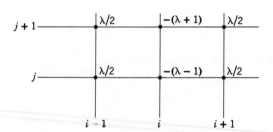

The truncation error is bounded by

$$(11.38) \qquad |T_{i,j}| \leq \frac{\lambda}{12} M h^4$$

with

$$|u_{xxxx}| < M$$

This bound is smaller than (11.36) by a factor of $6\lambda + 1$.

The bound in (11.38) is significantly smaller than (11.36) and thus on the basis of truncation error (11.37) is preferable to (11.35).

11.8 Solution of parabolic difference equations

We have introduced three difference approximations to $u_{xx} = u_t$, given by (11.30), (11.35), and (11.37). We now consider methods of solving each and make the relevant comparisons. In all cases the boundary and initial conditions are given by (11.28) and (11.29).

The first of the methods (11.30) are *explicit* equations for $u_{i,j+1}$ in the same sense that (11.19) was explicit for the hyperbolic case. From the first time line, $j = 0$, which is given by (11.29), we can calculate the second time line, $j = 1$, directly from (11.30) by letting $j = 0$. Once we have the second time line, we get the third from (11.30) by letting $j = 1$. We can proceed in this way for as many time lines as we wish.

This is completely analogous to the method described in Section 11.6 for hyperbolic equations. We should expect to face the same problems of stability and convergence. In the present parabolic case the process converges and is stable if

$$\lambda < \tfrac{1}{2}$$

or, equivalently, if

(11.39) $$k < \frac{h^2}{2}$$

This places a serious restriction on the size of the time step, more serious than the restriction (11.23) for the hyperbolic case. It is this factor that makes a consideration of the other methods (11.35) and (11.37) attractive.

Both (11.35) and (11.37) are implicit methods similar to (11.14) for elliptic equations. Consider first (11.35). We can write down the equations for the first time line, using the boundary and initial conditions (11.28) and (11.29).

$$(1 + 2\lambda)u_{1,1} - \lambda u_{2,1} = f(h) + \lambda T_0$$

$$-\lambda u_{1,1} + (1 + 2\lambda)u_{2,1} - \lambda u_{3,1} = f(2h)$$

$$-\lambda u_{2,1} + (1 + 2\lambda)u_{3,1} - \lambda u_{4,1} = f(3h)$$

$$\cdots \cdots \cdots \cdots$$

$$-\lambda u_{n-2,1} + (1 + 2\lambda)u_{n-1,1} = f(nh - h) + \lambda T_L$$

There are $n - 1$ linear equations in $n - 1$ unknowns $u_{i,1}$ for $i = 1$, $2, \ldots, n - 1$. We may solve them by Gauss elimination: despite the fact that they are sparse, they have a particular structure that makes elimination particularly attractive. Equations of this type are called *tridiagonal* because the only nonzero entries lie along the three diagonal rows. They may also be solved by Gauss-Seidel iteration. The diagonal term is $1 + 2\lambda$ and the sum of the off-diagonal terms is -2λ, so the iteration will converge. An extrapolation procedure can be used to accelerate the convergence.

Once we have found the first time line we can write down the equations for the second time line and again get a tridiagonal set of $n - 1$ equations in the $n - 1$ unknowns. These we solve before proceeding to the third line, and so on. *Each* time line requires the solution of $n - 1$ linear equations.

Since this is obviously much more work than the explicit method (11.30), one naturally asks whether it is ever worth the trouble. The answer to this question lies in the fact that (11.35) is stable and convergent for *all* $\lambda > 0$. We can therefore take much larger time steps. We should now try to determine in a more or less quantitative way whether there is a real economic advantage here.

A reasonable guess is that (11.35) will require about twice as much work per time step as (11.30). If we take $\lambda = 1$, then the work to reach a given time, using (11.35), is less. However, the truncation error goes up roughly as the square of the time step size, which may produce an intolerable error.

The last difference scheme (11.37) is also an implicit method, and it too requires the solution of $n - 1$ tridiagonal equations at each time step. The work required is, therefore, the same as that for (11.35). This method is stable for all λ also.

Notice that if we double λ in (11.37) we double the truncation error, whereas doubling λ in (11.35) quadruples the error. Thus (11.37)—the Crank-Nicholson method—is preferable to (11.35).

It should be noted, however, that for other parabolic equations (11.37) is not stable for all λ and thus (11.35) is sometimes of practical interest.

There are, of course, many other difference schemes, both explicit and implicit. This chapter has introduced only some simple ones. As usual, we end by noting that the methods presented do provide a practical way of handling many problems and that the reader has received an introduction to the subject that will enable him to study some of the more complete texts.

11.9   Case study 13: Temperature distribution in a square pipe

Consider a long square pipe with a square hole carrying a hot fluid. The pipe is half submerged in an ice bath so that the bottom half of the outside of the pipe is at a temperature of 0°C.   The top surface of the pipe is at 100°C.   We will suppose that the temperature varies linearly between the top of the ice bath and the top of the pipe.   The fluid on the inside is at 200°C.   The inside dimension of the pipe is 4 in. and the outside dimension is 10 in.   A cross section of the pipe is shown in Figure 11.5.

The temperature in the material of the pipe satisfies the partial differential equation

$$u_{xx} + u_{yy} = au_t$$

where a involves the specific heat, the thermal conductivity, and the density of the material.   We will assume that the fluid has been flowing long enough that all transient effects will have disappeared, that is, we are in a steady state.   Then $u_t = 0$, and we have

$$u_{xx} + u_{yy} = 0$$

inside the pipe and u is given on the boundary.   This is the Dirichlet problem discussed in Sections 11.3 and 11.4.

We are, of course, taking a *two*-dimensional problem, that is, we do not consider the lowering of the fluid temperature as the fluid flows along the pipe.   In other words, we shall study the temperature distributions at only one cross section.

We take 60 mesh spacings in both the x and y directions so that

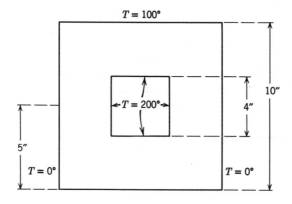

FIGURE 11.5   Cross section of the pipe in Case Study 13.

$h = 0.16667$ in. Then the boundary conditions are

$$u_{i,0} = 0 \qquad\qquad i = 0, 1, \ldots, 60$$

$$u_{0,j} = u_{60,j} = \begin{cases} 0 & j = 0, 1, \ldots, 30 \\ \frac{100}{30}(j - 30) & j = 31, 32, \ldots, 60 \end{cases}$$

$$u_{i,60} = 100 \qquad\qquad i = 1, 2, \ldots, 60$$

$$u_{i,42} = u_{i,18} = 200 \qquad\qquad i = 18, 19, \ldots, 41, 42$$

$$u_{42,j} = u_{18,j} = 200 \qquad\qquad j = 18, 19, \ldots, 41, 42$$

The difference equations are

$$u_{i,j} = \tfrac{1}{4}(u_{i-1,j} + u_{i,j-1} + u_{i+1,j} + u_{i,j+1})$$

for

$$i = 1, 2, \ldots, 59; \quad j = 1, 2, \ldots, 17$$

and

$$i = 1, 2, \ldots, 17, \quad 43, \ldots, 59; \quad j = 18, 19, \ldots, 42$$

and

$$i = 1, 2, \ldots, 59; \quad j = 43, 44, \ldots, 59$$

We can solve these equations by using the extrapolated Liebmann method to find the temperature at all points in the pipe.

The program shown in Figure 11.6 closely parallels the boundary condition equations just stated and the block diagram of Figure 11.3. The annoyance of not being able to use zero subscripts has been handled by adding 1 to every subscript shown in the text. Thus the points are numbered 1 to 61 instead of 0 to 60; the subscripts on the boundary of the hole in the middle run from 19 to 43 instead of 18 to 42, etc.

The first statement in the program reads values for OMEGA, the acceleration factor, EPS, the convergence test, and MAXIT, the maximum number of iterations that should be permitted. The statements down to number 5 set up the starting values and the boundary values in a quite close match with the equations above. The variables A and B are set up to save time in the heavily used computational loop. We write the extrapolated Liebmann formula as

$$u_{ij} = u_{ij} + \omega \left[\frac{1}{4} (u_{i+1,j} + u_{i-1,j} + u_{i,j+1} + u_{i,j-1}) - u_{ij} \right]$$

$$= \frac{\omega}{4} (u_{i+1,j} + u_{i-1,j} + u_{i,j+1} + u_{i,j-1}) + (1 - \omega)u_{ij}$$

The purpose of the new variables should be clear: there is no point in repeatedly dividing ω by 4 and subtracting ω from 1. The rest of the

```
          READ INPUT TAPE 7, 100, OMEGA, EPS, MAXIT
      100 FORMAT (2F10.0, 13)
          DIMENSION U(61, 61)
          DO 1 I = 1, 61
          DO 1 J = 1, 61
    1     U(I, J) = 0.0
          DO 2 J = 32, 61
          FJ = J
          BOUND = 100.0 * (FJ - 31.0) / 30.0
          U(1, J) = BOUND
    2     U(61, J) = BOUND
          DO 3 I = 2, 60
    3     U(I, 61) = 100.0
          DO 4 I = 19, 43
          U(I, 43) = 200.0
    4     U(I, 19) = 200.0
          DO 5 J = 19, 43
          U(43, J) = 200.0
    5     U(19, J) = 200.0
          ITN = 1
          A = OMEGA / 4.0
          B = 1.0 - OMEGA
   10     D = 0.0
          DO 14 J = 2, 60
          DO 14 I = 2, 60
          IF (I - 19) 50, 11, 11
   11     IF (43 - I) 50, 12, 12
   12     IF (J - 19) 50, 13, 13
   13     IF (43 - J) 50, 14, 14
   50     UNEW = A*(U(I+1,J) + U(I-1,J) + U(I,J+1) + U(I,J-1)) + B*U(I,J)
          RESID = ABSF (UNEW - U(I,J))
          IF (RESID - D) 15, 15, 16
   16     D = RESID
   15     U(I,J) = UNEW
   14     CONTINUE
          IF (D - EPS) 60, 61, 61
   61     ITN = ITN + 1
          IF (ITN - MAXIT) 10, 10, 62
   62     WRITE OUTPUT TAPE 10, 600, MAXIT
  600     FORMAT (21H FAILS TO CONVERGE IN, I5, 10HITERATIONS)
   60     CALL EXIT
          END
```

FIGURE 11.6   A program to find the temperature distribution is a square pipe, solving the LaPlace equation by the extrapolated Liebmann method. (Case Study 13.)

program follows the block diagram fairly closely, with the addition of the IF statements to prevent the solution from being carried out inside the hole and on its boundary.

We have not shown output steps.   It is indeed possible to print out all 2856 interior points.   However, trying to learn something from such a mass of figures is not only a strain on the eyes, but rather unilluminating.

A good solution is to let the computer print a diagram of the isotherms (lines of constant temperature) on a picture of the cross section, as in Figure 11.7.   The picture is not square because the vertical lines are spaced six to the inch, whereas the characters are spaced 10 to the inch; this is no real problem.   The diagram was written with a special computer program, which was itself written largely in FORTRAN. The diagram is used with Table 11.1, which gives the temperature corresponding to each symbol used for the isotherm lines.   For instance, we see that the letter A stands for a temperature range of 0°C to 11.7°C.   Naturally the complete listing is available if more details are needed, although we shall not reproduce it.

```
NNNNNNNNNNNNNNNNNNNNNNNNNNNNNNNNNNNNNNNNNNNNNNNNNNNNNNNNNNNNNNNNNNNNNNNN
NNNNNNNNNNNNNNNNNNNNNNNNNNNNNNNNNNNNNNNNNNNNNNNNNNNNNNNNNNNNNNNNNNNNNNNN
NNNNNNNNNNNNNNNNN                                  NNNNNNNNNNNNNNNNNN
   NNNNNNNNNN                                         NNNNNNNNNN
   NNNNNNNN              OOOOOOOOOOOOO                 NNNNNNNN
   NNNNNN         OOOOOOOOOOOOOOOOOOOOOOOOOO           NNNNNN
D    NNNNN       OOOOOOOOOOOOOOOOOOOOOOOOOOOOOOO       NNNNN    D
DD   NNNN      OOOOOOO                   OOOOOOO      NNNN    DD
DDD  NNN     OOOOO                         OOOOO     NNN    DD
DDD  NNN     OOO      PPPPPPPPPPPPPPP       OOO      NNN   DDD
DDD  NNN     OOO    PPPPPPPPPPPPPPPPPPPPP    OOO     NNN   DDD
 DDD NNN    OOO     PPPPP          PPPPP    OOO     NNN   DDD
  DD NNN    OO     PPPP              PPPP     OO    NNN    DD
C  DD NNN   OO   PPP     QQQQQQQQQQQQ    PPP   OO   NNN   DD  C
C  DD NN    OO  PP    QQQQQQQQQQQQQQQQQQQ    PP  OO   NN   DD  C
CC  DD N    OO PP P  QQQQ              QQQQ  P OO   N   DD  CC
C   DD N    OO PP QQ                      QQ PP OO   N   DD  C
CC DD  N    O   P QQ  RRRRRRRRRRRRRRRRRRR  QQ P  O   N   DD  CC
CC  D  N    O   P Q RRRRRRRRRRRRRRRRRRRRRRR Q P  O   N   D   CC
 C  D  N   O PP Q R                     R Q PP O   N   D  C
B CC D  N   O P   Q R                   R Q  P O   N   D CC B
B  C DD N   O P Q  R                     R  Q P O   N DD C  B
B  C DD N   O P Q RR                     RR Q P O   N DD C  B
 B C  D N   O P Q RR                     RR Q P O   N D  C B
 B CC D N   O P Q RR                     RR Q P O   N D CC B
 B  C D NN  O P Q RR                     RR Q P O NN D C  B
BB C  D NN  O P Q RR                     RR Q P O NN D C BB
A B C  D   N O P Q RR                     RR Q P O N  D C B A
A B C  DD N O P Q RR                     RR Q P O N DD C B A
A B C   D N O P Q RR                     RR Q P O N D  C B A
A B CC  D N O P Q RR                     RR Q P O N D CC B A
A BB  C D N O P Q RR                     RR Q P O N D C BB A
AA B  C D N O P Q RR                     RR Q P O N D C B AA
AA B  C D N O PP Q R                     R Q PP O N D C B AA
AA B C  D N   O P Q R                     R Q P O   N D C B AA
AA B C  D NN  O P Q R                     R Q P O NN D C B AA
AA B C  DD N  O P Q R                     R Q P O N DD C B AA
AA B C   D N  O P Q R                     R Q P O N D  C B AA
AA B CC  D N  O P Q R                     R Q P O N D CC B AA
AA B   C  D N  O P Q R                     R Q P O N D C  B AA
AA B   C  D    N O PP Q R                   R QP O N  D C  B AA
AA BB  C  DD N O P  R                   R P O N DD C  BB AA
AA BB  C   D N O P   QRRRRRRRRRRRRRRRRRRRRRRRRRQ P O N D  C BB AA
AA BB CC  D   N O P Q                     Q P O N  D CC BB AA
AA  B   C   D NN O P  QQQQQQQQQQQQQQQQQQQQQQQQ  P O NN D  C  B   AA
AA  B  CC DD N  O P                     PPP O N DD CC  B   AA
AA  BB CC   D  N   OO  PPPPPPPPPPPPPPPPPPPP  OO  N  D  CC BB   AA
AA  BB  CC DD  NN  OOO                     OOO  NN DD CC BB   AA
AAA   BB CC  DD  NN   OOOOOOOOOOOOOOOOOO   NN  DD  CC BB   AAA
AAA  BB  CC  DDD  NNN              NNN  DDD  CC  BB   AAA
AAA  BBB  CC   DDD    NNNNNNNNNNNNNNNNNNN   DDD   CC  BBB   AAA
AAA   BBB  CCC   DDDD                 DDDD   CCC  BB   AAA
AAAA   BBB   CCC   DDDDDDDDD  DDDDDDDDD   CCC   BBB   AAAA
AAAA   BBBB   CCCCC    DDDDDDDDD   CCCCC   BBBB   AAAA
AAAAA   BBBB    CCCCCCCC      CCCCCCCC    BBBB    AAAAA
AAAAA    BBBBB     CCCCCCCCCCCCCCC     BBBBB    AAAAA
AAAAAAA    BBBBBBBB              BBBBBBBB    AAAAAAA
AAAAAAAAAA     BBBBBBBBBBBBBBBBBBBBBBBBBBBB     AAAAAAAAA
AAAAAAAAAAAAAA                           AAAAAAAAAAAAA
AAAAAAAAAAAAAAAAAAAAAAAAAAAAAAAAAAAAAAAAAAAAAAAAAAAAAAAAAAAAAAAAAAAAAAAA
AAAAAAAAAAAAAAAAAAAAAAAAAAAAAAAAAAAAAAAAAAAAAAAAAAAAAAAAAAAAAAAAAAAAAAAA
```

FIGURE 11.7 Map of the isotherms in the pipe of Case Study 13. This was produced by a separate computer program.

Table   11.1

Symbol	Range, C°
A	0–11.7
B	23.6–35.3
C	47.1–58.7
D	70.6–82.3
N	94.2–105.8
O	117.9–129.4
P	141.4–152.9
Q	164.8–176.3
R	188.3–200.0

General information of the type provided by this plot is often the main interest at the start of a computer-aided investigation. In such cases it is frequently of interest to resolve the entire problem many times, varying some parameter; the general form of the variation of temperature with the parameter is made clearly understandable with the aid of diagrams produced by the computer.

Finally, we can get an insight into the effectiveness of extrapolation from Figure 11.8, in which the number of iterations required for convergence is plotted against the extrapolation parameter ω. Notice

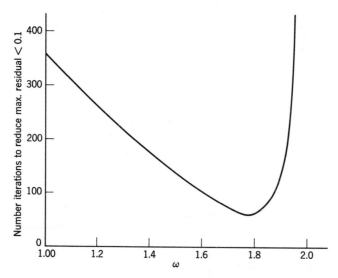

FIGURE 11.8   The number of iterations of the program of Figure 11.7 required for convergence, as a function of the extrapolation parameter ω. (Case Study 13.)

that the number of iterations required for the optimum ω of about 1.8 is far fewer than for the worst values tried and considerably better than the unextrapolated method, which amounts to setting $\omega = 1$. In fact, the number of iterations in the unextrapolated method is about seven times the number with the optimum ω.

Exercises

Note. Solving a few numerical examples of partial differential equations with paper and pencil or a desk calculator is a highly instructive experience. However, if more than a few exercises are to be done, which is desirable, it will be necessary to use the computer. The programs written for Exercises 17 to 22, together with the program in Figure 11.6, can be used with suitable modification to solve the numerical exercises that follow. This, too, is highly instructive.

1. Solve the elliptic equation $u_{xx} + u_{yy} = 0$ for the following square meshes, with boundary values as shown, using the Liebmann method and

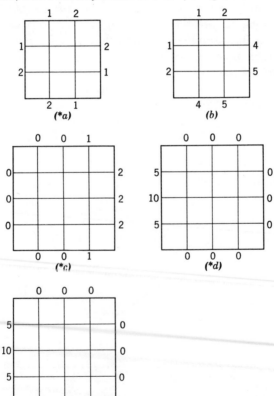

the difference equations approximations (11.6) and (11.7). Iterate until the maximum difference between successive values at any point is less than 0.005. You are free to make initial guesses other than zero and to use extrapolation to speed convergence.

*2. The mesh in Exercise 1d had three interior points in each direction. If we assume that the actual boundary condition approximated there was a linear increase from zero to 10, we can get a more accurate solution by drawing a new mesh with seven interior points in each direction. The left-hand boundary values will be 2.5, 5.0, 7.5, 10.0, 7.5, 5.0, and 2.5; all others are still zero.

Resolve Exercise 1d with a tolerance of 0.0001; then solve the related problem described here, also with a tolerance of 0.0001. Compare the solution of the old problem with the solution at corresponding points of the new problem. Why are there differences?

3. Extend the mesh of Exercise 2 one step farther to a grid having 15 interior points with appropriate boundary values. Solve with a tolerance of 0.0001 and compare with the solution of Exercise 2. It will be necessary to use extrapolation to get convergence in less than 100 iterations if zero guesses are used.

4. Solve three problems like those of Exercises 1d, 2, and 3 with the following change: the nonzero boundary values are on the right instead of the left. The final solutions obviously should be mirror images of the originals, but the number of iterations required will be different. Why?

5. Consider the following mesh and boundary values.

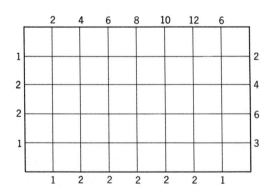

a. Using the unextrapolated Liebmann method ($\omega = 1$), solve successively with tolerances of 0.01, 0.001, 0.0001, and 0.00001.

*b. Does the fact that the difference between successive approximations is never greater than, say, 0.01 mean that the final values in such a solution are within 0.01 of true solution of the difference equations? Check by comparing values in the solutions having tolerances of 0.01 and 0.001.

*c. With the tolerance fixed at 0.0001, solve this system repeatedly with $\omega = 0.9, 1.0, \ldots, 1.9$. Compare the number of iterations required for convergence.

*d. Change the boundary value in the center of the bottom from 2.0 to 5.0 and resolve, using a tolerance of 0.0001 and any extrapolation factor you wish. Compare this solution with a previous solution of this problem in which the tolerance was 0.0001. Does this one change in a boundary value affect all solution points or only some of them?

6. Solve the hyperbolic (wave) equation $U_{xx} = U_{tt}$ by the explicit method (11.19). Take 21 points in the x-direction, with subscripts 1 to 21; let $h = 1.0$. Use the boundary condition

$$U(1, J) = U(21, J) = 0.0, \qquad J = 1, 2, \ldots$$

For an initial condition use the situation given in Figure 11.4, with $\delta = 2.0$, which we may describe by

$$U(I, 1) = 0.2(I - 1), \qquad I = 2, 3, \ldots, 11$$

$$U(I, 1) = 0.2(21 - I), \qquad I = 12, 13, \ldots, 20$$

To start the solution, write $U(I, 2) = U(I, 1)$, $I = 2, \ldots, 20$. Take $\lambda = 0.2$ and continue the solution to $j = 250$.

7. Resolve the problem of Exercise 6 with

a. $\lambda = 0.1$, $\quad j_{\max} = 400$
b. $\lambda = 0.4$, $\quad j_{\max} = 100$
c. $\lambda = 0.8$, $\quad j_{\max} = 50$
d. $\lambda = 1.0$, $\quad j_{\max} = 20$

*8. Same as Exercise 6, except that the initial condition is

$$U(I, 1) = U(I, 2) = 2 \sin \frac{\pi(I - 1)}{20}, \qquad I = 2, 3, \ldots, 20$$

Considering that we are starting the string vibrating in the shape of a sine wave, what would you expect the solution to do? Take the solution for $j = 202$, after which time there has been a complete oscillation, and plot the solution as a function of I. Similarly, plot the position of the midpoint $(I = 11)$ as a function of time.

9. Same as Exercise 8, except that the initial condition is

a. $U(I, 1) = U(I, 2) = 2 \sin \dfrac{2\pi(I - 1)}{20}$

b. $U(I, 1) = U(I, 2) = 2 \sin \dfrac{3\pi(I - 1)}{20}$

10. Same as Exercise 6, except that the initial condition is

$$U(2, 1) = U(8, 1) = 0.5$$

$$U(3, 1) = U(7, 1) = 1.0$$

$$U(4, 1) = U(6, 1) = 1.5$$

$$U(5, 1) = 2.0$$

$$U(I, 1) = 0.0, \qquad I = 9, 10, \ldots, 20$$

Would you expect this waveshape to perpetuate itself as the sine waves did? Plot conditions that will display the behavior of the string effectively under this initial condition.

*11. Resolve the problem in Exercise 6 after changing one boundary value:

$$U(13, 1) = U(13, 2) = 0.4$$

Compare the result with the previous one. Are all or only some of the solution points affected by the change?

*12. Solve the parabolic (heat) equation $U_{xx} = U_t$ by the explicit method of (11.30). Take 21 points in the x-direction, with subscripts 1 to 21; let $h = 1.0$. Use the boundary condition

$$U(1, J) = 100.0 \qquad J = 1, 2, \ldots$$

$$U(21, J) = 200.0 \qquad J = 1, 2, \ldots$$

For an initial condition use the temperature distribution as sketched:

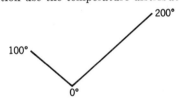

This may be described by:

$$U(I, 1) = 10(11 - I), \qquad I = 2, 3, \ldots, 11$$

$$U(I, 1) = 20(I - 11), \qquad I = 12, 13, \ldots, 20$$

Take $\lambda = 0.2$ and continue the solution to $j = 200$. From a consideration of the heat analogy, what would you expect the solution to approach for large time?

13. Resolve the problem of Exercise 12 with

a. $\lambda = 0.1, \qquad j_{max} = 400$
b. $\lambda = 0.4, \qquad j_{max} = 100$
c. $\lambda = 0.8, \qquad j_{max} = 50$
d. $\lambda = 1.0, \qquad j_{max} = 20$

14. Resolve the problem of Exercise 12 after changing one boundary value:

$$U(13, 1) = 200$$

Use $\lambda = 0.2$ and continue to $j = 200$. Compare the result with the previous one. Are all or only some of the solution points affected by the change?

15. Same as Exercise 12, except for an obvious change in boundary conditions and the initial condition is

a.

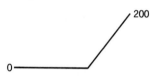

$$U(I, 1) = 0.0, \qquad I = 2, 3, \ldots, 11$$

$$U(I, 1) = 20(I - 11), \qquad I = 12, 13, \ldots, 20$$

b.

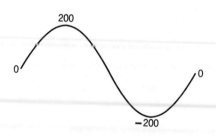

$U(2, 1) = U(8, 1) = 50$

$U(3, 1) = U(7, 1) = 100$

$U(4, 1) = U(6, 1) = 150$

$U(5, 1) = 200$

$U(I, 1) = 0.0, \qquad I = 9, 10, \ldots, 20$

c.

$$U(I, 1) = 200 \sin \frac{2\pi(I - 1)}{20}, \qquad I = 2, 3, \ldots, 20$$

16. Same as Exercise 12 but use the implicit method of (11.35) which requires solving a system like that shown in Section 11.8.   Try

a. $\lambda = 0.8,$ $j_{max} = 100$
b. $\lambda = 1.0,$ $j_{max} = 100$
c. $\lambda = 2.0,$ $j_{max} = 80$
d. $\lambda = 5.0,$ $j_{max} = 50$
e. $\lambda = 10.0,$ $j_{max} = 50$

*17. Write a program to solve the problem in Exercise 5, using the unextra-polated Liebmann method with a fixed tolerance of 0.001 and with the maximum number of iterations fixed at 50.   The program must be able to read data cards containing, in each case, a value of I, a value of J, and a boundary value $U(I, J)$; it should continue to read these cards until it detects one with an I subscript of zero.

18. Generalize the program in Exercise 17 as follows: let the maximum num-ber of mesh points in each direction be 50.   At the beginning of the program read a card containing the tolerance to be used, the value of the relaxation parameter, ω, the maximum number of iterations to be per-mitted, and the maximum values of the subscripts in the two directions.

*19. Write a program to solve the hyperbolic equation in Exercise 6 as follows: assuming for this exercise that you have a computer with a large storage, it is possible to waste storage space to simplify the program.   Set up a two-dimensional array with 21 elements in the I-direction and 500 in the J-direction.   Read from a data card the value of λ and the maximum number of steps in the J-direction.   Then, by program statements, generate the initial and boundary conditions.   (These statements can be changed to solve the equation for other initial conditions.)   Now an outer loop to control the J subscript (the time dimension) and an inner loop to control the I subscript (the x-dimension) can be used with the formula in (11.19).   It may be convenient, if desired, to make a nota-tional change so that J stands for the time line being computed, $J - 1$ stands for the time line preceding, and $J - 2$ stands for two time lines before, instead of what is shown in (11.19).   And, as always, the sub-scripts must run from 1 instead of the zero shown in the text because of the FORTRAN restriction to positive nonzero subscripts.

20. Modify the program in Exercise 19 to avoid the great waste of storage space.   Set up three one-dimensional arrays, each having 21 elements. They might be named something like UJP1(I), UJ(I), and UJM1(I), with the names intended to suggest the J-values with which each array is associated.   The initial conditions are set up in UJ(I) and UJM1(I); from these we compute new values in the UJP1(I) array and print them. Having done so, we now move the contents of the UJ(I) array into the UJM1(I) array, the UJP1(I) array into the UJ(I) array, and then go again into the program section for computing values of UJP1(I) from UJ(I) and UJM1(I).

21. Write a program to solve the parabolic equation of Exercise 12.   The program can be quite similar to the one written for Exercise 19 (or 20),

except that the initial condition is set up for only the first time line, and, of course, the difference formula is given by (11.30) instead of (11.19).

22. Write a program to solve a parabolic equation by the implicit method (11.35), which involves solving the system given in Section 11.8.

This will *not* require setting up a two-dimensional array for the coefficients. Gauss elimination can be expressed as a recursion relation; see Exercise 23. If the system is solved by iteration, the actual computation becomes particularly simple. The coefficients are simply $-\lambda$ and $(1 + 2\lambda)$ and can be written in arithmetic statements. If we consider that T_0 and T_L are, in fact, given by the values of U on the boundary ($I = 1$ and $I = 21$), the first and last equations follow exactly the same pattern as all others; the entire iteration formula compresses to one statement having subscripts controlled by a single DO statement. The logic of determining convergence and guarding against an endless loop if convergence is impossible can be quite similar to that used in Figures 8.9 and 8.15.

23. Consider a general system of n tridiagonal linear equations, which we will assume have a unique solution:

$$b_1x_1 + c_1x_2 \qquad\qquad\qquad\qquad = d_1$$

$$a_2x_1 + b_2x_2 + c_2x_3 \qquad\qquad\qquad = d_2$$

$$a_3x_2 + b_3x_3 + c_3x_4 \qquad\qquad = d_3$$

$$\vdots$$

$$a_{n-1}x_{n-2} + b_{n-1}x_{n-1} + c_{n-1}x_n = d_{n-1}$$

$$a_nx_{n-1} \quad + b_nx_n \quad = d_n$$

a. Show that the solution of this system is given by

$$x_n = d_n^*$$

$$x_r = d_r^* - c_r^*x_{r+1} \qquad r = n - 1, \ldots, 1$$

where

$$c_1^* = \frac{c_1}{b_1}$$

$$c_r^* = \frac{c_r}{b_r - a_rc_{r-1}^*} \qquad r = 2, \ldots, n$$

$$d_1^* = \frac{d_1}{b_1}$$

$$d_r^* = \frac{d_r - a_rd_{r-1}^*}{b_r - a_rc_{r-1}^*} \qquad r = 2, \ldots, n$$

b. Suppose that for some $r = 2, \ldots, n$

$$b_r - a_r c^*_{r-1} = 0$$

Show that

$$x_{r+1} = \frac{d_r - a_r d^*_{r-1}}{c_r}$$

provided $c_r \neq 0$. Discuss the case in which $c_r = 0$. Show also that the problem reduces to solving two systems, one consisting of r equations in r unknowns and the other having $(n - r - 1)$ equations in $(n - r - 1)$ unknowns.

What can be said about the solution of these two reduced systems if $c_k \neq 0$ for $k = r, r + 1, \ldots, n$?

24. Solve the five tridiagonal equations

$$2x_1 - \quad x_2 \qquad\qquad\qquad = 2$$
$$-x_1 + 2x_2 - \quad x_3 \qquad\qquad = 0$$
$$-x_2 + 2x_3 - \quad x_4 \qquad = 0$$
$$-x_3 + 2x_4 - \quad x_5 = 0$$
$$- \quad x_4 + 2x_5 = 1$$

25. Show that if we approximate the first derivative by

$$u_x \simeq \frac{u_{i+1,j} - u_{i-1,j}}{2h}$$

the truncation error is of the order h^2. This is called a *centered difference*. Note the similarity between this centered difference and the predictor formula (10.33).

26. a. Derive the approximation

$$u_{xy} \simeq \frac{u_{i+1,j+1} - u_{i+1,j-1} - u_{i-1,j+1} + u_{i-1,j-1}}{4hk}$$

Hint. Use centered differences twice.

b. Show that the truncation error is $O(h^2)$.

*27. Instead of using the forward difference (11.2), use the centered difference of Exercise 25 with (11.6) to obtain a difference approximation to the heat equation $u_{xx} = u_t$. Draw a stencil of the method.

This is usually called *Richardson's method*. It is unstable for all $\lambda = k/h^2$.

28. In the result of Exercise 27 replace $u_{i,j}$ by its average at $i, j + 1$ and $i, j - 1$, that is,

$$u_{i,j} = \tfrac{1}{2}(u_{i,j+1} + u_{i,j-1})$$

and obtain a new approximation to the heat equation. Draw the stencil of the method.

This is the *duFort-Frankel method*. It is convergent and stable for all $\lambda = k/h^2$.

Given the boundary and initial conditions (11.26) and (11.27) and using the duFort-Frankel method, can you find $u_{i,1}$ for $i = 1, 2, \ldots,$ $n - 1$? What would you do to get the calculations started?

*29. Recall that at $i, j + 1$

$$u_{xx}^{(j+1)} \sim \frac{u_{i+1,j+1} - 2u_{i,j+1} + u_{i-1,j+1}}{h^2}$$

and at i, j

$$u_{xx}^{(j)} \sim \frac{u_{i+1,j} - 2u_{i,j} + u_{i-1,j}}{h^2}$$

whereas at $i, j - 1$

$$u_{xx}^{(j-1)} \sim \frac{u_{i+1,j-1} - 2u_{i,j-1} + u_{i-1,j-1}}{h^2}$$

a. Write down three similar approximations to u_{yy} at $i + 1, j$; i, j; $i - 1, j$.

b. Let $h = k$ and let

$$u_{xx} = \tfrac{1}{12}u_{xx}^{(j+1)} + \tfrac{5}{6}u_{xx}^{(j)} + \tfrac{1}{12}u_{xx}^{(j-1)}$$

$$u_{yy} = \tfrac{1}{12}u_{yy}^{(i+1)} + \tfrac{5}{6}u_{yy}^{(i)} + \tfrac{1}{12}u_{yy}^{(i-1)}$$

Find an approximation to LaPlace's equation

$$u_{xx} + u_{yy} = 0$$

This is an extremely accurate approximation for LaPlace's equation. However, if the right-hand side is nonzero, it is no better than (11.14).

c. Draw the stencil of the method.

d. Can the Gauss-Seidel iteration method be used to solve these difference equations?

30. A well-known variational principle* states that of all functions $u(x, y)$ that have continuous first derivatives in a closed region R and satisfy the boundary condition $u(x, y) = f(x, y)$ on C, the boundary of R, the one that minimizes the integral

$$I = \iint\limits_{R} (u_x{}^2 + u_y{}^2)\, dx\, dy$$

---

* See, for instance, Forsythe and Wasow, Section 19.1.

is the solution of the Dirichlet problem

$$u_{xx} + u_{yy} = 0 \quad \text{in } R$$

$$u(x, y) = f(x, y) \quad \text{on } C$$

Replace the terms u_x and u_y by forward differences. Replace the integrals by sums and replace $dx\, dy$ by hk.

If I is to be a minimum, all of its first partial derivatives with respect to $u_{i,j}$ must vanish. Show that the vanishing of these derivatives is equivalent to the difference equations (11.14).

What changes would take place if backward differences were used for u_x and u_y?

*31. In Section 11.4 we solved the elliptic difference equations (11.14) by solving one equation at each point for one unknown; this is the Liebmann method.

Instead, suppose we try to solve several equations simultaneously for several unknowns. In particular, we will write down the $n - 1$ equations for a whole row or line ($i = 1, 2, \ldots, n - 1$ and j fixed). The unknowns will be the values of $u_{i,j}$ on that line, that is, $u_{1,j}, u_{2,j}, \ldots, u_{n-1,j}$. The $u_{i,j}$ on all other lines will be taken equal to the latest approximation.

We now solve these $n - 1$ equations for $n - 1$ unknowns to produce a new approximation for $u_{1,j}, u_{2,j}, \ldots, u_{n-1,j}$. We then go on to the next line, $j + 1$, and repeat the process. When all lines have been traversed, we say that one iteration has been completed.

a. Show that a tridiagonal set of equations must be solved to find the $u_{i,j}$ on each line. If we proceed this way from line to line, the process is called *line relaxation*. It is often more efficient than the Liebmann method, even though $m - 1$ sets of tridiagonal equations must be solved for each iteration.

b Write out all the equations for a square with four equal intervals in each direction. Let all of the boundary values be $+1$. Indicate the three tridiagonal sets of equations to be solved in each iteration. What do you notice about the equations for the first and third lines?

32. Instead of line relaxation (as described in Exercise 31), we could use column relaxation, that is, we could write the equations for all the points in a column and solve the resulting tridiagonal equations. Each of these equations would involve $m - 1$ unknowns, $u_{i,j}$ ($j = 1, 2, \ldots, m - 1$).

A particularly efficient computational scheme is to do row relaxation during odd-numbered iterations and column relaxation during even-numbered iterations. Write down the equations that express this process.

This is called an *alternating direction method*. It was developed by Peaceman, Rachford, Douglas, and others.

33. Show that the wave equation

$$u_{xx} = a^2 u_{tt}$$

can be reduced to

$$u_{yz} = 0$$

where

$$y = ax - t$$

$$z = ax + t$$

Hint. Use the chain rule to get $u_x = u_y y_x + u_z z_x$ and similar expressions.

*34. a. Write the difference equations (11.30) for the heat equation for the case $k = h^2$. Describe in words how $u_{i,j+1}$ is found in terms of the values on the jth row and draw the stencil.

  b. The difference equation in (a) is *unstable*. To verify this instability, let $h = 0.2$ and $k = 0.04$. Simulate an error in the initial data by letting $u_{i,0} = 0$ for $i \neq 10$ and $u_{i,10} = \epsilon$. Calculate the propagation of this error at $t = 0.16$ (four time steps ahead).

  Notice that some points, for example $i = 7$, $j = 1$, are unaffected, regardless of the size of ϵ. This is characteristic of parabolic and hyperbolic equations but not of elliptic. See Exercises 5d, 11, 14, and 36.

35. a. Write the difference equation (11.30) for the heat equation for the case $k = \frac{1}{2}h^2$. Describe in words how $u_{i,j+1}$ is found in terms of the values on the jth row. Draw the stencil.

  b. The difference equation in (a) is stable. Verify this fact by letting $h = 0.2$ and $k = 0.02$. Simulate an error in the initial data by letting $u_{i,0} = 0$ for $i \neq 10$ and $u_{i,10} = \epsilon$. Calculate the propagation of this error at $t = 0.16$ (eight time steps ahead).

  c. What is the sum of the errors on each line?

  d. Compare this result with that of the unstable method in Exercise 34. What is the maximum error at $t = 0.16$ in each case?

36. a. Write the difference equation (11.14) for LaPlace's equation for $h = k$. Describe in words how $u_{i,j}$ is found in terms of the neighboring points.

  b. Simulate an error in the boundary data by considering a square with six spaces in each direction ($i, j = 0, 1, \ldots, 6$). Let all boundary values be zero except for $u_{0,3}$ (midway on the lower boundary). Let $u_{0,3} = \epsilon$. Calculate the propagation of this error throughout the square.

  c. What points are unaffected by the error at the one boundary point? Compare this with the error propagation pattern in Exercises 34 and 35.

  d. Where does the maximum error occur?

37. Suppose that we wish to use line relaxation (Exercise 31) with the nine-point difference approximation of Exercise 29. What kind of linear equations must we solve at each line? Is the work involved more than with the simpler five-point approximation (11.14) discussed in Exercise 31?

38. Show that if we approximate $u_x(x_0, y_0)$ by

$$u_x = \frac{u(x_0 + h, y_0) - u(x_0 - h, y_0)}{2h}$$

the truncation error is

$$E_T = -\frac{h^2}{6} u_{xxx}(\xi, y_0)$$

where

$$x_0 - h < \xi < x_0 + h$$

This is analogous to the predictor formula (10.33) for ordinary differential equations.

39. Using the result of Exercise 38, show that an approximation for the mixed second derivative is

$$u_{xy} = \frac{u(x_0 + h, y_0 + k) - u(x_0 - h, y_0 + k) - u(x_0 + h, y_0 - k) + u(x_0 - h, y_0 - k)}{4hk}$$

with the following stencil

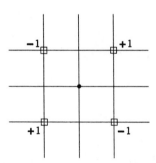

By expanding each term on the right in a series about x_0, y_0 show that the truncation error is approximately

$$E_T = -(h^2 u_{xxxy} + k^2 u_{xyyy})/6$$

plus higher order terms in h and k.

40. Show that the equation

$$u_{xx} - a^2 u_{tt} = 0$$

can be reduced to the wave equation $u_{xx} - u_{yy} = 0$ by the change of variables

$$ay = t$$

41. Consider a plane elastic membrane under a uniform tension T.

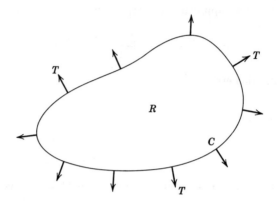

Suppose a constant pressure p is applied to the membrane in a direction perpendicular to the plane. Then the deflection z is given by the solution of

$$\frac{\partial^2 z}{\partial x^2} + \frac{\partial^2 z}{\partial y^2} = -\frac{p}{T} \quad \text{in } R$$

$$z = 0 \quad \text{on } C$$

Show that this can be reduced to the solution of the torsion problem (11.9 and 11.10).

—Appendix 1

Summary of FORTRAN
Input and Output Methods

The primary purpose of this appendix is to provide certain additional information about input and output methods. However, in order to make it more useful as a reference, certain information presented elsewhere is repeated here.

A1.1 Basics

Reading input data or writing output requires the programmer to provide four categories of information in the source program.

1. The selection of an input or output device, which is handled by using the appropriate statement: PRINT, READ INPUT TAPE, etc.

2. The variables to receive new input values or to have their values sent to an output device, as specified by the list of variables in the input or output statement.

3. The order in which the values are to be transmitted, as governed by the order in which the variables are named in the list.

4. The format in which the data appears for input, or is to be written for output, as specified by a FORMAT statement that must be referenced by the input or output statement.

Each of the four areas has been discussed and examples have been presented in preceding chapters. Each of them is the subject of further elaboration in the interest either of simplicity of programming or, more commonly, of more powerful techniques directed toward greater usefulness of the computer.

A1.2   The list of an input and output statement

The simplest type of list is one in which all the variables are named explicitly in the order in which they are to be transmitted. There are more complicated (and more powerful) types of lists, as discussed later. In all cases, however, the fundamental idea of "scanning" carries through: the first data field goes with the first variable name and the first field specification and so on.

The first additional list feature is a useful one that does not complicate the scanning process: it is permissible to use fixed point variables in a list as subscripts elsewhere in the same list. There are two restrictions, however.

1. When this is done with input, any variable used as a subscript must appear in the list as an input variable *before* it appears as a subscript. "Before" means in the sense of the scanning process; in fact, it always means "to the left."

2. A left parenthesis (other than a subscripting parenthesis) must appear between the list variable appearance and the subscript appearance. For a "simple" list this requires enclosing the subscripted variable in parentheses.

One useful way to take advantage of this flexibility is in reading elements of an array that appear in the deck in random order. Suppose, for instance, that the elements of a two-dimensional array are punched one-to-a-card, with the row and column number of each element punched on the card with it in the order I, J, A(I, J). The reading might be done with the statements

$$\text{READ 400, I, J, (A(I, J))}$$
$$\text{400 FORMAT (I2, I2, E14.7)}$$

The parentheses around A(I, J) are those required by Rule 2. Now, as each element is read, the information on the card is used immediately to specify where to store the element (i.e., to establish which element it is).

When entire arrays or parts of arrays are to be transmitted, it is often not necessary to name each element explicitly. To transmit an entire array, it is necessary only to name the array in a list without any subscripts. The name of the array must, of course, appear elsewhere in the program in a DIMENSION statement, but in the list it need not carry any subscripting information. The elements ordinarily have the same field specification; this one field specification may be given by itself in the FORMAT statement.   We can, for instance, write

$$\text{PRINT 21, A}$$
$$\text{21 FORMAT (E20.7)}$$

where A is an array of any size.   This is based on an additional feature of the scanning of the FORMAT statement; whenever the closing parenthesis of a FORMAT statement is reached, scanning starts again from the beginning (in this case).   In this example there is obviously only one field specification, which is the most elementary example of this situation: the one field specification is simply used over and over, until all variables have been transmitted.

Whenever an entire array is moved this way, the elements are transmitted in the "natural order" mentioned on p. 200: the sequence is such that the first subscript varies most rapidly and the last varies least rapidly.

When only some of the elements of an array are to be transferred, or when the "natural order" is not desired, it is often still possible to avoid naming each element explicitly.   They can instead be specified in the list in a way that parallels a DO loop, although it is not literally a DO loop.   For instance, the statements

$$\text{READ 200, (A(1, J),} \qquad \text{J = 1, 10)}$$
$$\text{200 FORMAT (10F7.0)}$$

would call for 10 numbers to be read from a card and stored as the first 10 elements of the first row of the array named A.   The same 10 numbers would be stored as the first 10 elements of the first *column* of A by

$$\text{READ 200, (A(I, 1),} \qquad \text{I = 1, 10)}$$

We see that the indexed variable (or variables), along with the indexing information, must be enclosed in parentheses.

Just as it is possible to have nests of DO's, it is possible to have nests of indexed variables in a list.   Suppose, for example, that we want to print 60 numbers, taking the first 12 as the first 12 elements of the first row of RESULT, the next 12 as the first 12 elements of the *third* row of RESULT, the next 12 as the first 12 in the *fifth* row, etc.   This can be done with:

$$\text{PRINT 91, ((RESULT (I, J), J = 1, 12), I = 1, 9, 2)}$$
$$\text{91 FORMAT (E20.7)}$$

In a certain sense this list may be thought of as equivalent to the DO nest:

$$\text{DO} \quad 462 \quad \text{I} = 1, 9, 2$$
$$\text{DO} \quad 462 \quad \text{J} = 1, 12$$
$$462 \text{ RESULT (I, J)}$$

In this analogy statement 462 is to be understood in the sense that "the next number printed is to be RESULT (I, J)." Thus it is seen that the idea of "inner" and "outer" DO's carries over to inner and outer list indexing. There may be a maximum of three nests.

We see here that the scanning of a list can become considerably more complicated than it is in a simple list that names each variable explicitly. Still, the sequence in which numbers are transferred is completely specified. We need to note how list scanning keeps in step with FORMAT statement scanning: as each new variable name is picked up from the list, another field specification is obtained from the FORMAT statement. The indexing of the list and the FORMAT statement variations discussed later make the picture more complex but do not change the basic idea of simultaneous scanning of the list and the field specifications.

Indexing may be set up to use fixed point variables earlier in the list as indexing parameters. When this is done, the parentheses that must enclose the indexed variable(s) and the indexing information will satisfy Rule 2 on p. 406.

A1.3 The FORMAT statement

It is the business of the FORMAT statement to describe how the information is arranged on input or is to be arranged on output. To each number transmitted there must correspond a field specification that lists the kind of information the field contains and what it "looks like" (or will look like, for output). The subject may conveniently be described under two headings: (1) what each of the types of field specifications does and (2) how the field specifications may be arranged in the FORMAT statement, in keeping with the scanning process.

We shall discuss six types of field specifications. In each case a complete field specification consists of the following:

1. A letter (I, F, E, H, X, or A) to designate the type of information and something about how it is to be handled.

2. A number to designate how many card columns or printer spaces are involved.

The E and F field specifications require a second number to prescribe decimal-point handling.

To save repetition, we may note some facts that apply to each of the field specifications I, F, and E.

On *input* a sign, if any, must be the first nonblank character of the field. The use of a plus sign is always optional; if no sign appears, the number is taken to be positive. Embedded blanks are taken to be zeros.

On *output* the number will appear at the right of the assigned field if more characters are specified for the field than there are characters in the number. If too few characters are specified, the sign and high-order digits will be lost and no indication given. Plus signs are not punched or printed.

In all six kinds it is permissible to specify that the same field specification applies to several successive fields by writing a *repetition number* in front of the field specification.

Field Specification I (Integer)

This is of the form Iw. I specifies conversion between an internal fixed point integer and an external decimal integer. The total number of characters in the field, including sign and any blanks, is w. Decimal points are not permitted.

Field Specification F (External Fixed Point)

This is of the form F$w.d$. The F indicates conversion between an internal floating point number and an external number written without an exponent. The total number of characters in the field, including sign, decimal point, and any blanks, is w. The number of decimal places after the (assumed) decimal point is d.

On *input* the use of an actual decimal point is optional: if one is supplied, it overrides d. Shown below are some sample data fields and the numbers to which they would be converted if read under control of F10.6.

Data Field	Converted Internal Number
+12345678	+12.345678
1234.5678	+1234.5678
−1.2345678	−1.2345678
.012345678	+.012345678
−1.2	−1.2
+1234567	+1.234567
123	+.000123

On *output* there will be d places to the right of the decimal point.

Field Specification E (Floating Point)

This is of the form E$w.d$. E specifies conversion between an internal floating point number and an external number written with an exponent. The total number of characters in the field in the external medium is w, including sign, decimal point, exponent, and any blanks. The number of decimal places after the decimal point (not counting the exponent) is d.

On *input* the use of an actual decimal point is optional; if one is supplied, it overrides d. The exponent part of the field is of the general form E $\pm ee$, the same as in a floating point constant in a statement. However, several short cuts are permitted to simplify card punching.

A positive exponent may appear with the $+$ omitted or replaced with a blank, that is, in the form E ee or Eee. If the first digit of the exponent is zero, it may be omitted. If the exponent is written with a sign, the E may be omitted. Thus the following are all permissible (and equivalent) forms for the exponent *plus* 2: E $+$ 02, E 02, E02, E $+$ 2, E2, $+$02, $+$2.

For example, observe that the following data fields convert to the same internal number if read in under the control of E14.7 (remember that an actual decimal point overrides d in the field specification):

$+$12345678E03   1234.5678E0

12345678.E $-$ 4 $+$0.12345678 $+$ 4

On *output* the number will normally appear in the form $\pm 0.nn$ $\cdots$ E $\pm ee$ (except that plus signs are replaced with blanks), where the number of places after the decimal point is specified by d.

A *scale factor* may be used by writing the field specification in the form sPnE$w.d$, where s is the scale factor, P stands for "place" or "point," and n is the repetition number. The effect of the scale factor is to move the decimal point s places to the right and decrease the exponent by s.

A scale factor has no effect on input with an E field specification. It has an effect on both input and output with an F field specification, but such usage is not common. When a scale factor is used, it applies to all subsequent E and F field specifications in the same FORMAT statement, as the scanning continues, until another scale factor is encountered. This means that if a scale factor is to apply to only one field specification, the one following it must have a scale factor of zero.

For routine printing of floating point results, the most common field specification is probably 1PE20.7. This prints the decimal point between the first and second digits, prints all the significant figures usually available, and provides plenty of space for easy reading.

Field Specification H (Hollerith)

This is of the form wH. The w characters immediately following the letter H are printed or punched in the position indicated by the position of the Hollerith field specification in the FORMAT statement. The Hollerith field specification is different from the others in that it does not go with a variable named in the list. Instead, it calls for the output of the text *itself*. Any character available in the computer system may be used, including the "character" *blank*. This is the only case in which a blank in a statement is not simply ignored. No indication of the presence of Hollerith text is required in the list of the output statement that refers to the FORMAT statement containing the text. Whenever a Hollerith field specification is encountered in the scanning of a FORMAT statement, the text following is written out and scanning continues without any variable from the list having been transmitted. It is permissible for an output record to consist of nothing but Hollerith text, which is sometimes useful. This can be done by putting nothing but Hollerith text in the FORMAT statement and giving no list with the output statement.

One of the most frequent applications of the Hollerith field specification is in controlling the spacing of the lines of printing. The first character of the line printed with a PRINT statement is actually not printed but is instead used to control spacing of the printer carriage. If the carriage control character is a blank, the normal single spacing occurs before the line is printed. If the carriage control character is zero, double spacing occurs before printing. If the character is 1, the paper spaces to the top of the next page before printing. The same considerations apply when a tape written with the WRITE OUTPUT TAPE statement (see later) is printed.

Field Specification X (Blank)

This is of the form wX. On input, the effect is to skip over w columns. The assumption is that the columns are blank and that the purpose is to avoid having to make the succeeding field longer than it really is. However, it makes no difference whether anything is punched in the columns skipped over; any punching will be ignored.

On output, the effect is to insert w blank printing positions in the line at this point in the scanning process.

Field Specification A (Alphanumeric)

This is of the form Aw. The variable involved must be alphanumeric for the field specification to be meaningful. An alphanumeric variable, if it is allowed by the particular FORTRAN system, is one that is named like a floating point variable but to which an alphanumeric "value" is given. This may be done with an input statement in which the field specification is A, or by an arithmetic statement in which the right-hand side is a Hollerith field specification. For instance, to give the alphanumeric variable HEAD the value X REAL we could write the statement

$$HEAD = 6HX\ REAL$$

The blank between X and REAL is intended; it is counted as a character. Any character available in the computer, including letters, digits, and special symbols such as punctuation marks, may be used in this way.

Usage varies for alphanumeric variables partly because different computers have different limits on the number of characters that can be placed in one variable. The interested reader should consult the appropriate manual for his system.

A1.4   Additional FORMAT statement features

Just as it is possible to repeat a field specification by writing a repetition number in front of it, it is also possible to repeat a *group* of field specifications. The group is enclosed in parentheses, and the desired number of repetitions is written before it. For instance, suppose that eight fields on a card are alternately described by I2 and F10.0. We can write 4(I2, F10.0) to get the desired action. This is *not* the same as 4I2, 4F10.0, which would describe a card with four I2 fields, then four F10.0 fields, rather than the intended alternation. Only one such level of grouping is permitted; that is, parentheses within parentheses are not permitted.

When the list of an input or output statement is used to transmit more than one *record* (card or line), with the different records having different formats, a slash (/) is used to separate the format specifications for the different records. For example, suppose that two cards are to be read with a single READ statement; the first card has only a four-digit integer and the second has six floating point numbers. We could write

$$FORMAT(I4/6E14.0)$$

It is possible to specify a special format for the first one or more records and a different format from the first group for all subsequent records. This is done by enclosing the last record specifications in parentheses. For instance, if the first card of a deck has an integer and a floating point number and all following contain two integers and a floating point number, we could write

FORMAT (I4, E14.0/(2I4, E14.0))

A slash always indicates the end of one record and the beginning of a new one. The closing parenthesis of the FORMAT statement marks the end of a record. The skipping of entire records (on the printer, usually) is called for by writing successive slashes. Note that the skipping of n records is called for by $n + 1$ successive slashes.

We are now able to summarize the scanning process. The list in the input or output statement specifies the variables to be transmitted and their sequence (taking into account any indexing). The associated FORMAT statement specifies the length and format of each field, as well as the length of each record if there is more than one. As the variables in the list are transmitted, the FORMAT statement is scanned from left to right to find the field specification associated with each variable. The scanning, of course, takes into account any repetition of field specification or of groups of them. Whenever Hollerith field specifications are encountered in scanning the FORMAT statement, they are handled in the proper place without the transmission of variables from the list. The transmission of variables is ended only when all named in the list have been moved, but any remaining Hollerith field specifications will be dealt with even after the transmission of the last variable named in the list. If variables remain to be transmitted when the last field specification in the FORMAT statement has been used, scanning begins again with the first field specification in the last set of parentheses in the FORMAT statement.

Examples of many of the advanced features discussed here have appeared in a few of the programs toward the end of the text, particularly Figures 9.9, 9.11, 10.10, and the answer to Exercise 19, Chapter 11.

A1.5 Magnetic tape operations

An important feature of all large computers is the availability of magnetic tape, which is used in two rather different ways.

The more common application is in speeding up input and output operations. Reading cards at a few hundred a minute is very slow compared with the internal arithmetic speed of a large computer and printing is little better. Therefore, except when the amount of input and output is very small, the usual procedure is to use magnetic tape to reduce the wasted computer time. This is done, in the case of input, by first taping the information on the cards with a separate card-to-tape converter that is not connected to the computer. While this is being done, the computer can be used for other work. When the problem is ready to be run, the magnetic tape is mounted on a tape unit that is connected to the computer, and the problem data is read in at about a hundred times the speed of card reading.

Similarly, problem results are written on magnetic tape rather than directly printed. When the problem is completed, the output tape is moved from the computer to a separate tape unit connected to a printer. The results are then printed while the computer is engaged in other work.

This perhaps sounds like more trouble than it is. In practice, the whole operation runs very smoothly, and the programmer ordinarily has nothing to do with the mechanics of the tape handling. The net result is a considerable increase in computer efficiency.

The other, less common use of magnetic tape provides intermediate storage for results during the solution of a problem. For instance, some problems involve very large arrays, which may be too big to fit in computer storage at one time. In such a case the intermediate results can be written on magnetic tape as they are computed and read back when they are needed.

The two tape applications require two different kinds of statements because of the simpler way the tape can be read and written if it is to be used only by the computer than if it must be usable by other equipment as well.

The READ INPUT TAPE statement is used to read a tape produced on the card-to-tape converter. It is handled just like a READ statement, with one minor exception: it is necessary to specify the number of the tape unit on which the reel of tape is mounted. This tape number is written before the FORMAT statement number. A typical statement would be

READ INPUT TAPE 5, 169, I, A, X1, SEG

The 5 specifies tape unit 5; in all other respects the statement is the same as a READ statement. The requirements of the FORMAT statement are the same, list indexing is the same, and the scanning process is the same.

The WRITE OUTPUT TAPE statement is similarly analogous to the PRINT statement. A typical statement would be

WRITE OUTPUT TAPE 6, 401, (X(I), Y(I), I = 1,6)

The choice of the tape unit is determined largely by the conventions established by the particular computer installation.

For operations with intermediate tapes, which are not involved with card reading or with printing, the READ TAPE and WRITE TAPE statements are used. These statements are different from other input and output statements because they do not require a FORMAT statement. A typical statement would be

WRITE TAPE 8, ARRAY

ARRAY is assumed to be large array; the name is written without subscripts, so that the entire array will be written. *The tape so written cannot be printed* because the data words are written just as they appear in computer storage, without conversion to a form suitable for printing. Its only meaningful function is to read it back into storage with a READ TAPE statement.

Three other statements are related to tape operations, although they do not themselves transmit information. BACKSPACE n, where n is the number of a tape unit, backs up the tape beyond one record. A record, in this case, means either the information corresponding to one card or printer line or all the information written by one WRITE TAPE statement. END FILE n puts a mark on the tape that will be recognized by the tape-to-printer converter as signifying the end of a printer run. The REWIND n statement returns the tape to its beginning. It may then be removed, if it is an input or output tape, or re-employed, if it is an intermediate tape. (Writing new information on a tape automatically erases what had been on it before.)

—Appendix 2

Miscellaneous Data

A Chebyshev polynomials

$T_0(x) = 1$
$T_1(x) = x$
$T_2(x) = 2x^2 - 1$
$T_3(x) = 4x^3 - 3x$
$T_4(x) = 8x^4 - 8x^2 + 1$
$T_5(x) = 16x^5 - 20x^3 + 5x$
$T_6(x) = 32x^6 - 48x^4 + 18x^2 - 1$
$T_7(x) = 64x^7 - 112x^5 + 56x^3 - 7x$
$T_8(x) = 128x^8 - 256x^6 + 160x^4 - 32x^2 + 1$
$T_9(x) = 256x^9 - 576x^7 + 432x^5 - 120x^3 + 9x$
$T_{10}(x) = 512x^{10} - 1280x^8 + 1120x^6 - 400x^4 + 50x^2 - 1$
$T_{11}(x) = 1024x^{11} - 2816x^9 + 2816x^7 - 1232x^5 + 220x^3 - 11x$

B Powers of x as functions of T_n (x)

$1 = T_0$
$x = T_1$
$x^2 = \frac{1}{2}(T_0 + T_2)$
$x^3 = \frac{1}{4}(3T_1 + T_3)$
$x^4 = \frac{1}{8}(3T_0 + 4T_2 + T_4)$
$x^5 = \frac{1}{16}(10T_1 + 5T_3 + T_5)$
$x^6 = \frac{1}{32}(10T_0 + 15T_2 + 6T_4 + T_6)$
$x^7 = \frac{1}{64}(35T_1 + 21T_3 + 7T_5 + T_7)$
$x^8 = \frac{1}{128}(35T_0 + 56T_2 + 28T_4 + 8T_6 + T_8)$
$x^9 = \frac{1}{256}(126T_1 + 84T_3 + 36T_5 + 9T_7 + T_9)$

$$x^{10} = \tfrac{1}{512}(126T_0 + 210T_2 + 120T_4 + 45T_6 + 10T_8 + T_{10})$$
$$x^{11} = \tfrac{1}{1024}(462T_1 + 330T_3 + 165T_5 + 55T_7 + 11T_9 + T_{11})$$

C   Formulas for telescoping power series

$$x = T_1$$
$$x^2 = \tfrac{1}{2}(1 + T_2)$$
$$x^3 = \tfrac{1}{4}(3x + T_3)$$
$$x^4 = \tfrac{1}{8}(8x^2 - 1 + T_4)$$
$$x^5 = \tfrac{1}{16}(20x^3 - 5x + T_5)$$
$$x^6 = \tfrac{1}{32}(48x^4 - 18x^2 + 1 + T_6)$$
$$x^7 = \tfrac{1}{64}(112x^5 - 56x^3 + 7x + T_7)$$
$$x^8 = \tfrac{1}{128}(256x^6 - 160x^4 + 32x^2 - 1 + T_8)$$
$$x^9 = \tfrac{1}{256}(576x^7 - 432x^5 + 120x^3 - 9x + T_9)$$
$$x^{10} = \tfrac{1}{512}(1280x^8 - 1120x^6 + 400x^4 - 50x^2 + 1 + T_{10})$$
$$x^{11} = \tfrac{1}{1024}(2816x^9 - 2816x^7 + 1232x^5 - 220x^3 + 11x + T_{11})$$

D   Approximations for some elementary functions

(From Duijvestijn and Dekkers, *op. cit.*, p. 73, Tables 8, 28, 36, 45, and 30)

1. $$\sin\left(\frac{\pi x}{2}\right) = c_1 + c_3 x^3 + c_5 x^5 + c_7 x^7, \qquad -1 \leq x \leq 1$$

$$c_1 = \quad 1.570790988$$
$$c_3 = -0.645892663$$
$$c_5 = \quad 0.079433971$$
$$c_7 = -0.004332882$$

The truncation error is
$$|e_T| \leq 0.6 \cdot 10^{-6}$$

2. $e^x = 1 + \dfrac{x}{\dfrac{-x}{2} + \left(\dfrac{k_0 + k_1 x^2}{1 + k_2 x^2}\right)}$, $-\log_e \sqrt{2} \leq x \leq \log_e \sqrt{2}$

where $k_0 = 1.00000\ 00020\ 967$
$\quad\quad\ k_1 = 0.09997\ 43507\ 186$
$\quad\quad\ k_2 = 0.01664\ 11490\ 538$

and
$$|e_T| \leq 10^{-10}$$

3.
$$\log_e (1 + x) = k_0 + \cfrac{x}{k_1 + \cfrac{x}{k_2 + \cfrac{x}{k_3 + \cfrac{x}{k_4 + \cfrac{x}{k_5}}}}}, \qquad 0 \leq x \leq 1$$

where $k_0 = 0.00000\ 00894$
$k_1 = 1.00000\ 91365$
$k_2 = 2.00058\ 59000$
$k_3 = 3.03119\ 32666$
$k_4 = 1.07877\ 48225$
$k_5 = 8.89527\ 84060$

and

$$|e_T| \leq 10^{-7}$$

4.
$$\tan\left(\frac{\pi x}{4}\right) = x \left[k_0 + \cfrac{x^2}{k_1 + \cfrac{x^2}{k_2 + \cfrac{x^2}{k_3}}} \right], \qquad -1 \leq x \leq 1$$

where $k_0 = 0.78539\ 80289$
$k_1 = 6.19223\ 44479$
$k_2 = -0.65458\ 87679$
$k_3 = 491.00139\ 34779$

and

$$|e_T| \leq 0.2 \cdot 10^{-7}$$

5.
$$\arctan x = x \left[k_0 + \cfrac{x^2}{k_1 + \cfrac{x^2}{k_2 + \cfrac{x^2}{k_3 + \cfrac{x^2}{k_4}}}} \right], \qquad -1 \leq x \leq 1$$

where $k_0 = 0.99999\ 752$
$k_1 = -3.00064\ 286$
$k_2 = -0.55703\ 890$
$k_3 = -17.03715\ 998$
$k_4 = -0.20556\ 880$

$$|e_T| \leq 0.2 \cdot 10^{-6}$$

Gauss quadrature abscissas and coefficients

	μ	A
$n = 2$	$\pm 0.57735\ 02692$	$1.00000\ 00000$
$n = 3$	$\pm 0.77459\ 66692$	$0.55555\ 55556$
	$0.00000\ 00000$	$0.88888\ 88889$
$n = 4$	$\pm 0.86113\ 63116$	$0.34785\ 48451$
	$\pm 0.33998\ 10436$	$0.65214\ 51549$
$n = 5$	$\pm 0.90617\ 98459$	$0.23692\ 68851$
	$\pm 0.53846\ 93101$	$0.47862\ 86705$
	$0.00000\ 00000$	$0.56888\ 88889$
$n = 6$	$\pm 0.93246\ 95142$	$0.17132\ 44924$
	$\pm 0.66120\ 93865$	$0.36076\ 15730$
	$\pm 0.23861\ 91861$	$0.46791\ 39346$

Answers to Selected Exercises

There are several acceptable answers to many of the exercises on programming questions. The one shown here is sometimes "better" than other possibilities, but there is sufficient space to define the criterion of "goodness" in only a few cases. In other problems there are several equally "good" answers; for instance, it makes no difference whether one writes $A = B + C$ or $A = C + B$. In short, the answers given here are correct, but not ordinarily *uniquely* correct. If another answer can be shown to be equivalent, it must be accepted unless other criteria are specified.

Chapter 1

Section 1.4 (page 7)

1. 256., 2.56, $-43000.$, $1.0E + 12$, $4.92E - 7$, -10.0, $-1.E - 16$.
3. 12,345.0 (comma not permitted); $+234$ (no decimal point); 1.6E63 (too large in most systems); $1E - 7$ (no decimal point).
5. Yes.
6. $-234.$ (decimal point not permitted); 23,400 (comma not permitted); 1E12 (E not permitted); $+1000000000000$ (too large in most systems).

Section 1.5 (page 9)

1. Fixed point: I, IJK, LARGE, KAPPA.
   Floating point: G, GAMMA, BT07TH, ZCUBED, CDC160, DELTA A1P4, ALGOL.
   Unacceptable: GAMMA421 (too many characters), IJK* (* not permitted); $J79 - 12$ ($-$ not permitted); R(2)19 (parentheses not permitted); ZSQUARED (too many characters); 12AT7 (does not begin with a letter); 2N173 (does not begin with a letter); EPSILON (too many

characters); A1.4 (decimal point not permitted); FORTRAN (too many characters).

Section 1.6 (page 14)

1. a. X + Y**3
   d. A + B/C
   f. A + B/(C + D)
   h. ((A + B)/(C + D))**2 + X**2
   j. 1. + X + X**2/2. + X**3/6.
   k. (X/Y)**(G − 1.0)
2. b. (X + 2.0)/(Y + 4.0). Constants may be written in any other equivalent form, such as (X + 2.)/(Y + 4.).
   e. ((X + A + 3.1416)/(2.0 * Z))**2
   g. (X/Y)**(R − 1.0)
   j. A + X*(B + X*(C + D*X))

Section 1.8 (page 19)

1. a. 13.0, floating.
   b. zero, floating.
   e. 4, fixed.
   f. 4.0, floating.
   k. 1.3333332, floating.
   n. 8.0, floating (could be 7.9999999 or 8.00000001).
   o. 5, fixed.
3. a. DELTA = BETA + 2.0
   c. C = SQRTF(A**2 + B**2) or
      C = SQRTF(A*A + B*B)
   d. R = 1.414214
   g. Y = COSF(2.0 * X) * SQRTF(X / 2.0)
   h. G = G + 2.0
4. a. AREA = 2. * P * R * SINF(3.1416 / P)
   c. ARC = 2.0 * SQRTF(Y**2 + 1.3333*X**2)
   e. S = −COSF(X)**(P + 1.0)/(P + 1.0)
   f. G = 0.5* LOGF((1. + SINF(X))/(1. − SINF(X)))
      Preferably written as two statements to avoid computing the sine function twice:
      S = SINF(X)
      G = 0.5 * LOGF((1. + S)/(1. − S))
   i. E = X*ATANF(X/A) − A/2.*LOGF(A**2 + X**2)
   l. Q = (2./(3.1416*X))**0.5*(SINF(X)). Since
      $(2/x)^{1/2}(1/\pi)^{1/2} = \sqrt{2/\pi}/\sqrt{x} = 0.7978/\sqrt{x}$,
      this can be written more compactly and thus requires less time in the object program:
      Q = 0.7978/SQRTF(X)*SINF(X)
   n. Y = 2.5065*X**(X + 1.)*EXPF(−X)

Section 1.9 (page 27)

1. READ 94, A, B, C
    94 FORMAT (3F10.0)
    RADICL = SQRTF(B**2 − 4. * A * C)
    X1 = (−B + RADICL)/(2. * A)
    X2 = (−B − RADICL)/(2. * A)
    PRINT 93, A, B, C, X1, X2
    93 FORMAT (5E20.8)

3. READ 97, A, E, H, P
    97 FORMAT (4F10.0)
    X = E*H*P/(SINF(A)*(H**4/16. + H**2*P**2))
    PRINT 98, A, E, H, P, X
    98 FORMAT (5E20.8)

5. READ 300, A, X, S
    300 FORMAT (3F10.0)
    Y = SQRTF(X**2 − A**2)
    Z = X*S/2. −A**2/2.*LOGF(ABSF(X + S))
    PRINT 50, A, X, S, Y, Z
    50 FORMAT (5E20.8)

Section 1.10 (page 30)

1. IF(X − Y) 11, 11, 12
    11 BIG = Y
    GO TO 13
    12 BIG = X
    13 Continuation of program

4. 400 IF (THETA − 6.2832) 402, 401, 401
    401 THETA = THETA − 6.2832
    GO TO 400
    402 Continuation

5. IF (ABSF(XREAL) − 1.) 16, 82, 82
    16 IF (ABSF(XIMAG) − 1.) 81, 82, 82

6. IF (SQRTF(XREAL**2 + XIMAG**2) − 1.) 187, 459, 459

10a. IF (X− 0.999) 67, 63, 21
    21 IF (X − 1.001) 63, 63, 67

10b. IF (ABSF(X − 1.) − 0.001) 63, 63, 67

Section 1.11 (page 32)

1. READ 20, ANNERN
    IF (ANNERN − 2000.00) 40, 40, 50
    40 TAX = 0.00
    GO TO 100
    50 IF (ANNERN − 5000.00) 60, 60, 70
    60 TAX = 0.02 * (ANNERN − 2000.00)
    GO TO 100
    70 TAX = 60.00 + 0.05 * (ANNERN − 5000.00)

```
100  PRINT 30, ANNERN, TAX
 20  FORMAT (E10.0)
 30  FORMAT (2E20.8)
     STOP
     END
```

3.
```
     X = 1.0
 61  Y = 16.7*X + 9.2*X**2 - 1.02*X**3
     PRINT 62, X, Y
 62  FORMAT (2E20.8)
     IF (X - 9.9) 63, 64, 64
 63  X = X + 0.1
     GO TO 61
 64  STOP
     END
```

4. For the first suggested method replace the IF statement in solution above with IF(ABSF(X−9.9) − 1.E−4) 63, 64, 64. Second suggested method leads to the following program, if we note that there are 90 values to be computed.

```
     X = 1.0
     N = 1
 61  Y = 16.7*X + 9.2*X**2 - 1.02*X**3
     PRINT 62, X, Y
 62  FORMAT (2E20.8)
     IF (N - 90) 63, 64, 64
 63  X = X + 0.1
     N = N + 1
     GO TO 61
 64  STOP
     END
```

Chapter 2

1. Write
$$e = iR$$
where e = volts
   i = amperes
   R = ohms
and let e_e, e_i, e_R be the respective absolute errors. Then from the problem data

$$e_R = 10\% \text{ of } 10 \text{ ohms} = \pm 1$$

$$e_i = \pm 0.1 \text{ amp}$$

Then
$$e_e = Re_i + ie_R$$
$$= 10 \cdot (\pm 0.1) + 2.0 \cdot (\pm 1)$$

and
$$|e_e| \le 10 \cdot |\pm 0.1| + 2.0 \cdot |\pm 1| = 3 \text{ volts}$$

Therefore
$$e = 20 \pm 3 \text{ volts}$$

The relative error is
$$\left| \frac{e_e}{e} \right| \le \left| \frac{\pm 3}{20} \right| = 0.15$$

Also
$$\left| \frac{e_e}{e} \right| \le \left| \frac{e_i}{i} \right| + \left| \frac{e_R}{R} \right| = \left| \frac{0.1}{2} \right| + |\pm 10\%| = 0.05 + 0.10 = 0.15$$

5. $u = a + a$

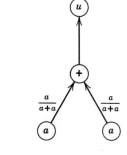

$$\frac{e_u}{u} = \frac{a}{a + a} \cdot i_a + \frac{a}{a + a} \cdot i_a + r$$
$$= i_a + r$$
$$\left| \frac{e_u}{u} \right| \le |i_a| + |r| \le 10^{-t+1}$$

$$v = 2a$$

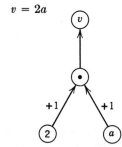

$$\frac{e_v}{v} = +1 \cdot i_2 + 1 \cdot i_a + r$$

$$= +1 \cdot 0 + 1 \cdot i_a + r$$

$$\left| \frac{e_v}{v} \right| \le |i_a| + |r| \le 10^{-t+1}$$

6. $u = a + a + a$

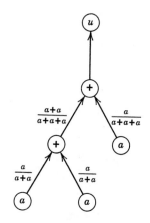

$$\frac{e_u}{u} = \frac{a+a}{a+a+a} \left(\frac{a}{a+a} \cdot i_a + \frac{a}{a+a} \cdot i_a + r_1 \right) + \frac{a}{a+a+a} \cdot i_a + r_2$$

$$= \frac{1}{3} i_a + \frac{1}{3} i_a + \frac{2}{3} r_1 + \frac{1}{3} i_a + r_2$$

$$\left| \frac{e_u}{u} \right| \le |i_a| + \left| \frac{2}{3} r_1 \right| + |r_2| \le \frac{8}{3} \cdot 5 \cdot 10^{-t}$$

$$u = 3a$$

$$\frac{e_v}{v} = +1 \cdot i_3 + 1 \cdot i_a + r$$

$$= +1 \cdot 0 + i_a + r$$

$$\left| \frac{e_v}{v} \right| \le |i_a| + |r| \le 2 \cdot 5 \cdot 10^{-t}$$

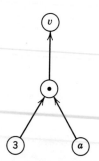

If $a = .6992$, $a + a = 1.3984$, which rounds to 1.398, $(a + a) + a = 2.0972$, which rounds to $2.097 = u$. $3a = 2.0976$, which rounds to $2.098 = v$.

8. $u = x \cdot (x \cdot (x \cdot x))$

$$\frac{e_u}{u} = i_x + i_x + r_1 + i_x + r_2 + i_x + r_3$$

$$\left|\frac{e_u}{u}\right| \le |4i_x| + |r_1| + |r_2| + |r_3| \le 7 \cdot 5 \cdot 10^{-t}$$

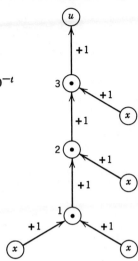

$v = (x^2)^2$

$$\frac{e_v}{v} = i_x + i_x + r_1 + i_x + i_x + r_2 + r_3$$

$$\left|\frac{e_v}{v}\right| \le |4i_x| + |r_1| + |r_2| + |r_3| \le 7 \cdot 5 \cdot 10^{-t}$$

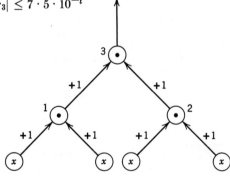

11. $u = ax + bx^2$

With all inherent errors taken to be zero,

$$\frac{e_u}{u} = \frac{bx^2}{ax + bx^2}(r_1 + r_2) + \frac{ax}{ax + bx^2} \cdot r_3 + r_4$$

$$\left|\frac{e_u}{u}\right| \le \left|\frac{a}{a + bx} \cdot r_3\right| + \left|\frac{bx}{a + bx} \cdot r_1\right| + \left|\frac{bx}{a + bx} \cdot r_2\right| + |r_4|$$

$$\leq 5 \cdot 10^{-t} + \frac{bx}{a + bx} \cdot 5 \cdot 10^{-t} + 5 \cdot 10^{-t}$$

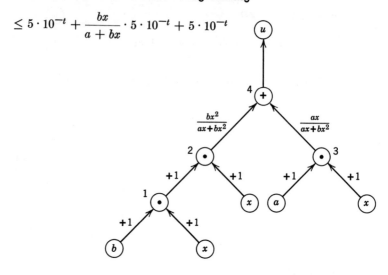

$$v = x \cdot (a + bx)$$

$$\frac{e_v}{v} = \frac{bx}{a + bx} \cdot r_1 + r_2 + r_3$$

$$\left| \frac{e_v}{v} \right| \leq \left| \frac{bx}{a + bx} \right| \cdot 5 \cdot 10^{-t} + 5 \cdot 10^{-t} + 5 \cdot 10^{-t}$$

Let the symbol $\simeq$ stand for the rounded result.   Then

$$bx = 0.29885994 \simeq 0.2989$$
$$bx^2 = 0.12858678 \simeq 0.1286$$
$$ax = 0.32802750 \simeq 0.3280$$
$$ax + bx^2 = 0.4566 = u$$
$$a + bx = 1.0614 \simeq 0.1061 \cdot 10^1$$
$$x(a + bx) = 0.4564422 \simeq 0.4564 = v$$

The exact answer is 0.456597.

16.
$$u = \frac{a - b}{c}$$

With all inherent errors taken to be zero,

$$\frac{e_u}{u} = r_1 + r_2$$

$$\left| \frac{e_u}{u} \right| = |r_1| + |r_2| \le 10^{-t+1}$$

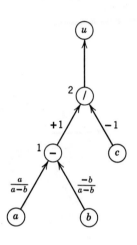

$$v = \frac{a}{c} - \frac{b}{c}$$

$$\frac{e_v}{v} = \frac{a/c}{a/c - b/c} r_1 - \frac{b/c}{a/c - b/c} r_2 + r_3$$

$$= \frac{a}{a - b} r_1 - \frac{b}{a - b} r_2 + r_3$$

$$\left| \frac{e_v}{v} \right| \le \left| \frac{a}{a - b} r_1 \right| + \left| \frac{b}{a - b} r_2 \right| + |r_3|$$

If $a \simeq b$ this is approximately equal to

$$\frac{2a}{a - b} \cdot 5 \cdot 10^{-t} + 5 \cdot 10^{-t}$$

which can be very large if $a - b$ is small.

$$u = \frac{(a - b)}{c} = \frac{(0.41 - 0.36)}{0.70} = \frac{0.05}{0.70} = 0.071428 \simeq 0.71 \cdot 10^{-1}$$

$$v = \frac{a}{c} - \frac{b}{c} = \frac{0.41}{0.70} - \frac{0.36}{0.70} = 0.5857 - 0.51428 \simeq 0.59 - 0.51 = 0.80 \cdot 10^{-1}$$

18. $\quad x_1 = \dfrac{-b + \sqrt{b^2 - 4ac}}{2a} \qquad\qquad x_1' = \dfrac{-2c}{b + \sqrt{b^2 - 4ac}}$

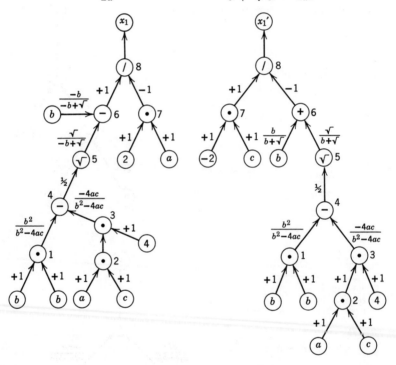

$$\frac{e_{x_1}}{x_1} = \frac{\sqrt{b^2 - 4ac}}{-b + \sqrt{b^2 - 4ac}} \left[\frac{1}{2} \left(\frac{b^2}{b^2 - 4ac} r_1 - \frac{4ac}{b^2 - 4ac} (r_2 + r_3) + r_4 \right) + r_5 \right. $$
$$\left. + r_6 - r_7 + r_8 \right]$$

with $b^2 \gg 4ac$, this gives approximately

$$\left| \frac{e_{x_1}}{x_1} \right| \leq \frac{b}{-b + \sqrt{b^2 - 4ac}} \left(\frac{|r_1| + |r_4|}{2} + |r_5| \right)$$

which can be very large.

$$\frac{e_{x_1}'}{x_1'} = \frac{-\sqrt{b^2 - 4ac}}{b + \sqrt{b^2 - 4ac}}\left[\frac{1}{2}\left(\frac{b^2}{b^2 - 4ac}r_1 - \frac{4ac}{b^2 - 4ac}(r_2 + r_3) + r_4\right) + r_5\right]$$
$$- r_6 + r_7 + r_8$$

with $b^2 \gg 4a$, this gives approximately

$$\left|\frac{e_{x_1}'}{x_1'}\right| \leq \frac{1}{2}\left[\frac{1}{2}(|r_1| + |r_4|) + |r_5|\right] + |r_6| + |r_7| + |r_8|$$

$$x_1 = \frac{-0.4002 + \sqrt{0.16016004 - 0.00032}}{2}$$

$$\frac{-0.4002 + \sqrt{0.1602 - 0.0003}}{2}$$

$$= \frac{-0.4002 + 0.3999}{2} = -0.1500 \cdot 10^{-3}$$

$$x_1' = \frac{-0.00016}{0.4002 + 0.3999}$$

$$= -0.2000 \cdot 10^{-3} = \text{exact root}$$

Chapter 3

1. a. 4 terms (through $x^7/7!$);   6 terms.
   c. 6 terms (through $1/9 \cdot x^9$);   13 terms.

6. $a_0 = a_2 = a_3 = a_4 = a_4 = 0$; $a_1 = 1$

8. a. $a_0 = \frac{2}{\pi}$; $a_1 = 0$; $a_2 = \frac{-4}{3\pi}$; $a_3 = 0$; $a_4 = \frac{-4}{15\pi}$

   b. $\sqrt{1 - x^2} = \frac{2}{15\pi}(23 - 4x^2 - 16x^4)$

   c. At $x = 0.5$ the Chebyshev series gives 0.891268; the correct value is 0.866025; the Taylor series is $\sqrt{1 - x^2} = 1 - x^2/2 - x^4/8$, which gives 0.867188.

10. $T_0^*(x) = 1$; $T_1^*(x) = 2x - 1$; $T_2^*(x) = 8x^2 - 8x + 1$;
   $T_3^*(x) = 32x^3 - 48x^2 + 18x - 1$

12. $e^x \simeq 1 + \left(1 + \frac{7}{64 \cdot 7!}\right)x + \frac{x^2}{2!} + \frac{1}{3!}\left(1 - \frac{56}{64 \cdot 7!}\right)x^3$

$$+ \frac{x^4}{4!} + \frac{1}{5!}\left(1 + \frac{112}{64 \cdot 7!}\right)x^5 + \frac{x^6}{6!}$$

19. a. EX = 1.0 + X*(1.0 + X*(0.5 + X*(0.166667 + X*
                     (0.0416667 + X*(0.00833333 + X*0.00138889)))))
   b. EX = 1.0 + X*(1.0 + X/2.0*(1.0 + X/3.0*
                     (1.0 + X/4.0*(1.0 + X/5.0*(1.0 + X/6.0)))))

20.

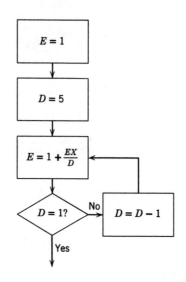

$$E = 1.0$$
$$D = 5.0$$
29 $E = 1.0 + E*X/D$
$$IF(D - 1.0)\ 34,\ 34,\ 47$$
47 $D = D - 1.0$
$$GO\ TO\ 29$$
34 Continuation

26. SINE $= -3.66519143 * (X - 11.47221432 / (X + 8.03055026 / X))$

28. $b_1 = \dfrac{\pi}{2}$

$b_3 = -\dfrac{31}{294}\left(\dfrac{\pi}{2}\right)^3$

$c_2 = \dfrac{3}{49}\left(\dfrac{\pi}{2}\right)^2$

$c_4 = \dfrac{11}{5880}\left(\dfrac{\pi}{2}\right)^4$

31. $k_1 = a$

$k_2 = \dfrac{1}{b - ad}$

$$k_3 = \frac{(b - ad)^2}{(b - ad)d - c}$$

$$k_4 = \frac{(b - ad)d - c}{(b - ad)c}$$

Chapter 5

1. 0.7071.   No, because for x near $+0.5$, $f'(x)$ is greater than 1.

4. $x_{n+1} = x_n - \dfrac{x_n^3 - c}{3x_n^2} = \dfrac{2x_n^3 + c}{3x_n^2}$

7. For the root of interest, $x \neq 0$, so divide through by it first to simplify: $0.1x - \log x = 0$. If we convert to natural logarithms to take the derivative, the iteration formula can be simplified to

$$x_{n+1} = x_n - \frac{x_n - 10 \log_{10} x_n}{1 - \dfrac{4.3429}{x_n}}$$

The root is $x = 1.3713$.

9. 1.100, -2.300, 2.673.

12. $x = 2.753;\ |\epsilon| \simeq 0.127$.

21.   X = A
    26 XNEW = (X**2 + A)/(2.0 * X)
        IF (ABSF(X − XNEW) − 0.0001) 21, 24, 24
        IF (ABSF(X − XNEW)) 21, 24, 24
    24 X = XNEW
        GO TO 26
    21 SQRTA = XNEW

22.   READ 8, X0, A0, A1, A2, A3, A4, A5, A6
     8 FORMAT (8F10.0)
        FXO = A0 + X0*(A1 + X0*(A2 + X0*(A3 +
     1   X0*(A4 + X0*(A5 + X0*A6)))))
        PRINT 9, A0, A1, A2, A3, A4, A5, A6, X0, FX0
     9 FORMAT (9F15.6)

33. $x = 1.932$, $y = 0.517$.   Yes.

Chapter 6

9. a. 1.00018
   b. 1.08193
   c. 1.00491
   d. 1.58190

For high accuracy, it is better to integrate backward to reduce roundoff error.

10. a. GAUSS = 5.0 * EXPF(−5.0) *

    1   (0.17132449*(EXPF(5.0*0.93246951)

                              + EXPF(−5.0*0.93246951))

    1 + 0.36076157*(EXPF(5.0*0.66120939)

                              + EXPF(−5.0*0.66120939))

    1 + 0.46791393*(EXPF(5.0*0.23861919)

                              + EXPF(−5.0*0.23861919)))

  b.   I = 1
       SUM = EXPF(−10.0)
   23 X = I
       SUM = SUM + 2.0 * EXPF(−10.0 + X)
       I = I + 1
       IF(I − 10) 23, 39, 39
   39 TRAP = 0.5 * (SUM + 1.0)

  c.   I = 1
       SUM = EXPF(−10.0)
   23 X = I
       SUM = SUM + 4.0 * EXPF(−10.0 + X)
       SUM = SUM + 2.0 * EXPF(−9.0 + X)
       I = I + 2
       IF(I − 9) 23, 39, 39
   39 SIMP = 0.33333333 * (1.0 + (SUM + 4.0 * EXPF(−1.0)))

  d.   I = 0
       RECT = 0.0
   23 X = I
       RECT = RECT + EXPF(−10.0 + X)
       I = I + 1
       IF(I − 10) 23, 39, 39
   39

'13. In Figure 6.7 replace statements 32–61 with the following:

   32 END1 = 1.0/(A**5*(EXPF(1.432/(T*A)) − 1.0))
      END2 = 1.0/(B**5*(EXPF(1.432/(T*B)) − 1.0))
      BMH = 1.0/((B−H)**5*(EXPF(1.432/(T*(B−H))) − 1.0))
      SIMP = 64.77*H/3.0*(4.0*(SUM4 + BMH) + 2.0*SUM2
    1   + END1 + END2)/T**4
      TRAP = 64.77*H/2.0*(2.0*(SUM4 + SUM2 + BMH)
    1   + END1 + END2)/T**4
      PRINT 61, T, SIMP, TRAP
   61 FORMAT (3E20.8)

29. a. 13, 47.
    b. 7, 30, 53.
    c. 4, 20, 40, 56.

Chapter 7

1.   DIMENSION X(3)
      DIST = SQRTF(X(1)**2 + X(2)**2 + X(3)**2)
3.   DIMENSION A(2, 2), B(2, 2), C(2, 2)
      C(1, 1) = A(1, 1) * B(1, 1) + A(1, 2) * B(2, 1)
      C(1, 2) = A(1, 1) * B(1, 2) + A(1, 2) * B(2, 2)
      C(2, 1) = A(2, 1) * B(1, 1) + A(2, 2) * B(2, 1)
      C(2, 2) = A(2, 1) * B(1, 2) + A(2, 2) * B(2, 2)
5. Without DO statement:

      DIMENSION A(30), B(30)
      I = 1
      D = 0.0
   23 D = D + (A(I) − B(I))**2
      I = I + 1
      IF (I − 30) 23, 23, 39
   39 D = SQRTF(D)

With DO statement:

      DIMENSION A(30), B(30)
      DO 23 I = 1, 30
   23 D = D + (A(I) − B(I))**2
      D = SQRTF(D)
6. Without DO statement:

      DIMENSION X(50), DX(49)
      I = 1
   23 DX(I) = X(I+1) − X(I)
      I = I + 1
      IF (I − 49) 23, 23, 39
   39

With DO statement

      DIMENSION X(50), DX(49)
      DO 23 I = 1, 49
   23 DX(I) = X(I+1) − X(I)
9.   DIMENSION Y(50)
      S = Y(I) + U*(Y(I+1) − Y(I−1))/2.0
     1   + U**2 * (Y(I+1) − 2.0*Y(I) + Y(I−1))/2.0

11. Without DO statement:

```
    DIMENSION A(7), B(7)
    READ 21, A
 21 FORMAT (7F10.0)
    READ 21, B
    I = 1
    SUM = 0.0
 23 SUM = SUM + A(I)*B(I)
    I = I + 1
    IF (I - 8) 23, 39, 39
 39 ANORM = SQRTF(SUM)
    PRINT 22, ANORM
 22 FORMAT (E20.8)
```

With DO statement:

```
    DIMENSION A(7), B(7)
    READ 21, A
 21 FORMAT (7F10.0)
    READ 21, B
    SUM = 0.0
    DO 23 I = 1, 7
 23 SUM = SUM + A(I)*B(I)
    ANORM = SQRTF(SUM)
    PRINT 22, ANORM
 22 FORMAT (E20.8)
```

13.
```
    DIMENSION M(20)
    DO 23 I = 1, 20
 23 M(I) = I * M(I)
```

14.
```
    DIMENSION R(40), S(40), T(40)
    DO 32 I = 1, M
 32 T(I) = R(I) + S(I)
```

16.
```
    DIMENSION F(50)
    MM1 = M - 1
    DO 43 I = 2, MM1
 42 F(I) = (F(I - 1) + F(I) + F(I + 1))/3.0
```

17.
```
    DIMENSION B(50)
    BIGB = B(1)
    NBIGB = 1
    DO 40 I = 2, 50
    IF(BIGB - B(I)) 60, 40, 40
 60 BIGB = B(I)
    NBIGB = I
 40 CONTINUE
```

20.
```
    DIMENSION A(15, 15), X(15), B(15)
    DO 61 I = 1, 15
```

```
        B(I) = 0.0
        DO 61 J = 1, 15
    61  B(I) = B(I) + A(I, J)*X(J)
22.     DIMENSION RST(20, 20)
        DPROD = RST(1, 1)
        DO 1 I = 2, 20
     1  DPROD = DPROD * RST(I, I)
23.     DO 67 I = 100, 300
        X = I
        X = X / 100.0
        Y = 41.926 * SQRTF(1.0 + X*X) + X**0.333333 * EXPF(X)
    67  PRINT 68, X, Y
    68  FORMAT (2E20.8)
```

27. Many ways are possible.   Here is one.

```
        SUM = 0.0
        DO 93 I = 12, 48, 2
        X = I
        X = X / 10.0
    93  SUM = SUM + SQRTF(1.0 + X**2) * EXPF(-X)
        TRAP = 0.1*(SQRTF(2.0)*EXPF(-1.0) + 2.0*SUM
                                 + SQRTF(26.0)*EXPF(-5.0))
```

Here is another possibility.

```
        SUM = 0.0
        DO 93 I = 2, 20
        X = I
        X = 0.8 + 0.2 * X
    93  SUM = SUM + SQRTF(1.0 + X**2) * EXPF(-X)
        TRAP = 0.1*(SQRTF(2.0)*EXPF(-1.0) + 2.0*SUM
                                 + SQRTF(26.0)*EXPF(-5.0))
```

31. Replace statement 41 and the eight statements following it with

```
        B = A(1)
        C = B
        DO 40 I = 2, 4
        B = A(I) + Z*B
    40  C = B + Z*C
        B = A(5) + Z*B
34.     DIMENSION GRAPH(41)
        X = 0.0
   100  S = SINF(X)
        I = 20.0*(S + 1.05)
        GRAPH(I) = 1HX
        PRINT 101, GRAPH
```

```
101 FORMAT (1H , 41A1)
    GRAPH(I) = 1H
    X = X + 0.2
    IF (X − 7.0) 100, 100, 102
102 STOP
    END
```

Chapter 8

1. $x = 3$, $y = 6$, $z = -1$.

3. $x = 3.000$, $y = -2.000$, $z = 6.000$.

6. $x = 1 + i$, $y = 2 - i$.

8. Without row interchanges, $x = -1.400$, $y = 0.7406$.
With row interchanges, $x = -1.590$, $y = 0.7409$.

14. $x = 2.222$, $y = 3.333$, $z = 4.444$.

17. Without interchanges, $\delta_x = 1.5 \cdot 10^{-2}$, $\delta_y = 1 \cdot 10^{-2}$.
With interchanges, $\delta_x = 2.5 \cdot 10^{-2}$, $\delta_y = 1 \cdot 10^{-2}$.
The difference reflects the fact that these are bounds; the actual error can be less than the bound. These are clearly not *minimum* bounds, which would be much more powerful.

18. a. $\delta_x = 3.1 \cdot 10^{-2}$ $\delta_y = 1.8 \cdot 10^{-2}$ $\delta_z = 0.8 \cdot 10^{-2}$
b. $\delta_x = 28.4 \cdot 10^{-2}$ $\delta_y = 16.3 \cdot 10^{-2}$ $\delta_z = 7.6 \cdot 10^{-2}$
c. $\delta_x = 31.5 \cdot 10^{-2}$ $\delta_y = 18.1 \cdot 10^{-2}$ $\delta_z = 8.4 \cdot 10^{-2}$
d. $\delta_x = 12.0$ $\delta_y = 6.9$ $\delta_z = 3.2$

20. $x = 1.003$, $y = -2.990$, $z = 3.994$.

27. II = NROW(I)
KK = NROW(K)
A(II, J) = A(II, J) − FACTOR * A(KK, J)

37. Since
$$\sum_{i=1}^{N} i = \frac{N(N+1)}{2}$$

$$\sum_{i=1}^{N} i^2 = \frac{N(N+1)(2N+1)}{6}$$

we get

$$Na + \frac{N(N+1)}{2} b = \Sigma y$$

$$\frac{N(N+1)}{2} a + \frac{N(N+1)(2N+1)}{6} b = \Sigma xy$$

38. $N \log a + \Sigma x_i b = \Sigma \log y_i$
$\Sigma x_i \log a + \Sigma x_i^2 b = \Sigma (x_i \log y_i)$

Chapter 9

1. DENOMF(X) = X**2 + SQRTF(1.0 + 2.0*X + 3.0*X**2)
   ALPHA = (6.9 + Y) / DENOMF(Y)
   BETA = (2.1*Z + Z**4) / DENOMF(Z)
   GAMMA = SINF(Y) / DENOMF(Y**2)
   DELTA = 1.0 / DENOMF(SINF(Y))
3. S34F(X, A) = SQRTF(X**2 − A**2)
   SFK = 0.5*(V*S34F(V, R) − R**2*LOGF(ABSF(V + S34F(V, R))))
   PSB = S34F(X(I), B)**7/7.0 +2.0*B**2(*S34F(X(I), B)**5/5.0
   1   + B**4*S34F(X(I), B)**3/3.0

   It is better in both cases to use two statements, one to compute the
   function, the second to evaluate the expression.
5. FUNCTION Y(X)
   IF (X) 10, 11, 12
   10 Y = 1.0 + SQRTF(1.0 + X*X)
   RETURN
   11 Y = 0.0
   RETURN
   12 Y = 1.0 − SQRTF(1.0 + X*X)
   RETURN
   END

   F = 2.0 + Y(A + Z)
   G = (Y(X(K)) + Y(X(K + 1)))/2.0
   H = Y(COSF(6.2832*X)) + SQRTF(1.0 + Y(6.2832*X))
7. FUNCTION SUMNR(A, K)
   DIMENSION A(20, 20)
   SUMNR = 0.0
   DO 69 I = 1,20
   69 SUMNR = SUMNR + ABSF(A(K, I))
   SUMNR = SUMNR − ABSF(A(K, K))
   RETURN
   END
9. SUBROUTINE AVERNZ(A, N, AVER, NZ)
   DIMENSION A(50)
   AVER = 0.0
   NZ = 0
   DO 19 I = 1, N
   AVER = AVER + A(I)
   IF (A(I)) 19, 18, 19
   18 NZ = NZ + 1
   19 CONTINUE
   AN = N
   AVER = AVER / AN
   RETURN
   END

```
        CALL AVERNZ(ZETA, 20, ZMEAN, NZCNT)
11. DEQF(X, Y) = Y - 2.0 * EXPF(-X)
    DEQF(X, Y) = 2.0 * X + (X**2 - Y) * SINF(X) / COSF(X)
    DEQF(X, Y) = Y**3 - Y / X
    DEQF(X, Y) = COSF(X) - SINF(X) - Y
    DEQF(X, Y) = 2.0 * Y / X + X**2 * EXPF(X)
13. FUNCTION YNEXT(X, Y, H)
    DEQF(X, Y) = Y - 2.0 * EXPF(-X)
    AK1 = DEQF(X, Y)
    AK2 = DEQF(X + H/2.0, Y + H*AK1/2.0)
    AK3 = DEQF(X + H/2.0, Y + H*AK2/2.0)
    AK4 = DEQF(X + H, Y + H*AK3)
    YNEXT = Y + H / 6.0 * (AK1 + 2.0 * (AK2 + AK3) + AK4)
    RETURN
    END
```

Chapter 10

2. a. 31.64
   b. 34.87
   c. 35.85
   d. 36.64
   e. 37.07
   f. 36.85
   g. 37.07
   h. 36.85
   i. 37.50
   j. 36.82
   k. 36.69
   l. 36.76
11. Euler's method.

```
        DEQF(X, Y) =
        READ 16, X, Y, H, XLAST
    16  FORMAT (4F10.0)
        PRINT 17, X, Y, H
    17  FORMAT (1P3E20.7)
    20  Y = Y + H * DEQF(X, Y)
        X = X + H
        PRINT 17, X, Y
        IF (X - XLAST) 20, 21, 21
    21  STOP
        END
```

For improved Euler method, replace statement 20 with the following two statements:

```
20 YP = DEQF(X, Y)
   Y = Y + H / 2.0 * (YP + DEQF(X + H, Y + H*YP))
```

For modified Euler method, replace statement 20 with the following two statements:

```
20 YP = DEQF(X, Y)
   Y = Y + H * DEQF(X + H/2.0, Y + H/2.0*YP)
```

Fourth-order Runge-Kutta.

```
   DEQF(X, Y) =
   READ 16, X, Y, H, XLAST
16 FORMAT (4F10.0)
   PRINT 17, X, Y, H
17 FORMAT (1P3E20.7)
   H2 = H / 2.0
20 AK1 = DEQF(X, Y)
   AK2 = DEQF(X + H2, Y + H2*AK1)
   AK3 = DEQF(X + H2, Y + H2*AK2)
   AK4 = DEQF(X + H, Y + H*AK3)
   Y = Y + H/6.0*(AK1 + 2.0*AK2 + 2.0*AK3 + AK4)
   X = X + H
   PRINT 17, X, Y
   IF (X - XLAST) 20, 21, 21
21 STOP
   END
```

Text predictor-corrector method.

```
   DEQF(X, Y) =
   READ 16, X, Y, H, XLAST, TOLER
16 FORMAT (5F10.0)
   PRINT 17, X, Y, H, TOLER
17 FORMAT (1P4E20.7)
   X0 = X
   Y0 = Y
   H2 = H / 2.0
   AK1 = DEQF(X0, Y0)
   AK2 = DEQF(X0+H2, Y0+H2*AK1)
   AK3 = DEQF(X0+H2, Y0+H2*AK2)
   AK4 = DEQF(X+H, Y0+H*AK3)
   X1 = X0 + H
   Y1 = Y0 + H/6.0*(AK1 + 2.0*AK2 + 2.0*AK3 + AK4)
   PRINT 17, X1, Y1
40 X2 = X1 + H
   Y2 = Y0 + 2.0*H*DEQF(X1, Y1)
   ITN = 1
```

```
   41 Y2NEW = Y1 + H2*(DEQF(X1, Y1) + DEQF(X2, Y2))
      IF (ABSF(Y2 - Y2NEW) - TOLER) 68, 67, 67
   67 IF (ITN - 10) 66, 64, 64
   66 Y2 = Y2NEW
      ITN = ITN + 1
      GO TO 41
   64 PRINT 88
   88 FORMAT (35H FAILS TO CONVERGE IN 10 ITERATIONS)
      STOP
   68 PRINT 17, X2, Y2
      IF (X - XLAST) 20, 21, 21
   20 X0 = X1
      Y0 = Y1
      X1 = X2
      Y1 = Y2
      GO TO 40
   21 STOP
      END
```

17. Let $z = y'$.   Then

$$z' = F(x) - y$$

$$y' = z$$

Iterations of the corrector are still required because the y-value on the right of the first equation is a result produced by the predictor and is no more accurate than the z-value.

22. a. $A_0 + A_1 = 1$
   $-A_1 + B_0 = 1$
   $A_1 \quad\quad = 1$

25. a. Milne

b. $A_0 + A_1 + A_2 \quad\quad = 1$
   $-A_1 - 2A_2 + B_0 + B_1 = 1$
   $A_1 + 4A_2 - 2B_1 \quad\quad = 1$
   $-A_1 - 8A_2 + 3B_1 \quad\quad = 1$
   $A_1 + 16A_2 - 4B_1 \quad\quad = 1$

d. Fifth.

27. a. Implicit

b. $a_0 + a_1 \quad\quad\quad = 1$
   $-a_1 + b_{-1} + b_0 + b_1 = 1$
   $a_1 + 2b_{-1} - 2b_1 \quad = 1$
   $-a_1 + 3b_{-1} + 3b_1 \quad = 1$
   $a_1 + 4b_{-1} - 4b_1 \quad = 1$

c. Because the equations are singular.   In fact, the last three equations for the three unknowns a_1, b_1, and b_{-1} are singular.

d. $a_0 = 1 - a_1$

$b_{-1} = \dfrac{5 - a_1}{12}$

$b_0 = \dfrac{2a_1 + 2}{3}$

$b_1 = \dfrac{5a_1 - 1}{12}$

Chapter 11

1a. a.

	1	2	
1	1.333	1.667	2
2	1.667	1.333	1
	2	1	

c.

	0	0	1	
0	0.1875	0.5000	1.1875	2
0	0.2500	0.6250	1.2500	2
0	0.1875	0.5000	1.1875	2
	0	0	1	

d.

	0	0	0	
5	2.634	1.250	0.491	0
10	4.286	1.875	0.714	0
5	2.634	1.250	0.491	0
	0	0	0	

2.

0.0000	0.0000	0.0000	0.0000	0.0000	0.0000	0.0000
2.5000	1.8731	1.3400	0.9281	0.6247	0.4041	0.2405	0.1120	0.0000
5.0000	3.6525	2.5588	1.7479	1.1668	0.7513	0.4461	0.2074	0.0000
7.5000	5.1782	3.4950	2.3380	1.5436	0.9882	0.5851	0.2717	0.0000
10.0000	6.0654	3.9052	2.5656	1.6814	1.0730	0.6344	0.2945	0.0000
7.5000	5.1782	3.4951	2.3380	1.5436	0.9883	0.5851	0.2718	0.0000
5.0000	3.6526	2.5589	1.7480	1.1670	0.7514	0.4461	0.2075	0.0000
2.5000	1.8731	1.3401	0.9282	0.6248	0.4042	0.2406	0.1120	0.0000
0.0000	0.0000	0.0000	0.0000	0.0000	0.0000	0.0000

The differences are caused by the truncation error in approximating the differential equation by a difference equation. The size of the truncation error of course depends on h and k; by doubling the number of intervals we have in effect halved h and k.

5. b. Not at all. In fact, given that successive approximations differ by less than ϵ, it is quite difficult, if not impossible, to say just *how* close the approximation is to the true value. In methods of practical interest the problem is not severe, however.

c.

ω	Iterations required
0.9	44
1.0	37
1.1	30
1.2	24
1.3	18
1.4	17
1.5	20
1.6	26
1.7	34
1.8	53
1.9	Had not converged in 90 iterations

d. *All* interior points are affected. This is always true of elliptic equations.

8. The string vibrates indefinitely in the shape of a sine wave. It goes through zero as a straight line; it reaches a maximum in the negative direction, at which point the negative values match the starting positive values very closely. Plotting the position of the midpoint as a function of time yields a cosine curve.

11. Only some of the solution points are affected. Imagine a graph of the solution in which x runs horizontally and time vertically. Choose scales on the axes so that the units are the same; in our problem, with $\lambda = 0.2$, one step on the x-axis corresponds to five time steps. Then draw two 45° lines out from the point of the "disturbance" at 13, 1. The effect of the disturbance will not be felt outside these lines, except for a slight "smear." The lines are called *characteristics*.

12. After infinite time the solution will be a linear increase from 100 to 200°. After 20 time units ($\lambda = 0.2$, $j = 101$) the distribution is

I	Temperature
1	100.00
2	94.44
3	89.17
4	84.46
5	80.56
6	77.72
7	76.13
8	75.95
9	77.31
10	80.27
11	84.87
12	91.08

I	Temperature
13	98.85
14	108.07
15	118.61
16	130.32
17	143.03
18	156.55
19	170.69
20	185.24
21	200.00

17.
```
   13 DIMENSION U(6, 9)
   11 READ 13, I, J, VAL
      FORMAT (2I1, F10.0)
      IF (I) 15, 15, 14
   14 U(I, J) = VAL
      GO TO 11
   15 ITN = 1
   17 D = 0.0
      DO 18 I = 2, 5
      DO 18 J = 2, 8
      UNEW = 0.25 * (U(I+1,J)+U(I-1,J)+U(I,J+1)+U(I,J-1))
      RESID = ABSF (UNEW - U(I, J))
      IF (RESID - D) 18, 18, 19
   19 D = RESID
   18 U(I, J) = UNEW
      IF (D - 0.001) 20, 27, 27
   27 ITN = ITN + 1
      IF (ITN - 50) 17, 17, 55
   55 PRINT 56
   56 FORMAT (35H FAILS TO CONVERGE IN 50 ITERATIONS)
      CALL EXIT
   20 PRINT 21, (((I, J, U(I, J)), J = 1, 9), I = 1, 6)
   21 FORMAT (5(2I3, F14.6))
      CALL EXIT
      END
```
The output statement here uses some advanced techniques that are discussed in Appendix 1. The results could be printed in many other acceptable ways.

19.
```
      DIMENSION U(21, 500)
   13 READ 3, FLAMBD, MAXJ
    3 FORMAT (F10.0, I3)
      PRINT 12, FLAMBD
   12 FORMAT (8H1LAMBDA=, F10.4)
      B = FLAMBD * FLAMBD
      A = 2.0 * (1.0 - B)
```

```
      DO 6 I = 2, 11
      FI = I
      U(I, 1) = 0.2 * (FI − 1.0)
  6   U(I, 2) = U(I, 1)
      DO 7 I = 12, 20
      FI = I
      U(I, 1) = 0.2 * (21.0 − FI)
  7   U(I, 2) = U(I, 1)
      DO 8 J = 1, 500
      U(1, J) = 0.0
      U(21, J) = 0.0
      DO 99 J = 1, 2
      PRINT 39, J
 39   FORMAT (1H0, I10)
 99   PRINT 40, (U(I, J), I = 1, 21)
 40   FORMAT (11F11.6 / 10F11.6)
      DO 19 J = 3, MAXJ
      DO 9 I = 2, 20
  9   U(I, J) = A*U(I,J−1) + B*(U(I+1,J−1)+U(I−1,J−1))
                                              − U(I,J−2)
      PRINT 39, J
 19   PRINT 40, (U(I, J), I = 1, 21)
      CALL EXIT
      END
```

27. $u_{i,j+1} - u_{i,j-1} = 2\lambda(u_{i-1,j} - 2u_{i,j} + u_{i+1,j})$

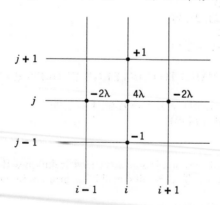

29. a. $u_{yy}^{(i+1)} = \dfrac{u_{i+1,j+1} - 2u_{i+1,j} + u_{i+1,j-1}}{k^2}$

$u_{yy}^{(i)} = \dfrac{u_{i,j+1} - 2u_{i,j} + u_{i,j-1}}{k^2}$

$u_{yy}^{(i-1)} = \dfrac{u_{i-1,j+1} - 2u_{i-1,j} + u_{i-1,j-1}}{k^2}$

b. $u_{i+1,j+1} + u_{i+1,j-1} + u_{i-1,j-1} + u_{i-1,j+1}$
$$+ 4(u_{i+1,j} + u_{i,j-1} + u_{i-1,j} + u_{i,j+1}) = 100u_{i,j}$$

c.

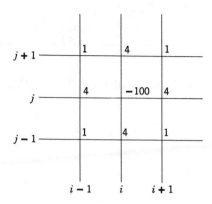

d. Yes.

31. a. $-u_{i-1,j}^{(n)} + 4u_{i,j}^{(n)} - u_{i+1,j}^{(n)} = u_{i,j+1}^{(n-1)} + u_{i,j-1}^{(n)}$

where n is the iteration number and the jth row is being computed. The right-hand sides do not involve the jth row and are considered fixed.

b. For line 1

$$\begin{aligned}
4u_{1,1}^{(n)} - u_{2,1}^{(n)} &= 2 + u_{1,2}^{(n-1)} \\
-u_{1,1}^{(n)} + 4u_{2,1}^{(n)} - u_{3,1}^{(n)} &= 1 + u_{2,2}^{(n-1)} \\
-u_{2,1}^{(n)} + 4u_{3,1}^{(n)} &= 2 + u_{3,2}^{(n-1)}
\end{aligned}$$

For line 2

$$\begin{aligned}
4u_{1,2}^{(n)} - u_{2,2}^{(n)} &= 1 + u_{1,3}^{(n-1)} + u_{1,1}^{(n)} \\
-u_{1,2}^{(n)} + 4u_{2,2}^{(n)} - u_{3,2}^{(n)} &= u_{2,3}^{(n-1)} + u_{2,1}^{(n)} \\
-u_{2,2}^{(n)} + 4u_{3,2}^{(n)} &= 1 + u_{3,3}^{(n-1)} + u_{3,1}^{(n)}
\end{aligned}$$

For line 3

$$\begin{aligned}
4u_{1,3}^{(n)} - u_{2,3}^{(n)} &= 2 + u_{1,2}^{(n)} \\
-u_{1,3}^{(n)} + 4u_{2,3}^{(n)} - u_{3,3}^{(n)} &= 1 + u_{2,2}^{(n)} \\
-u_{2,3}^{(n)} + 4u_{3,3}^{(n)} &= 2 + u_{3,2}^{(n)}
\end{aligned}$$

Note that

$$u_{i,3}^{(n)} = u_{i,1}^{(n+1)} \qquad i = 1, 2, 3$$

so that only two sets of equations need to be solve in each iteration. The reader will find it instructive to determine why this is so.

34. **a.** $u_{i,j+1} = u_{i+1,j} - u_{i,j} + u_{i-1,j}$

To find $u_{i,j+1}$ we take the sum of the two values diagonally below and subtract the value directly below.

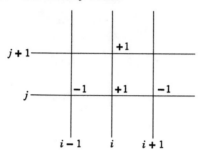

b.

	$i=6$	$i=7$	$i=8$	$i=9$	$i=10$	$i=11$	$i=12$	$i=13$	$i=14$	
$t=0.16$	ϵ	-4ϵ	10ϵ	-16ϵ	20ϵ	-16ϵ	10ϵ	-4ϵ	ϵ	$j=4$
$t=0.12$	0	ϵ	-3ϵ	6ϵ	-7ϵ	6ϵ	-3ϵ	ϵ	0	$j=3$
$t=0.08$	0	0	ϵ	-2ϵ	3ϵ	-2ϵ	ϵ	0	0	$j=2$
$t=0.04$	0	0	0	ϵ	$-\epsilon$	ϵ	0	0	0	$j=1$
$t=0.00$	0	0	0	0	ϵ	0	0	0	0	$j=0$

Index

449